FROM PEASANT TO EMPEROR: THE LIFE OF LIU BANG

A Novel of Han China

Victor Cunrui Xiong

 airiti Press

FROM PEASANT TO EMPEROR: THE LIFE OF LIU BANG

Contents

Part II. The Chu-Han War

Part III. The Emperor

Author's Note

Liu Bang was a household name in China more than 2,000 years ago and still is today. He was one of Mao Zedong's favorite historical figures. Mao said, "Liu Bang was one of the greatest among the feudal emperors," and "King Xiang (Xiang Yu) was no statesman; the King of Han (Liu Bang), on the other hand, was a first-rate statesman."

Among Liu Bang's claims to eternal fame, two are probably the most significant. First, he defeated his rivals in a brutal civil war to found his own Han dynasty, which was to last 400 years, and has since become the ethnic identity of the majority Chinese. Second, he rose from the lowly rank of a peasant who hardly had a penny to his name to the pinnacle of power and ascended the imperial throne. So his is a pauper-to-prince story par excellence.

This book about Liu Bang is a "faction," that is, a hybrid of fact and fiction. In penning it, I draw heavily on the traditional or primary sources, while making sure that all the characters and place names are real, so are the major events. I do attempt, however, to provide missing links that help explain the causes, motivations, and results of events. I also introduce a host of minor characters and events seemingly tangential to the central story. This kind of "side-shadowing" is intentional, because it provides a sense of authenticity.

In this book, the only untranslated Chinese unit of length measure is *li* (里). In Qin-Han times, 1 *li* was slightly shorter than half a kilometer. Traditional place names are followed by their underlined present-day equivalents or approximate locations in parentheses. For example: Luoyang (east of Luoyang, Henan). In the Glossary at the end of the book are listed historical figures, place names, and special terms that occur in the novel, with simple explanations.

Lastly, I would like to thank the Burnham Macmillan Endowment Fund of the Department of History, Western Michigan University, for its financial support, Mr. Derek Robert Benson of the same department for copy-editing the manuscript, and my wife Xiaoqing Li for her faith in me.

Victor Cunrui Xiong

January 2018

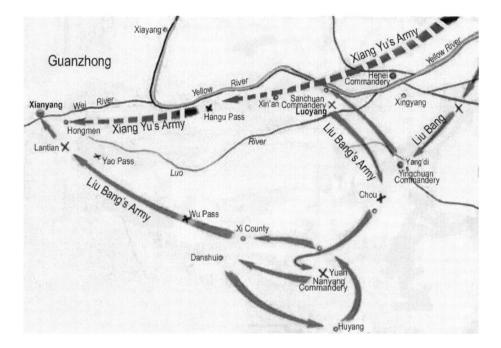

Map 1. Routes of Liu Bang's Army and Xiang Yu's Army, 206 BCE

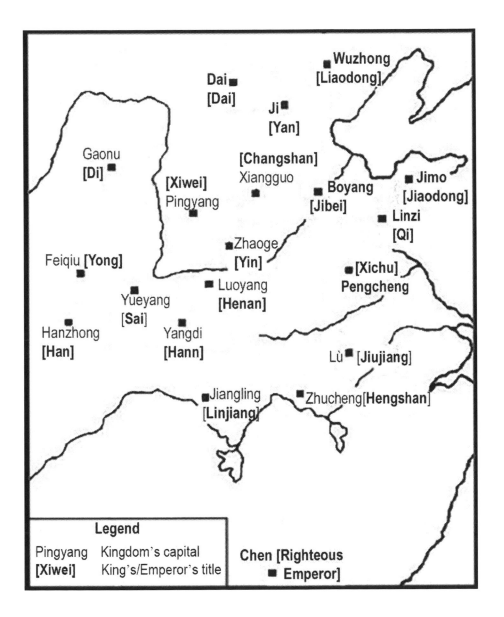

Wuzhong
[Liaodong]

Dai
[Dai]

Ji
[Yan]

Gaonu
[Di]

[Changshan]
Xiangguo

Jimo
[Jiaodong]

[Xiwei]
Pingyang

Boyang
[Jibei]

Linzi
[Qi]

Zhaoge
[Yin]

Feiqiu [Yong]

[Xichu]
Pengcheng

Luoyang
[Henan]

Yueyang
[Sai]

Hanzhong
[Han]

Yangdi
[Hann]

Lù [Jiujiang]

Jiangling
[Linjiang]

Zhucheng [Hengshan]

Legend

Pingyang　Kingdom's capital
[Xiwei]　King's/Emperor's title

Chen [Righteous
■ Emperor]

Map 2. Fiefdoms under Xiang Yu

iv

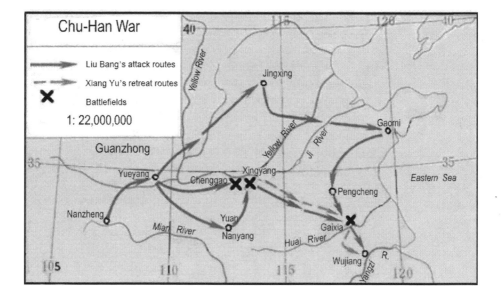

Map 3. Chu-Han War

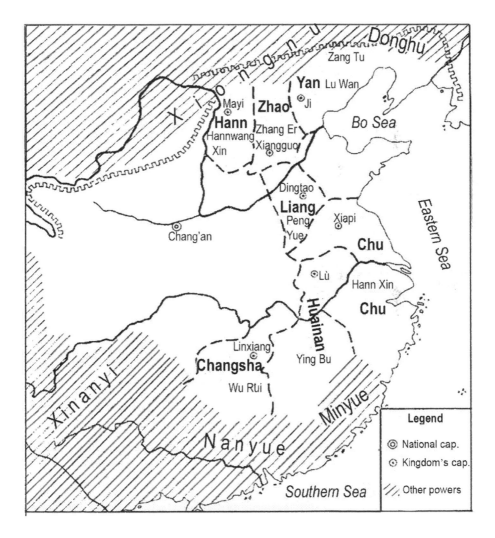

Map 4. Kingdoms under Liu Bang

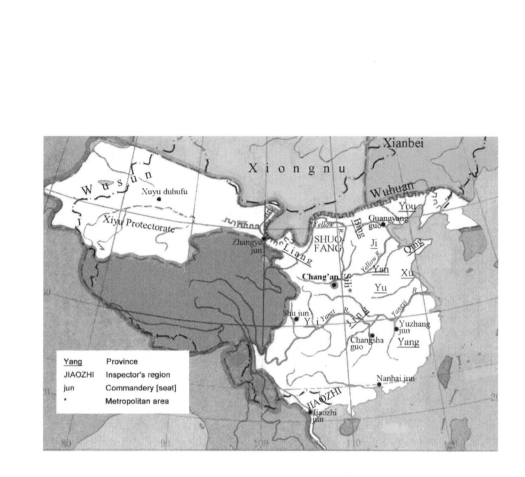

Map 5. Provinces under the Western Han

Ban Gu

Ban Gu, director of the Library of the Orchid Pavilion (Palace Library) under Emperor Zhang, was a towering figure in both literature and history. His reputation as a literary writer rests on his elegant *fu*-rhapsodies. His fame as historian derives from his magnum opus, the *Book of the Han* (Hanshu). *The Life of Liu Bang* could have been written by him.

Dedicatory Letter

Your Majesty's subject Ban Gu, risking death and bowing twice in obeisance, presents to His Majesty the Emperor* the following letter:

After working diligently for the last four springs and autumns, Your Majesty's humble subject has completed the biography of the Exalted Progenitor (Gaozu),† entitled *From Peasant to Emperor: The Life of Liu Bang*, and is submitting one copy of it to Your Majesty for review. The original has been deposited in the permanent collection of the Library of the Orchid Pavilion, of which Your Majesty's humble subject is currently the director.

This book can be read as a companion to the "Basic Annals of the Exalted Progenitor" and the "Basic Annals of the Exalted Emperor" chapters and related biographical chapters in Sima Qian's *Grand Scribe's Records* (Shiji) and in Your Majesty's subject's *Book of the Han* (Hanshu). It is an attempt to flesh out these chapters by providing a much more detailed account of the Exalted Progenitor and key historical figures, whose lives crossed paths with him, and of events that were of military and political significance to the Han.

In penning this book, Your Majesty's humble subject strove to live up to the lofty standards set by his predecessor, Sima Qian—author of the monumental *Grand Scribe's Records*—who is known for his honesty, candor, and integrity.

To Your Majesty from his subject and servant Ban Gu,

risking death and bowing twice in obeisance

wuchen day, 4th month,

1st year of Zhanghe (May 21, 87 CE)

---

* Emperor Zhang, né Liu Da, of the Eastern Han (r. 75–88 CE).
† Liu Bang, founding emperor of the Western Han.

Part I.

Turmoil under Heaven

Yellow Stone (218 BCE)

In the West, the Second Punic War broke out, and Hannibal brought his massive Carthaginian army across the Alps into Italy, posing a direct threat to the heart of the Roman Republic.

ZHANG LIANG EMERGED FROM the brick archway of the west gate of the county town Xiapi (southeast of Xuzhou, Jiangsu) and stepped onto the Si River Bridge. It was teeming with peasants and small vendors in drab garments, walking, pushing wheel-barrows, riding in donkey carts. Wearing a sackcloth kirtle and a bamboo hat, Zhang Liang fit right in. As he was approaching the further end of the long wood bridge, he pulled down his hat and started walking briskly toward the western suburb.

"Hey, kid! Pick up my shoes, will you?" a husky voice called out.

"Where, sir?" asked Zhang Liang as he caught sight of an old man of small stature with disheveled, long white hair. Wearing a tattered kirtle, the man was standing at the edge of the bridge, bare-footed. Though a bit startled, Zhang Liang managed to keep up the façade of politeness, because he had been brought up to respect the old. Surely he felt uncomfortable with the way he was addressed—he was well past 30.

"There." The old man pointed to a pair of hemp shoes lying below in the sand near the bridge.

Zhang Liang picked up the shoes, and placed them at the feet of the old man.

"Good kid. But, don't you want to finish the good work you started?" The old man sat down.

Zhang Liang knelt down and put the shoes on the old man's bare feet with as much respect as he could muster.

"Thank you! You are a great kid." With Zhang Liang's help, the old man got to his feet, and the two strangers parted company.

As Zhang Liang was reflecting on the bizarre experience, he heard a voice calling out, "Hey kid!" The old man had turned around and caught up with him.

"Yes?" asked Zhang Liang. Beneath his quiet demeanor, he was annoyed.

"Five days later, early in the morning, I will meet you again here." The old man was pointing a finger at the spot Zhang was standing.

"For what purpose, may I ask, sir?" Zhang Liang had been very careful about meeting strangers ever since he had made a failed attempt on the First Emperor's life and had been put on the court's most wanted list.

"Haven't you heard of this book called the *Taigong's Art of War* ?"

"Yes, who hasn't? But after it was condemned all copies have been destroyed."

"All but one. And I've got the surviving copy." The old man paused as he stared at Zhang Liang intensely from under his bushy eyebrows.

"So?" a suspicious Zhang asked. "Are you going to show it to me?"

"Yes, at our next meeting."

***

FIVE DAYS LATER, Zhang Liang, dressed again as a peasant, arrived at the west end of the bridge just before sunrise. He wanted to be there early enough to check out the meeting place and to make sure Qin soldiers were not lying in wait for him. Then he saw the old man in the distance, sitting all by himself. Zhang rushed forward to greet him.

"How long have you been here, sir?" asked Zhang Liang.

"Quite some time," answered the old man gruffly.

"I am awfully sorry. But..."

"But what?" The old man was apparently angry. "Is this how you treat an appointment? With an elderly man, no less!"

Zhang Liang did not know what to say.

"We have to put off the meeting for five more days," said the old man surly.

Originally, Zhang Liang had agreed to the meeting out of curiosity. After all, the author of the book Jiang Taigong was regarded as the greatest strategist who had ever lived. It was he who had helped King Wu defeat the Shang and found the Zhou dynasty. Few ancients could match him in vision and wisdom. Now the prospect of seeing Jiang's book began to seriously interest him. When the waiting period was over, he got up at the first cockcrow and arrived at the Bridge when it was still dark. To his dismay, the old man was already there.

"Late again, boy," said the old man as he shook his head. "See you in another five days. This will be your last chance."

In the five days that followed, Zhang Liang lived in anticipation. When the day of appointment finally arrived, he got up a little past midnight and went racing to the meeting place. No one was there. He spent the next few hours waiting until the old man made his appearance at the crack of dawn, carrying a wicker hamper with him.

In a thicket nearby, out of view from passersby, they sat down on a patch of grass beneath the crown of a tree. Still out of breath, the old man asked with a smile, "Don't you have a question? For example, why me?"

"Indeed, sir, why me?"

"Well, you are a good kid and you show respect for the old. But more importantly, I saw in your face a great destiny. You will be the preceptor to a son of a dragon—the conqueror of all under Heaven."

He lifted the hamper lid to reveal a dozen or so closely packed silk scrolls. "Here is the book. And it's yours."

Zhang Liang dropped on his knees and made a deep obeisance, as was required by ritual at the first meeting with one's teacher. Then he said, "I don't know how to thank you enough, sir," as he picked out the first scroll to examine.

"About nine years later," the old man continued, "there will be a rebellion nationwide and it will involve you."

"Is that so?" asked Zhang without lifting his eyes.

"Don't worry," the old man continued, "you'll be fine. Twelve years on, when the entire realm under Heaven is at peace, you will pass through Jibei Commandery. There at the foot of the Gucheng Mountain (southwest of Pingyin, Shandong), you will find a uniquely shaped yellow stone. That yellow stone is me. You can honor me then if you like."

"Absolutely, sir," said Zhang Liang. He had unrolled the scroll, and the cinnabar book title in archaic Large Seal Script—*Taigong's Art of War* (Taigong bingfa)—written on silk came into view. This was the legendary work on military strategy, tactics, and political intrigues allegedly predating Sunzi's *Art of War*. It was banned by the current government because it was judged highly subversive and thus dangerous.[1]

Zhang Liang was immediately engrossed in reading the scroll. About 10 minutes had passed before he muttered, "People stopped using this script years ago. I wonder..." He raised his head to look around and only saw trees and bushes, their leaves rustling. The old man had vanished.

---

[1] The *Taigong's Art of War* was probably completed much later than conventionally believed.

The Magistrate's Party (218 BCE)

IN THE COUNTY TOWN PEI (in <u>Peixian</u>, <u>Jiangsu</u>), north of Pengcheng (<u>Xuzhou</u>), word had gone out that the county magistrate was going to hold an open-house party in honor of a distinguished guest staying in his mansion. On the evening of the event, Xiao He, head of the County's Personnel Section, volunteered his service as the gatekeeper.

"We have too many guests today, Fourth Brother," Xiao said to one of the visitors waiting in line at the gate, "and we have to place those whose donation is less than 1,000 cash in the lower section of the main hall, away from the guest of honor. How much are you going to donate?"

"This much," said Liu Bang, as he handed over a bamboo slip on which was written "10,000 cash."

With the bamboo slip in hand, Xiao He went in. When he came out again, he was accompanied by a sprightly old man. After introducing himself, Mr. Lü, the guest of honor, led Liu Bang inside and invited him to sit down next to himself, in the most sought-after seat in the hall.

A middle-aged man with no money, Liu Bang had grown up in the neighboring county town of Feng. For years he had worked as a peasant, but had yet to show any interest in farming. When he was in his 20s, all he cared about, it would seem, were women and wine. He slept around with quite a few of them and even fathered a boy, Liu Fei, with a certain Ms. Cao. But Liu Bang could not afford to marry the woman nor did he want to raise their son born out of wedlock. So Ms. Cao kept him.

As a drinker, Liu Bang particularly enjoyed visiting two taverns in town, Wang's and Wu's. Since he did not have money to support his drinking habits, he resorted to buying drinks on credit. The owners of the taverns, both middle-aged women, took notice of his handsome looks, and discovered, to their surprise, each time their shops were visited by Li Bang business boomed. So one after another they canceled his debt, and allowed him to drink free of charge.

When he was about 30, Liu Bang passed an official test and became community head (*tingzhang*) of Sishui in Pei County in charge of hundreds of households. He left his hometown Feng (west of Pei) to take up office in the east. But his prospects did not improve that much at all, since his new post was unranked and was outside the official hierarchy.

***

NOW THE MAGISTRATE'S PARTY was over and the visitors began to file out. It was well past midnight. Liu Bang had been having a great time. He had never tasted such a great variety of wine: paddy wine, rice wine, millet wine, pepper wine, pine needle wine, cypress needle wine…. His favorite was cinnamon wine, which was pungent and potent without being overly heady. As he was sipping his goblet of wine, someone tugged at his sleeve and asked, "Do you know why I came to Pei?"

"No, Mr. Lü." Liu Bang shook his head.

"To get away from my personal enemy. I got involved in a feud, and my enemy threatened to kill my family. I'm here now with my wife, two sons, and two daughters. If you don't terribly mind…." The elderly man paused for a few moments as his eyes shifted to the goblet on the table before whispering faintly into Liu's ear, "I want you to marry my 23-year-old daughter."

"What?!" The usually loquacious Liu Bang was stumped. He was accustomed to being called by such sobriquets as "drunkard," "drifter," and "jerk," and could not figure out how to respond. By then Mr. Lü had turned his head and moved away, led by a feisty woman well past 40.

"Are you out of your mind, Old Man?" asked the woman when they were out of the earshot of Liu Bang. "In these parts, everybody knows our eldest daughter is a beauty, and you always say that she shall marry a man of great nobility. The magistrate is a great friend of yours; you even turned him down when he proposed. Now you want to marry her off to that good-for-nothing pushing 40?"

"Come on, you know very well our daughter is already past the best age for marriage. Once she is 25, she is finished. Besides, Mr. Liu donated the largest amount tonight."

"Nonsense! It is just a promise he can't keep."

"To tell you the truth, Wife, I can't help it," said Mr. Lü, freeing his hand from his wife's grip. "Haven't you noticed there is something august about him? Look at his tall nose and majestic bearing."

"But he has hardly a penny to his name!"

"I don't care," said Mr. Lü curtly.

A few moments later, the old man found Liu Bang again and made him a formal marriage offer. Liu accepted it with a deep obeisance.

The Mangdang Mountains (210 BCE)

The Romans under Fabius Maximus and others had resisted Hannibal's invasion of Italy with some success. But the outcome of the Second Punic War was by no means conclusive. Spain was still in the hands of the Carthaginians. Meanwhile, a young Roman general, Scipio Africanus, leading a Roman army, invaded Spain.

IN THE FIRST EIGHT YEARS of their marriage, Liu Bang's wife Ms. Lü had given birth to a daughter, Yuanyuan (also known as Liu Luyuan), and a son, Yingying (also known as Liu Ying), about seven years apart. Since Liu Bang had not increased his interest in farming, his main source of income, his family lived in grinding poverty.

One hot summer afternoon, Ms. Lü and her daughter Yuanyuan, not yet eight years of age, were taking a break from work in a millet field in the shade of a pagoda tree, their clothes soaked through with sweat. They had been weeding. Yuanyuan picked up her little brother in swaddling clothes lying at the foot of the tree. Her mother poured water from a pottery jar into a bowl. As she was bringing the bowl to her lips a shabbily dressed old man came out of nowhere to beg for water. Without hesitation, she handed him her bowl. The old man gulped down the water, exchanged a few words with her, and went on his way.

Liu Bang emerged from the field hut nearby and waddled to the tree, flask in hand. He asked somewhat tipsily, "Who has woken me up from my sweet dreams?"

"You lazy ne'er-do-well," answered his wife. "Nobody but an old diviner begging for water."

"An old diviner?" asked Liu Bang, becoming alert. "Where has he gone?"

Ms. Lü pointed towards the dirt road leading into the distance.

Liu Bang walked swiftly down the road as his wife asked loudly, "Hey, when are you going to start working in the field?"

When he returned a few moments later, he asked his wife, with a grin on his face: "Do you know what the old man told me?"

"How should I know?"

"Soon I am going to have a change of destiny; I will be a man of great nobility! A dragon-slayer!"

A dragon-slayer was someone who killed a large snake or python; in folklore he is a metaphor for a dynastic founder. Liu could never have imagined becoming a dragon-slayer, literally or otherwise. Still, he was fascinated with the prediction. In fact, in spite of his humble origin, he had always aspired to greatness. And the prediction seemed to suggest that something big was going to happen.

***

THEN A ONCE-IN-A-LIFETIME opportunity landed in his lap. He was chosen by the county to transport 100 corvée laborers to Guanzhong to the west (the Wei River valley in south Shaanxi). There they would work on the First Emperor's Mausoleum at Mount Li, near Xianyang, the capital.

A few years back, Liu Bang himself had been to Xianyang (north of Xi'an, Shaanxi). While there he happened to be among tens of thousands of onlookers when the imperial procession was moving along the main avenue. The guard of honor on horseback, the sea of banners, the armed cavalry escort, the ornately decorated carriage drawn by six tall stallions.... As a lowly peasant from Pei on corvée duty, Liu Bang was very, very impressed.

This time was different. He would go there not as a laborer but as a foreman. *You'll never know*, he said to himself. *This might be the opportunity to change my destiny.*

***

ABOUT ONE WEEK INTO the journey, he and his party arrived in Suiyang (south of <u>Shangqiu</u>, <u>Henan</u>), a town much bigger than Pei. When he saw this nondescript tavern, Liu Bang stopped the march and went inside with two assistants, Lu Wan and Xiahou Ying.

Soon, the rice wine Liu ordered came in a jar. He sniffed its fragrant aroma. "I didn't know Suiyang wine could be this good," exclaimed Liu as he poured it into three dark-brown pottery bowls on the table. The three men started drinking.

After the first jar was finished, Liu Bang pounded his fist on the table and shouted, his face crimson-red, "We are doomed!"

"Fourth Brother," said Xiahou, the oldest of the three, "we can perhaps find them with the help of the commandery government."

"No way!" reacted Lu Wan, who was Liu Bang's lookalike. "All of us would have to answer for it if you alert the authorities."

"How many deserters so far?" asked Liu Bang.

"At last count, five," answered Xiahou. "If we don't report it to the government and they find out about it later, we'll really be in trouble."

"Well, buddy," said Liu Bang, "I've got news for you. For each laborer who deserted, one of us has to be beheaded... *beheaded*! That's the law."

"We are done for, aren't we?" asked Lu Wan.

"Well, there is only one way out," said Liu Bang, as he pointed towards the east.

"The Mangdang Mountains, the Paradise of Outlaws?" asked Lu Wan.

"Yes," answered Liu Bang with decision. "I've made up my mind."

"Fourth Brother, as always, I am with you," said Lu Wan.

By then, Xiahou Ying was in tears.

"Come on, Ying," said Liu Bang. "If you don't want to join us, you can go back to Pei."

"Yes, I do want to join you, Fourth Brother. But I am going to miss my family."

"Aren't we all?" said Liu Bang, as he wiped his wet eyes with the sleeve of his gray sackcloth kirtle.

Moments later, when Liu Bang was facing the corvée laborers sitting by the roadside, he said, with a grave but determined look on his face:

"Brothers, I am sorry you are strung together like this. From this moment on, you are free."

The laborers, with the help of Lu Wan and Xiahou Ying, freed themselves from the ropes that linked them together, came forward one by one to thank Liu for his generosity and took the road. In the end, about a dozen remained. One swarthy young man of muscular build, with fearless eyes and a tousled beard, knelt down in front of Liu Bang and said pleadingly, "Take us with you—me and my brothers! We want to be your followers!"

"You've got a familiar accent," said Liu as he helped the young man to his feet. "You are from Pei?"

"Yes. My name is Fan Kuai. I grew up in Pei."

"No wonder."

"I used to work as a butcher in that dog meat store in the marketplace."

"Yes, I remember. Butcher Fan! The store is just next to the drugstore."

"Exactly. Across the street is that tavern."

"They've got the best wine in town. Oh, I miss my days in Pei." With tears in his eyes, Liu said, "But I can never go home again. The authorities will go after me. I have nowhere to go but the woods."

"Where?" asked Fan Kuai.

"The Mangdang Mountains. Are you still willing to follow me?"

"Yes, we are!" was the answer, which was echoed by Fan's peasant comrades.

Thus, accompanied by Lu Wan, Xiahou Ying, Fan Kuai, and a small rabble of peasants clothed in rags, Liu Bang started the long trek to the Mangdangs.

On the last stretch of the journey, they formed a single file as they scaled a jungled slope on a narrow path. A young man picking his way forward at the head of the group stopped with a start when he was confronted with a black-striped, silver-white snake of enormous size blocking the way. It slithered towards him as it thrust its red tongue in and out. With a quick stroke of his broadsword Liu Bang cut it into two halves. After that they were able to complete the remainder of the journey and reached their destination without incident.

Once in the mountains, these law-abiding subjects of the Qin began to live the lives of true outlaws. They slept in caves and makeshift shelters. They gathered wild plants and fruits and hunted wild game—hares, deer, wolves, feral dogs, and birds—for food. On occasion, they conducted raids on villages and waylaid caravans. At Liu Bang's insistence, they only robbed the rich and shared their loot equally. Gradually, Liu earned a reputation as a fair-minded leader. In a matter of months, his following grew to several hundreds. For better or for worse, this experience altered his destiny.

The Shaqiu Palace (210 BCE)

THE FIRST EMPEROR Ying Zheng had a lot to brag about. Having crushed the six competing powers (the Six States), he had united China and founded the first empire, to which the Han would be the immediate successor. He had dislodged the mighty Xiongnu nomads from Henandi (in the north of the Ordos Loop) in the great bend of the Heshui (Yellow River), and taken measures to effectively standardize the written script (using the Qin Small Seal Script to replace the scripts of the Six States), the currency (replacing the coinages of the Six States with the Qin *banliang* coin), weights and measures, and the axial length of carriages (making it possible to travel long-distance without having to switch vehicles). He had mobilized the male labor force of the entire country to build a countless number of massive palaces in the capital Xianyang and in commanderies all over the country, to erect the longest defensive wall in history (known as the Great Wall) to keep the northern barbarians at bay, and to construct his mammoth mausoleum at Mt. Li.[2]

Guided by occultists, experts in longevity and immortality, the First Emperor had begun to experiment with cinnabar pills more than a decade before and was now consuming them with greater frequency and at higher dosage. His immediate goal was to reduce his weight to such an extent that he could start practicing the art of becoming invisible.

---

[2] This is the only tumulus in ancient China that rivals the Great Pyramid of Khufu in scale.

Early in the year, the First Emperor had set off on a tour of inspection. Having visited the south and the Qi area (<u>Shandong</u>), he headed up north with Henandi (in the <u>Ordos</u> <u>Loop</u>) as his northernmost destination, where his favorite son Fusu and his mentor General Meng Tian were posted.

In July, he broke his journey in Shaqiu, Julu (in south <u>Hebei</u>). Shaqiu was home to one of the many "touring palaces" the Emperor had built for himself that dotted along his travel routes.

On the eighth day of his stay, the Emperor attended a grand banquet in his honor. It began with a kind of meat potage flavored with red chili, ginger, shallot, and a variety of spices. The main course consisted of lamb, beef, pork, pheasant, crucian carp, bear's paw, suckling pig, and even leopard embryo.

The next day, the Emperor did not get up early in the morning as usual. He had spent most of the previous night drinking and feasting. The eunuch officer on duty, reluctant to disturb His Majesty, waited until noon. He then entered the sleeping chamber to remind His Majesty that it was time to take the longevity drug. To his horror, the Emperor was lying listlessly in bed with white foam oozing from his mouth.

A palace physician was immediately summoned. After checking the Emperor's pulse and tongue, he gave his diagnosis: "Heat stroke." By then more palace physicians had gathered, accompanied by court occultists. They got into a fierce argument on how to cure the symptoms as the Emperor lay unconscious.

"There is too much 'internal heat' trapped inside the body. We should treat him with blood-letting and 'cooling' medicines such as turtle blood," a physician suggested.

"Heat is good," countered an occultist. "This is a sign that the Emperor is getting close to achieving invisibility, the first step towards immortality. It is exceptionally meaningful now that His Majesty is approaching his 50th birthday. He should double the dose of the elixir."

Another physician soon offered a counterargument, only to be rejected by another occultist. Thus the debate continued; neither side would budge.

Two hours later the Emperor woke up and the left side of his body had gone limp. He struggled painfully to speak, but only managed to make a few guttural sounds. When pressed to make a choice between the two rival plans of treatment, he nodded his assent to the occultists. There would be no need for bloodletting or drinking turtle blood. Instead, he would take more cinnabar pills.

Two months on, the Emperor had recovered his faculty of speech to a limited extent, but his body had shrunken to a skeleton with a thin layer of skin.

On September 10th, as the First Emperor lay dying inside the palace (or he was ready to be received as a transcendent in Heaven), he dictated his testamentary edict to Zhao Gao, head eunuch and director of the Palace Livery Office. He then handed over to him the imperial gold seal and the imperial bronze tiger tally, which he had kept under his pillow. Holding the eunuch's hand, the Emperor stammered, "Gi...gi...give these and the edict to Fu...Fusu," and closed his eyes, never to open them again.

***

ZHAO WRAPPED UP the edict on silk, the seal, and the tally in a white silk bundle, and rushed out. In the covered passageway he ran into Li Si, the leader of the bureaucracy, and said, "I have got something extremely important to report, Chancellor." Li Si motioned his attendant gentlemen to step aside.

"The Emperor has expired," Zhao Gao whispered.

"May he rest in peace in Heaven. When are we going to break the news to the public?"

"Not now, Chancellor. We are more than 2,000 *li* away from the capital. Much of the military is in the hands of General Meng Tian and Prince Fusu on the northern frontier. We don't want to give people an excuse to make trouble, do we?"

"I guess not, Director."

With these words, they parted company.

***

THAT EVENING ZHAO GAO brought the ill tidings to Huhai, Prince Fusu's younger brother. Suddenly seized with sorrow and fear, the 20-year-old young man broke out crying.

Zhao Gao waited patiently until the prince quieted down and blurted out, "The Emperor is no more. What's going to happen to the Great Qin? And to me?"

Zhao opened the silk bundle he carried with him, revealing the three treasures: the edict, seal, and tally, and said, "The late Emperor wanted me to give these to Fusu."

"That means Elder Brother will succeed as Emperor?"

"Not necessarily," said Zhao Gao.

The young man looked in perplexity at the smooth countenance of the eunuch in his early 50s, which was devoid of any facial hairs except for the grayish thin eyebrows, and asked, "You are not suggesting...?"

"Yes, the seal and the tally are now in our hands, and the throne is yours just for the taking."

"But the edict?"

"It has no legal effect until stamped with the imperial seal. We can easily replace it with a different one."

After a long pause, the prince said, "But this is a matter of great importance. We'd better consult the chancellor first."

"Leave that to me, Your Highness," said Zhao Gao.

***

THAT LI SI'S RESPONSE to Zhao Gao's scheme to place Huhai on the throne was a categorical no came as a surprise. *The old curmudgeon!* thought Zhao. *He framed his erstwhile classmate and friend, the great Master Hann Fei, and caused his death. All because of jealousy! Now he talks sanctimoniously about "treason"!*

Suppressing his anger, Zhao Gao said persistently, "Forget about my plan for a moment. Let me ask you this: between you and General Meng Tian, who is more talented, more capable of strategic thinking, more meritorious, more willing to do the hard work, and more trusted by Prince Fusu?"

"Of course Meng Tian," answered Chancellor Li Si without hesitation.

"Then, if Fusu succeeds to the throne, you are finished. Why? Because, as emperor he will no doubt appoint Meng Tian as chancellor. If you want to quit politics and retire in the country by then, won't it be too late?"

Li Si knitted his thick white eyebrows as he listened.

"Fusu's younger brother Huhai, on the other hand," Zhao resumed, "is benevolent, kind, almost gullible. In a word, perfect for the throne."

"So I might as well," said Li Si with a cold smile, "be hanged for a sheep as for a lamb."

"That makes two of us! Remember Meng Tian's brother Meng Yi? He once sentenced me to death for a trivial offense. Had it not been for the timely intervention of the late Emperor, I would have lost my head years ago. Do you think the Mengs would let me off the hook once they were in power?"

"Listen, I am 70 years old now," said the chancellor, "and am getting tired of all the palace intrigues that have plagued the country for as long as I can remember. All I want now is to be able to take a stroll with my son and yellow doggy every morning near my house. Can I be spared this time? "

"No, unless you want to risk extirpation of your entire family."

The old chancellor was quiet for a long time until the eunuch asked in an irritatingly shrill voice, "You want to join us? Yes?"

Resignedly, the chancellor nodded his head.

Prince Huhai (210 BCE)

THE IMPERIAL PROCESSION RESUMED its course after Shaqiu. Along the way, each time the imperial carriage drawn by six horses made a scheduled stop, senior court officials and local government leaders would gather—the former to report on government business and the latter to pay homage; and delicate foods would be presented for His Majesty's enjoyment. But nobody was allowed to see the Emperor in person except for the two eunuch attendants who served as liaisons between the sovereign and the outside world. No one was surprised by this arrangement, since it was widely known that the Emperor had begun practicing the art of invisibility.

After the imperial procession went through the Jingxing Pass (in the Taihang Mountains), a putrid smell seeped into the air from the imperial carriage. On Zhao Gao's orders, a large quantity of salted fish was purchased locally, and each carriage or wagon was loaded with as much as one bushel of them. Although the fishy odor drowned out the stench of the decomposed corpse, many people suspected foul play. But nobody dared to complain.

The procession then moved northwest to reach Jiuyuan Commandery (in the Ordos Loop). After a brief stay, the imperial carriage under the escort of several hundred mounted guards sped away to the south on the Jiuyuan-Xianyang thoroughfare. By the time it arrived in the capital, it was well past midnight.

The next morning, key court officials and officers in the capital were summoned to a court assembly in the main basilica. The passing of the Emperor was announced. Thereupon, Huhai ascended the throne.

An elaborate funeral was held at Mount Li in the eastern suburb, where the late Emperor was laid to rest in his extravagant mausoleum embedded in a man-made mound and surrounded by several immense pits, in which were buried his underworld army, comprised of thousands of larger-than-life-size terra cotta officers and men with their weapons, horses, and chariots.

All imperial concubines who had failed to give birth to a son were forced to commit suicide so as to accompany the Emperor to the netherworld. Several dozen craftsmen went down to the tomb chambers four-stories underground to deploy booby-traps. With their job done, they started making their way back. When they were about halfway up the long sloping passageway, they on instruction closed and sealed the middle gate behind them. Now the light emanating from the outside was becoming increasingly visible. Suddenly, they were attacked and brought down by a barrage of arrows. As the poor craftsmen lay dying, the exterior gate banged shut. No one came to their rescue. What really mattered was to keep the secret of the tomb sealed forever.

***

IN THE MAIN HALL of the Qin Northern Frontier Command Headquarters (south of Yulin, north Shaanxi), the court envoy, a middle-aged eunuch officer who had just arrived with his suite, presented to Commanding General Meng Tian and Prince Fusu his credentials and produced a slender bamboo tube sealed with sealing clay bearing the impress of the imperial seal. The prince examined the seal and testified to its authenticity. The messenger broke the seal and took out a silk document. The general and the prince knelt on their knees as the messenger read out the testamentary edict:

> ...*Prince Huhai shall be appointed crown prince. General Meng Tian and Prince Fusu, because of their failure to pacify the northern frontier despite a tremendous loss of life over a decade, are condemned to death by suicide....*

With tears streaming down his face, Prince Fusu dashed out of the hall. A few moments later, as General Meng found him alone in his bedroom inside an enormous mansion, the distraught prince was holding a broadsword in his hand. The general rushed forward and seized the sword by the hilt, saying, "Prince, don't take your life yet. I have reason to believe that this edict is a forgery. Just think, if His Majesty wanted to kill us, why did he allow Your Highness and me to command an army of 300,000 on the northern border?"

The prince, with tears rolling down his cheeks, did not answer.

The next day, the eunuch officer found, to his great annoyance, that the prince and general were still alive. He issued a warning: if they refused to follow the imperial edict, he would start penalizing their subordinate officers. The prince could not take the heat and fell on his sword. The general refused to do the same, and was conducted under armed guard to Yangzhou (north of Zichang, Shaanxi), a small town in Shang Commandery.

"Well then," said the Emperor Huhai to Zhao Gao one week after enthronement, "now that Elder Brother is dead, there is no need to execute Meng Tian. He is our greatest general after all."

"Yes, he is the greatest general alive, Your Majesty," said the eunuch.

"Then he should be reinstated. Don't you agree?"

"Your Majesty, I have to say 'No,'" the eunuch answered.

"But why?" asked the Emperor.

"Your Majesty, have you forgotten that Meng Yi, Tian's brother, strenuously opposed your appointment as crown prince? Apparently, the Mengs may have changed their mind by now, but at heart they are always your opponents."

"I agree Meng Yi has to die. But Meng Tian defeated the Xiongnu (Huns) and dislodged them from Henandi (in the <u>Ordos Loop</u>). Without him, how can we defend the northern border?"

"Your Majesty, trust me, there are other great generals, such as Zhang Han, Zhongli Mo, and Long Ju, to name a few. The trouble is, when the truth about Fusu's death eventually comes out, Meng Tian, as his mentor, will surely rebel. It is far better to use a mediocre general who is loyal than a brilliant general who is not!"

Huhai fell silent. Zhao continued, "If Your Majesty has no objection, I will take care of the rest." As he said so, he produced two previously prepared edicts on silk.

As Huhai was reading them, the court seal-keeper was called. Without knowing how to counter Zhao's argument, the Emperor gave in to his demand. The seal-keeper spread the imperial documents on the table, and the Emperor lifted the imperial seal of jade. Then surprisingly a voice called out, "Your Majesty, I entreat you to reconsider."

"Why, Uncle Ziying?" asked the Emperor.

The 20-year old uncle with a childlike face answered, "Just look at the fate of the states of Zhao and Qi. Both collapsed after loyal officers had been slandered and killed."

"But," said Zhao Gao to the Emperor, "Meng Tian's loyalty to Your Majesty is questionable."

"If the general is executed, there will be grave consequences," said Ziying.

"Nothing is more important than preserving the throne," said Zhao Gao.

"You insist that I issue the edicts?" the Emperor asked the eunuch.

"Absolutely, Your Majesty," answered Zhao Gao.

The Emperor impressed the seal on the silk documents.

The execution orders were sent with poisoned wine to the Meng brothers held in two separate places. Meng Yi, the younger of the two, took the wine without a word. General Meng Tian, however, said with a long sigh, "For three generations, the Mengs have served as trusted officers of the Qin. With a force of 300,000 under my command, I could have started an uprising, even when I was kept in custody. I didn't do it. Because my ancestors taught me never to forget the kindness of the late Emperor, and I would rather die than disobey the teaching of my ancestors." He picked up his goblet of wine and drank it all.

Princes and Princesses (209 BCE)

This year marked a turning point in the Second Punic War. The Roman general Fabius Maximus captured Tarentum (in south Italy). Another Roman general Scipio Africanus defeated the Carthaginians in Spain. Hannibal was in serious trouble.

BY EARLY SUMMER, the Emperor Huhai had begun to feel secure on the throne. Months had gone by, and nobody had come forward to challenge his legitimacy. Life in the palace settled into a routine and a sense of boredom set in.

After a morning court session, the Emperor said to his mentor and de facto regent Zhao Gao, "After Shaqiu, for a long time, I was haunted by the fear of being called out by some senior officers as an imposter, a charlatan."

"Your Majesty should not be afraid any longer. We have silenced the opposing voices so thoroughly that there is not a single courtier left who dares to say 'no' to your demand."

"Really?"

"Beyond a shadow of a doubt, Your Majesty."

"Great!" shouted the Emperor. "I am told that life is short, like driving six stallions past a narrow crevice. Now that I hold dominion over all under Heaven, I want to indulge myself in sensual pleasures so that the country will be at peace, the people will be joyful, and I will live my life to the fullest. Is that doable?"

"Of course, Your Majesty."

"But I am worried that time is slipping away."

"Your Majesty is still young. There is plenty of time to do whatever Your Majesty wants."

"Really?"

"Obviously."

"What I want is to indulge my eyes and ears and to live a life of extravagance and sensual pleasure until the day I die. Is that doable?"

"Yes, yes, it is doable," answered the eunuch. "This is what a sage sovereign can do, but a fatuous sovereign cannot even dream of doing. However, now is not the time yet. Allow me to explain, Your Majesty.

"The death of Fusu has caused much suspicion among the princes, princesses, and senior court officials. The princes and princesses are all your brothers and sisters, and the officials were all appointed by the late Emperor. They are not pleased with Your Majesty as Emperor. Although they keep their mouths shut at court, they are willing to replace you at any moment. I shudder everyday at the prospect that something terrible will happen. How can you give yourself up to extravagance and sensual pleasures now of all times?"

"What do you advise me to do?" asked the Emperor, ruffled.

"Aggressively enforce the laws on the books. For example, 'the law of culpability by association.' It allows one to cast a wide net to ensnare your enemies."

"What exactly do you mean by 'culpability by association?'"

"It means 'if someone commits a crime, not only he himself but also his relatives and associates will suffer the consequences.' It is an effective deterrent against crime."

"Indeed, it is."

"But it is not enough. We should create stricter laws and harsher punishments. The aim is to *physically* eliminate the princes and princesses and those senior officials appointed by the late Emperor in short order. At the same time, we should do our utmost to satisfy the demands of the common people. Make the poor rich; make the base people noble; and appoint Your Majesty's favorites to key positions. This way, Your Majesty will acquire the virtue of *yin*, and gain the trust of your subjects. Since riddance of those royal and court vermin will benefit the masses, it will be immensely popular with them. Only then can Your Majesty begin to seek pleasure."

"I see, Mentor. Once again you have proven to be an invaluable asset to my court. Had it not been for your sagacious advice, I would have gone astray."

"I just do my duty as your humble servant. So Your Majesty is aggreeable to the measures I just proposed?"

"Of course. I can't wait to see them take effect," said the Emperor.

***

WITH THE EMPEROR'S BLESSING, Zhao Gao became the de facto chief justice and chief enforcer of a system of law and punishment that was among the harshest in history. Capital punishment alone took many forms, including decapitation, hanging, flaying alive, burying alive, cooking alive in oil, the severing of the body, quartering, and others. After the execution, the remains were often subjected to gruesome treatments that would have the mangled corpse exposed in a marketplace for days, the severed head hoisted on a stake for public viewing, or the flesh ground to a paste and burned, and the ashes scattered. The criminal's kinsmen and associates were subject to extirpation.

Many top officials were framed and executed together with their close relatives and intimates by Zhao Gao's overzealous henchmen. The entire court lived in fear.

The princes and princesses did not fare any better. The first target was Prince Jianglü and his two younger brothers. After they were incarcerated in the Inner Palace, an imperial envoy arrived to announce their death sentences for failure to carry out their duty as subjects. A desperate Jianglü asked, "Can you tell me how we have failed?"

The envoy did not say a word.

"I think we have always done the right thing. We have never once misbehaved or even uttered a wrong word at court. Tell me, how we have failed?"

"Don't ask me," the envoy finally answered. "I just follow my orders."

Jiānglü screamed at the top of his lungs, "Heaven, heaven, heaven! We are innocent!"

The three brothers broke out crying before killing themselves with swords.

Another prince was so stricken with fear that he wanted to flee. Only the consequences of his action—clan extirpation—deterred him. In the end he wrote a letter to the throne, which said,

> *During the time the late Emperor was alive, whenever I paid him a visit, he treated me to a great meal; whenever I followed him on a tour, he allowed me to ride in an imperial carriage; he showered me with generous gifts, including fine vestments and treasured horses. When he passed away, I should have followed him to the Beyond, but did not. That shows me to be an unfilial son and a disloyal subject. As an unfilial and disloyal person, I have no reason to go on living in this world. I would like to ask permission to join the late Emperor in the next world and be buried in the Mount Li Mausoleum. May Your Majesty have pity on me!*

"The letter brought me to tears, Mentor," the Emperor said to Zhao Gao. "The prince was one of my best childhood friends. I want to pardon him. What do you think?"

"For that reason alone, Your Majesty should pardon him," said Zhao Gao. "However, it will set a dangerous precedent. All these royal princes and princesses are related to you. Some of them were your intimates. The problem is: once you grant the first pardon, before you know it, you will find one reason after another to pardon most, if not all, of them."

Zhao Gao paused briefly to wait for the Emperor's response. But the Emperor was quiet, and Zhao continued, "Don't you remember? Our plan is to make all of them worry about their own death every day so that they won't have time to conspire against the throne."

"But still, the death of this prince will be on my conscience."

"As Emperor, you can't afford to have a conscience all the time. If you feel bad, you can provide his family with some financial assistance to show you care."

"All right, Mentor," said the Emperor begrudgingly.

So the prince's request for suicide was granted together with 100,000 cash for his burial expenses.

The other surviving royal offspring were not so lucky. Twelve more princes were executed in Xianyang's marketplace and 10 princesses were killed by dismemberment in the suburbs. Their assets were confiscated to the palace. Hundreds of people were implicated because of their association with the condemned, and were sent to their death as well.

The Storm of Daze Township (209 BCE)

ON AN AUGUST DAY in Daze Township (in Suzhou, Anhui; southwest of Xuzhou, Jiangsu) just north of the Huai, Chen Sheng was running hastily through a torrential downpour until he stopped in front of a thatched-roof cottage, one of dozens of similar-looking ones in the hamlet. He kicked in the ramshackle bamboo door and entered. Taking off his rain-drenched straw cape and bamboo hat, Chen, a tall man in his late 20s, revealed a brownish kirtle made of coarse hemp. He was immediately greeted by Wu Guang, a middle-aged man in his early 40s in similar coarse attire.

"Brother Chen, how is it?" asked Wu.

Chen Sheng shook his head and said in a grave voice, "Bad news. A long section of the road ahead has been swept away by flood. There is no way we can reach Yuyang (north of Beijing) on time."

Wu Guang fell silent, looking glum.

"According to the Qin law," Chen Sheng said, "the punishment for being late for garrison duty is death. I..." His voice became shaky as he continued, "I am not afraid of death. But what's going to happen to my wife and children? And the 900 peasant brothers under our care?"

"It's not fair!" Wu Guang said in an agitated voice, with tears welling up in his eyes. "Since I am going to die anyway, I want to die fighting, not with my hands tied behind my back like a miserable criminal."

There was a long pause, and the sound of raindrops grew louder.

"Well, I've got a plan," said Chen Sheng calmly.

"Yes? What is it?"

"I heard that originally it was Fusu who was set up as crown prince, not Huhai. Huhai had Fusu killed and usurped the throne. The masses all think Fusu is a benevolent prince, but don't know he is dead. And then there is this great Chu general Xiang Yan in these parts, who used to fight the Qin, and is well loved by his soldiers. People don't know he is dead either. If we launch an uprising in the name of Fusu and Xiang Yan, we can immediately attract a large following. That will greatly increase our chances of victory. What do you think?"

"Great!" exclaimed Wu Guang. "All we need now is a divine confirmation."

They paid a secret visit to a physiognomist, who, after a careful study of their faces, said, "Both of you will accomplish something big in the next few days. But first you need to invoke the help of the ghosts."

Back in the cottage, Chen and Wu had a discussion on how to find a medium to help them communicate with the ghosts. They knew there were shamans among the conscript soldiers. The problem was how to get in touch with them without alerting the authorities. Even if they did find a shaman, convincing him to work for them was by no means guaranteed.

Suddenly, Chen Sheng stood up, as if something had hit him, and murmured, "Now I know what he really wants us to do."

"Who?" asked Wu Guang.

"The diviner! He wants *us* to awe the soldiers into submission!"

***

THE NEXT MORNING, it stopped raining. A young conscript soldier had just bought a large carp from a fishmonger and was preparing it for cooking. With half a dozen fellow soldiers looking on, he sliced open the belly, and was surprised to find therein a small piece of white silk, which bore a short sentence in cinnabar, "Make Chen Sheng king!"

That night, the hamlet shrine turned crimson with campfires. Many soldiers came out to watch the spectacle. Indistinctly, they heard in the distance something like a fox bark. Some of them detected a hidden message, "Revive Chu! Make Chen Sheng king!" One soldier panicked and took to flight, while shouting, "Ghosts! Ghosts!" The rest followed, stampeding back to camp.

For the remainder of the night, the entire hamlet became restless as the soldiers gossiped and quarreled about the white silk and fox bark, and their meaning.

The next morning, in the hamlet square, the two Qin commandants in charge and Chen Sheng and Wu Guang were seated at a long table drinking rice wine. Overwhelmed by the strength of the booze, the Qin officers started rambling about whipping conscript soldiers who dared to challenge their authority. Wu Guang tried to remind them of a more serious issue—they would be late for garrison duty.

"What should we do?" asked Wu.

"Keep going!" answered one of the officers in a knee-jerk reaction. "The road will be repaired soon."

"But by law we will be executed."

Shaken out of his stupor, the officer shouted, "Coward! Coward!"

"I am not," replied Wu.

"Bullshit!" the officer growled as he lashed Wu with a whip.

Wu raised his left arm to ward off the blows. Suddenly the lashing stopped. The officer had thrown away the whip and was about to unsheathe the sword he wore at his hip. Wu grabbed his hand and wrestled the scabbard away from him. Pulling out the sword, Wu hacked the officer down. The other commandant rushed to confront Wu, sword in hand, while shrieking out attack orders to his guards, only to tumble forward onto the ground, having been run through from behind by Chen Sheng.

That evening, the 900 conscript soldiers were gathered in the square surrounded by several dozen guards, some of whom were holding torches. Standing on a makeshift stage, Wu Guang announced to the crowd, "Brothers! You have seen the white silk and heard the call of the ghosts." Pausing to point to his partner standing next to him, he continued, "Both show that Chen Sheng is our man!"

Amidst a deafening roar of cheers, Chen Sheng, silhouetted against the reddish background of the torch-lit night, waved his arms several times. When the cheering finally died down, he began to speak in a stentorian voice, "Brothers! We are late for duty. That means death. Even if we are not dead and are allowed to go on garrison duty, seven out of ten will die in a matter of months. If we run away and get caught, we will be quartered. Brothers! There is only one way to live. That is, to band together and fight this corrupt government! If we have to go out, let's go out with a bang, like true heroes. Besides, people become generals and chancellors—is it because they have it in their blood?"

"No!" the excited conscript soldiers answered in unison.

"If you are with Wu Guang and me, say 'Yes!'"

"Yes! Yes! Yes!" was the resounding reply.

"Great! To show you really want to join us, do this," said Chen Sheng, as he pulled his right arm out of his tunic, baring his right chest and shoulder. The conscript soldiers did the same. Then Chen Sheng and Wu Guang led them to the shrine where an altar had been erected.

On the altar were placed the severed heads of the two Qin officers. Chen Sheng knelt down to make a sacrifice to the gods and ghosts, and rising, he declared the establishment of his peasant insurgent army, the first in recorded history, in the name of Prince Fusu and the Chu general Xiang Yan.

***

THE FOLLOWING DAY AT DAWN, the Qin court astrologer noticed that the sun rose in the east while a bright star was still shining. The two heavenly bodies moved upwards in tandem for hours before the star vanished. This was the famous phenomenon known as the "apparition of Venus in broad daylight," in which the *yin* star Venus rivaled the sun, the grand *yang*, that symbolizes the sovereign. It was predictive of a serious threat posed by an outside force to the throne.

Zhang Er and Chen Yu: Friends for Life (209 BCE)

IN LESS THAN THREE WEEKS, Chen Sheng's rebels sacked half a dozen towns and cities, the largest of which was Chen (<u>Huaiyang</u>, <u>Henan</u>), the seat of Chen Commandery. By now, his ragtag army of 900 had grown into a formidable fighting force with 700 carriages, 1,000 horses, and 30,000 foot soldiers. At the city of Chen, Chen Sheng summoned a meeting with local worthies, including several well-educated gentlemen, known as *dafu* (counselors), who abhorred Qin tyranny.

"Brothers," Chen Sheng addressed the meeting, "a few weeks ago, we staged an uprising against the tyrannical Qin, just to stay alive. Today, we are strong enough to capture territory from the Qin and take on their regular army. It is time we set up our own government."

A chorus of cheers erupted in the hall. Wu Chen, Chen Sheng's friend and lieutenant, took the floor, "Brothers, we have decided to formally found the kingdom of Zhang-Chu (pan-Chu)."

One elderly man stood up and said, "I would like to propose that General Chen Sheng be crowned king." The hall echoed with the sounds of approval.

***

AFTER THE MEETING, Chen Sheng met two of the gentlemen—Zhang Er and Chen Yu—in private, and said, "I heard that the Zhang-Chen friendship can be compared to the Guan-Bao friendship—is that true?"

"Like Guan Zhong and Bao Shuya," answered the gray-haired Zhang Er in his mid-50s, "Chen Yu and I are great friends. But Guan and Bao were of similar age, and we are not."

"Mr. Zhang Er is more like a father to me," said Chen Yu, who, more than 20 years Zhang Er's junior, had a boyish look on his face.

"Still, we took an oath that binds us together for life," added Zhang Er.

"Wonderful," said Chen Sheng. "I heard you used to work for the government, Zhang Er."

"Well," replied Zhang. "I was a retainer in the household of Lord Xinling."

"One of the Four Lords of the Warring States," said Chen Sheng.

"After the lord died, I became magistrate of Waihuang. It was during this time that I got to know Chen Yu."

"He took me under his wing," said Chen Yu respectfully.

"And?" asked Chen Sheng.

"After the Qin overran the Wei capital Daliang (Kaifeng) and Waihuang to its east, we fled south to Chen," said Zhang.

"What did you do then for a living?"

"Both of us were working as gatekeepers, just to get by. In fact, when the city fell, we were starving."

"So you welcomed our rebel army?"

"With open arms," said Zhang. "Not only because they gave us food, also because we fully support the anti-Qin cause. This corrupt government deserves to be overthrown."

"I am glad you came to Chen. Otherwise, I would have missed you," said Chen Sheng. "Since both of you are learned and familiar with history and government, I sincerely ask you to give us some advice on policy."

"Your Highness, thank you for the opportunity," said Zhang Er, "You started the first rebellion against the tyrannical, abusive Qin. It is a great achievement, for which the public will be eternally grateful. However, to set up this kingdom of Zhang-Chu and to declare yourself king so soon after the capture of Chen seems a bit premature and—please excuse me for using the term—self-serving."

"What then do you think I should do, Mr. Zhang?" asked Chen Sheng.

"Please allow my young friend to explain."

"Yes?" Chen Sheng now turned to Chen Yu.

"Your Highness," said Chen Yu, "our view is that you should delay enthronement and lead the main force west to capture territory in the Central Plain and beyond and to revive the Six States under the leadership of the descendants of their former kings. This will force the Qin to confront many opponents at the same time, and all towns and cities under Heaven will come over to your side. Before very long, you will be the ruler—the Emperor—of the entire realm."

"Well, young man, we have conquered a sizeable territory with hundreds of thousands of residents. I am already their actual leader. What harm can it do if I take the king's title? As for Emperor, it is a title invented by the tyrannical First Emperor. I am not interested in becoming one."

Both Zhang Er and Chen Yu emerged from the meeting disappointed with the leader of the rebellion. Because of his background as peasant with little education, they believed, Chen Sheng only lived in the moment and did not possess a long-term vision. Worse still, he was full of conceit and unwilling to listen to the opinions of others.

In the heady days that followed the founding of the kingdom and the crowning of Chen Sheng, Zhang Er and his young friend Chen Yu swallowed their disappointment and proposed another strategy—sending a force to capture the Zhao area (central and south Hebei) to the north. It won King Chen Sheng's prompt approval. He dispatched an expeditionary force of 3,000 men, under the command of his comrade-in-arms, Wu Chen. Zhang Er and Chen Yu were to serve as his lieutenants.

Wu Rui and Ying Bu: The Great Outlaws of the South (209 BCE)

THE QIN EMPIRE UNDER Huhai had become a tinderbox. When Chen Sheng and Wu Guang struck the first spark, the fire of rebellion broke out and spread in every direction from the Huai to the Central Plain, from the Jiangshui (Yangzi) valley to the Wei valley where the Qin court was based. Many heroes came out of the woodwork to carve out their own domains. In the south the most storied hero was Wu Rui. He lived in Poyang County (northeast of <u>Poyang</u>, north <u>Jiangxi</u>), a small area sandwiched between Lake Peng to the west and the Jiuhua Mountains to the east. Unlike most rebel leaders, who were commoners, Wu had a distinguished family background. One of his ancestors, Fuchai, had been the King of the powerful state of Wu, which had dominated much of the south about 300 years before.

In the wake of the outbreak of the Chen Sheng Rebellion, Wu Rui, then in his early 30s, raised a rebel army of several thousands. Most of his soldiers were non-Sinitic Viets, who were quite different from the people to the north. They spoke a different language, tattooed their faces and bodies, cut their hair short, lived in stilt houses, chewed betel nuts to blacken their teeth, and practiced head-hunting. Thoroughly comfortable with the local culture, Wu Rui had been a popular magistrate. The locals called him the Lord of Po and whole-heartedly supported his effort to set up a separate government.

***

TO THE NORTH OF Poyang was a forested wilderness that extended along the south bank of the Jiangshui (<u>Yangzi</u>). There a large gang of outlaws had made their home. The ringleader was a young man called Ying Bu in his mid-20s. In spite of his relative young age, Ying was already something of a legend.

When he was still a teenager living in Lù County (north of <u>Lu'anshi</u>, <u>Anhui</u>), his handsome looks, athletic figure, and personal charm attracted the attention of a stranger, who, after examining his features, predicted, "You shall be king after a penal punishment."

As a young adult, Ying Bu got involved in a tavern brawl, in which he and his friends beat members of a rival gang black and blue. Someone then tipped off the authorities and Ying Bing was thrown into prison. Since the crime he had committed was light, he was to receive a lightest form of punishment called "blacking."

When the day arrived, he was taken out of his prison cell into the torture chamber. As he was lying supine on a rough-hewn board, two burly men tied him down with rope. A third man approached his head, holding a red-hot horse-branding iron. Ying Bu closed his eyes. The torturer pressed the iron against the center of his forehead and an excruciating pain shot through him. The whole procedure lasted about a few seconds, but felt like an eternity. When Ying Bu opened his eyes again, the torturer was dusting his wound with a kind of black powder, which would give the scar a dark color for years to come. This was how he acquired the sobriquet "Qing Bu," meaning, "Branded Bu" or "Bu the Branded."

Soon after his release, he was conscripted to work on the First Emperor's mausoleum at Mount Li, hundreds of *li* away from home. There he emerged as leader of conscripted laborers. In the wake of the First Emperor's death, Ying Bu escaped back to the central Jiangshui valley, bringing several thousand followers with him. They now took shelter in the Poyang wilderness.

Through the help of a mutual friend, Wu Rui the magistrate-turned-rebel and Ying Bu the leader of the wilderness outlaws met for the first time. They instantly took a liking to each other. While Wu Rui was impressed with the courage, charisma, and vision of Ying Bu, he was most struck by his majestic bearing. To him, that was suggestive of great nobility. Ying Bu, for his part, was greatly flattered by the tremendous respect he, a notorious outlaw, received from Wu, a member of the old aristocracy of the south. At the end of the meeting, Wu Rui proposed the junction of the two forces under their command, and the marriage of his pretty daughter to Ying Bu, despite his lowly station and disfigurement. A grateful Ying Bu accepted both proposals with deep gratitude.

Lord of Pei (209 BCE)

BY MID-OCTOBER, the town of Pei (northwest of Xuzhou, Jiangsu) south of the Huai was stirred to action. It started with the magistrate's plan to launch his own rebellion against the Qin in response to Chen Sheng. Xiao He, head of the County's Personnel Section, advised caution, saying, "There are still a lot of Qin supporters in the government. To stage a rising now can be a dangerous move."

His colleague Cao Shen agreed.

"To be on the safe side," Xiao He continued, "you should get help from the outlaws who were originally from Pei. With their help, the local people will follow your orders. To my knowledge, there are several hundreds of them in the Mangdangs under the command of Liu Bang."

"That drunkard?" asked the magistrate, with suspicion.

"Life in the mountains has changed him," said Xiao He. "In fact, he has been sober for quite some time."

"Oh?" said the magistrate in disbelief.

"There is hardly any wine in the mountains."

"I see." The magistrate paused for a while before he said, "Send him a message first, will you?"

"Yes, Magistrate. I will see to it," answered Xiao He.

***

ONE WEEK LATER, Liu Bang's rabble of an army was on the move. When they were halfway to Pei, Liu Bang ordered his men to stop for a rest. Liu dismounted and lay beneath a pagoda tree to take a nap. Under Lu Wan's direction, several makeshift stoves were set up and army cooks began to prepare the midday meal comprised of millet, dried veggie soup, and salt-cured meat.

As Liu Bang dozed off, one of his minions came to make an urgent report.

"Fuck off, you son-of-bitch," growled Liu, who felt drowsy and did not like to be disturbed.

"But these two suspected spies we captured insisted on seeing you, Master. They claim to have important intelligence."

Suddenly becoming alert, Liu Bang sat up and said, "Why don't bring them here? Now!"

Liu Bang was horrified when he recognized that the suspected spies were none other than Xiao He and Cao Shen. With disheveled hair and tattered clothes, they looked wretched. Xiao He, in particular, showed a careworn expression on his face that had added years to his age.

"What's happened, Mr. Xiao?" asked Liu Bang, having motioned to his men to untie both of them.

"I am all right, Fourth Brother. But the magistrate has changed his mind," said Xiao He.

"Why?"

"Probably, he doesn't want to get involved with the Mangdang outlaws after all. But I really don't know."

"We barely made out alive," said Cao Shen.

"Shall we call off the march?" asked Lu Wan.

"Not yet," Liu Bang answered calmly.

Through debriefing the two escapees, Liu Bang learned that Pei was defended by a small force with low morale. He issued an order to resume marching.

By the time Liu's army reached Pei in the early afternoon, the town had closed its four gates. Without siege engines and scaling ladders, Liu Bang's soldiers could not take it. The best they could do was to starve it into submission. But time was not on their side. Anything could happen within the space of a few days. So Liu Bang decided to try something different. He wrote an open letter addressed to the town residents, which said:

> People in the entire realm have suffered under Qin rule for too long. The local lords have risen against the tyrannical government. However, your magistrate continues to support it. If you, the residents of Pei, eliminate him and set up a worthy in his place, your families will be held harmless. If not, there is no guarantee that you and your children will not become fair game in the ensuing battle.

On Liu's orders, dozens of copies were made of the letter on silk. They were tied to arrows, which were then shot into the town over the walls by Lu Wan, Xiahou Ying, Fan Kuai, and others.

By nightfall, white flags were raised over the city walls, and the gates were thrown open. Liu Bang's rebel troops were welcomed as liberators by the locals, who had just done away with their magistrate.

Liu Bang was dined and wined and celebrated as a great hero. The council of the local elders chose him to be the leader of Pei. But Liu balked at the idea. Despite his personal ambition for power and success, he was not sure if he had what it took to assume such an important post—he had no formal experience either as an administrator or as a commanding officer. However, Xiao He and Cao Shen, the two original proponents of the idea, urged him to reconsider, arguing that lack of formal experience or training could not detract from the fact that he possessed a rare talent for managing people, and that was the crucial attribute for a successful leader. Other possible candidates, including Xiao and Cao themselves, were not nearly as good. Eventually, after Xiao and Cao, both extraordinary administrators and organizers, agreed to serve as his close advisers, Liu Bang accepted the offer. Thereupon, Liu Bang was raised to lord of Pei by the council.

***

ON A PROPITIOUS DAY selected by a diviner, in the main courtyard of the County Government Office, Liu Bang made sacrifices to the Yellow Emperor (Huangdi), the legendary ancestor of the Sinitic people, and Chiyou, a militant sovereign of far antiquity. For the occasion, an ox had been butchered, and its blood used to smear a ceremonial drum and a red flag emblazoned with the character "Pei." The color red was chosen because in the ancient concept of Five Phases cosmology, red is the color of the Fire Phase, the successor to and conqueror of the Metal Phase, which, with white as its color, had been the phase of the Qin.[3]

The occultists were quick to point out that the white snake Liu Bang had slain was in fact the white dragon, the son of the White Emperor, whom Liu Bang as the son of the Red Emperor was destined to replace. Both Emperors, according to the occultists, belonged to the small group of divine rulers, known as the Five Celestial Sovereigns, who took turns to dominate the world below. Subsequently, Liu Bang was given the sobriquet of "dragon-slayer." This rhetoric was intended to highlight the fact that Liu Bang was not merely another "local lord," but someone who, sanctioned by the gods, was destined to deliver all under Heaven from the tyranny of the Qin and rule over the realm.

---

[3] This view would be abandoned soon. Western Han cosmologists normally identified Qin and Han as belonging to the same Water Phase. It was not until the Eastern Han that Han was officially identified with the Fire Phase.

Among Liu Bang's staunchest supporters, apart from Xiao He, Cao Shen, and Fan Kuai, were Lu Wan and Xiahou Ying. Both Lu and Xiahou had been Liu's childhood friends. Lu Wan and Liu Bang were born on the same day in the same neighborhood in Feng. Their families knew each other very well, and they themselves grew up as close intimates, going to the same school, wearing each other's clothes, and celebrating their milestones such as birthdays together. At play or school they always kept each other company as if they were twin brothers. But there were some vital differences. While Lu Wan and Liu Bang were of similar medium height and even resembled each other, Lu was not nearly as handsome as Liu. Whereas Lu Wan exuded innocence, Liu Bang evinced intelligence. Lu Wan was always the follower, and Liu Bang the leader.

Xiahou Ying was about two or three years senior to Liu Bang and Lu Wan, but looked much older, with a weather-roughened long face. After he became an official in charge of carriages in Pei, he continued to be friends with Liu Bang. Whenever he passed by Sishui, where Liu served as community head, he would drop by Liu's home and chat with him for hours. Once Liu Bang horsed around with Xiahou and hurt his arm by accident. Someone tipped off the authorities and Liu Bang was run in. Xiahou volunteered to vouch for him when he was put on trial. As a result, Liu got away with a light punishment, flogging. It was Xiahou's testimonials that eventually secured Liu Bang's release from jail after only one year.

***

BY THE TIME Liu Bang became the Lord of Pei, several major rebel regimes had arisen all over the realm: one in Qi (Shandong), one in Yan (north Hebei), one in Wei (north Henan), one in Wu (seat: Suzhou, Jiangsu), and one under Ying Bu and Wu Rui in the town of Poyang (in north Jiangxi). In addition, there was the state of Zhang-Chu founded by Chen Sheng north of the Huai (in south Henan). Minor warlords, such as Wang Ling and Yong Chi, both from the town of Pei, were simply numerous.

Most of the rebellious activities were confined to the Central Plain, the northeast, and the south. One of Chen Sheng's generals, Zhou Wen, however, broke this pattern by advancing west to strike at the capital Xianyang, in the heart of the Wei valley in Guanzhong (in south Shaanxi north of Hanzhong). Although Zhou Wen subsequently suffered a serious setback at the hands of the Qin general Zhang Han and the Qin capital was saved, Guanzhong was shaken to the core and the Qin Empire was teetering on the verge of collapse.

Xiang Liang and Xiang Yu in Kuaiji (209 BCE)

OF ALL THE REBEL GROUPS that had risen following the Chen Sheng Rebellion, the one in Wu (Jiangsu) seemed to have the greatest legitimacy. Its leader was Xiang Liang, a native of Chu and son of General Xiang Yan, in whose name Chen Sheng had launched his rebellion. Xiang Liang had made Kuaiji (Suzhou) his home a long time before, after he had killed a family enemy in a blood feud in his hometown and fled with his nephew Xiang Yu. Later other Xiangs had joined them.

Over time, the Xiangs had become respected members of the Kuaiji community. Xiang Liang did his best to give his nephew, virtually his adopted son, a decent education, teaching him the art of swordsmanship and the art of war in the tradition of Jiang Taigong of the Western Zhou, Sunzi (Master Sun or Sun Wu) of the Spring and Autumn era, and Sun Bin (Sunzi's descendant) and Wu Qi of the Warring States era.

When the Chen Sheng Rebellion broke out, it filled Xiang Liang with hope and excitement. The long-awaited opportunity—to revive Chu, to revenge the death of his father, and to destroy the much-hated Qin—had finally arrived.

By that time, Xiang Yu, the nephew, had grown into a muscular, well-built, tall man of 23 with physical strength that was virtually beyond this world. The most remarkable features of his square face were its piercing eyes under heavy eyebrows. Each of his eyes had two pupils, a rare feature only found in truly great men like Shun (a predynastic sage-king).

Uncle and nephew drew up a secret plan to launch their own rebellion by killing the commandery governor of Kuaiji and taking over his office. Then a summons arrived from the governor himself, requiring their immediate presence in his office to discuss some important matters.

"Is it safe to go?" asked Xiang Yu.

"I suppose so," answered Xiang Liang. "Only you and I know about our plan. It could not have been leaked out."

"How about the plan itself?"

"It depends. We just have to act as we see fit."

Momentarily, the two Xiangs were brought to the heavily guarded audience hall of the Commandery Government Office. The middle-aged governor dismissed his guards with a wave of his hand. A secret discussion ensued. The Xiangs were astonished to learn the governor's true intention: join the rebel king Chen Sheng himself. However, since he habitually treated the Xiangs not as equals, but as minions who would do his bidding, the Xiangs were not exactly pleased. Then, the governor made a request.

"Now that I have let you into my secret," said the governor, "I can't allow you to leave without taking an oath of loyalty."

"Yes, Governor. We'll take the oath," said Xiang Liang. Cocking his eye, he continued, "It is about time."

Suddenly, Xiang Yu bared his sword, and lunged toward the governor. Terrified, the governor made an attempt to run while shrieking "Murder!" But he was blocked by Xiang Liang, brandishing his sword. Xiang Yu came up from behind and lopped off his head with one blow.

About a dozen bodyguards, armed with swords and spears, had rushed into the room to engage the Xiangs. Without much effort, the Xiangs made short work of them. But soon more soldiers joined the melee. With his uncle covering his back, Xiang Yu parried their blows with address, and struck them down one by one.

By the time the Xiangs finished the fight, more than 100 people who had dared to challenge them had perished. And the rest of the establishment cowered in submission. Xiang Liang emerged from the entrance of the Governor's Office, with his nephew by his side, holding in one hand by the top-knot the governor's severed head and in the other the governor's seal with its ornamental ribbons.

***

AT AN EMERGENCY MEETING Xiang Liang called with local high officials and magnates, he announced, "This is an uprising."

All present voiced their assent. In short order, Xiang Liang, now self-styled governor of Kuaiji, raised an army of 8,000 with his nephew Xiang Yu as general and his little brother Xiang Bo and nephew Xiang Zhuang as commandants.

Modu and the Xiongnu (209 BCE)

Having been defeated by Scipio Africanus in Spain, Hasdrubal Barca led the remnants of his Carthaginian troops to Italy to join his brother Hannibal.

TO THE NORTH OF the realm lay the immense Xingnu territory.[4] While they were still under the leadership of the *chanyu* Touman, the Xiongnu were threatened by two nomadic powers: Donghu to the east and Yuezhi to the west. To the south was the mighty Qin, whose army under General Meng Tian had dislodged them from the lush graze lands of Henandi (in the Ordos Loop) during the reign of the First Emperor.

Following an age-old convention, the chanyu Touman set up his eldest son, Modu, as crown prince when he was still a young teenager. An average-looking man with a short stature, Modu had a slightly swarthy complexion, a broad chest, and narrow eyes. Apart from his royal blood, he was known for his agility, strength, courage, and sharp mind.

Not long afterwards, Touman's favorite consort gave birth to a son. As this younger half-brother of Modu's grew up, Touman began to toy with the idea of replacing Modu with him as crown prince. Before he could act on it, Touman

---

[4] The Xiongnu were a proto-Turkish or proto-Mongol nomadic people who were at this time active in Siberia and Mongolia. A branch of them would appear as the Huns in Europe in the fourth century CE, where, under their king Attila, the Scourge of God, they would terrorize the Visigoths, the Ostrogoths, and the settled communities of the Roman Empire.

received a request from the Yuezhi for a royal hostage. Without hesitation, he sent Modu on this treacherous mission.[5]

During his sojourn among the Yuezhi, Modu was initially given a royal treatment that befitted his status until his father launched a surprise attack on them, probably as a way to eliminate his eldest son. The Yuezhi retaliated by taking Modu, the royal hostage, into custody. While waiting for his execution, Modu overpowered his guards and escaped on a stolen horse.

Touman was impressed with Modu's courage and intelligence. He cast aside his prejudice, and put his son in charge of an elite cavalry force of 10,000.

"I am proud of you, my son," said Touman. "Don't be upset by what I did before. I sent you to Yuezhi precisely because I wanted you to gain some valuable experience in real life."

"Yes, Your Majesty. I am grateful," answered Modu reverently.

***

AS SOON AS he assumed command of the cavalrymen assigned him, Modu began to train them with vigor and discipline. He demanded absolute loyalty. With that in mind, he invented a kind of whistling arrow and issued a peculiar order: *Whenever I shoot a whistling arrow at a target, all must do the same. Those who fail to do so shall be beheaded.*

One day when Modu was practicing archery with some of his men, suddenly he raised his bow and shot a whistling arrow at his beloved warhorse. All present were too shocked to react. On another occasion, Modu shot a whistling arrow at his pretty wife. His attendants and guards did not understand his intention and took no action. "Our master must have made two errors in a row," one of them said. Then, to the surprise of everybody, Modu ordered to have all those who had failed to shoot arrows at his horse and wife, including some of his favorite riders, arrested and summarily executed in front of his men. The message came through loud and

[5] The Yuezhi, the ancestors of the Kushans, were a nomadic Indo-European people then roaming the Qilian Mountains in the Hexi Corridor.

clear: his commands, no matter how absurd, were meant to be executed to the letter.

Not long afterwards, while out hunting, he shot a whistling arrow again, this time, at his father's favorite warhorse, all in his company followed suit and killed the steed.

On a bright, sunny day, Touman went on a hunting trip, galloping on a gentle mountain slope while Modu and his entourage followed closely behind. Suddenly, Modu pulled out his bow and shot a whistling arrow at his father, and all of his cavalrymen did the same in a mechanical action. Touman tumbled off his horse, his body bristling with arrows, and died instantly.

Modu turned his horse and headed back swiftly, accompanied by his elite cavalry.

At the Xiongnu main camp, on Modu's orders, his myrmidons dragged his half-brother and his mother from their yurts, killing both on the spot; and others rounded up unfriendly senior officers, and executed them in public. Modu then declared himself *chanyu*, the supreme leader of the Xiongnu, and sent emissaries to neighboring countries to spread the news.

Authoritarian Rulership

THE NEWS OF REBEL ARMIES capturing cities and towns in the Central Plain and elsewhere kept the Emperor Huhai on pins and needles. He was particularly disturbed by a recent rebel attack on the capital led by Zhou Wen, one of Chen Sheng's generals. Although General Zhang Han had repelled the attackers, and Xianyang was unharmed, the Emperor was furious that the rebels could get so close to the palace. He took Chancellor Li Si to task, asking sharply, "Why are the bandits running amuck?"

"Your Majesty..." Li Si stammered as sweat broke out on his forehead.

"How could you, a top official with the rank of the Three Dukes, allow that to happen?"

"As a leading court official," Li Si resumed, after pausing to put his thoughts together, "I bear unshirkable responsibility. I will work tirelessly to help improve the situation. On the other hand, there is something Your Majesty can do."

"Do you expect me, the Son of Heaven, to get involved in the dirty business of governing? What are people like you for?"

"No, no, I did not mean that Your Majesty should get involved in the nitty-gritty of government affairs. But Your Majesty can be more proactive in policy making."

"You've lost me there," said the Emperor fretfully.

"Has Your Majesty ever heard of 'authoritarian rulership?'"

"No. But what does that have to do with anything? Can it help prevent rebellion?"

"Allow me to explain, Your Majesty."

The Emperor nodded his head, and Li Si continued, "It was advocated by great Legalist masters like Shen Buhai of the state of Hann. For instance, Shen said, 'For those sovereigns who reign over all subjects under Heaven but still cannot act at will, the subjects are nothing but fetters. This is so because those sovereigns fail to practice authoritarian rulership.'

"And what exactly is authoritarian rulership? In brief, it is a way of ruling all subjects under Heaven in accord with the will of the ruler. Failing that, a ruler is no different from a commoner, and does not deserve to control his subjects. Under authoritarian rulership, however, the ruler alone makes all the policy decisions and the high officials have no decision-making power at all. That will make it possible to eradicate the pernicious ideas of benevolence and righteousness, and suppress the unpalatable arguments of the remonstrators. Consequently, everyone, official or nonofficial, will be so busy trying to avoid mistakes that they will have no time to even think of making trouble."

The Emperor regarded the idea with suspicion, but decided to give a try. To his pleasant surprise, in the name of authoritarian rulership, he could bypass the chancellor, the co-chancellor, and other top advisers in making major policy decisions. Soon he started promoting officials based on their ability to levy taxes, and rewarding his officers based on the number of people they executed. As more and more people were thrown into jail and more and more corpses of executed inmates were displayed in the marketplace, many people were driven to despair, desperation, and rebellion.

Meeting of Liu Bang and Zhang Liang (208 BCE)

IN THE TOWN OF LIU, the seat of Liu County (southeast of <u>Peixian</u>, <u>Jiangsu</u>), a new Chu king was enthroned. It gave Zhang Liang hope that the king might be that son of a dragon, whose appearance had been prophesied by the old man of the yellow stone and confirmed in the *Taigong's Art of War*.

But the meeting with King Jingju turned out to be a disappointment. It was obvious that he was only a puppet in the hands of one of Chen Sheng's former generals who had set him up.

While Zhang Liang was getting ready to leave Liu, he received in the local inn where he stayed a visitor, Liu Bang. Intrigued by Liu Bang's "royal physiognomy," Zhang did a *Yijing* divination, which indicated that Liu Bang was a "dragon in hiding." For his part, Liu Bang was favorably impressed with Zhang Liang's tall stature, graceful bearing, effeminate but noble manner, elegant speech, and full forehead, which suggested great wisdom.

"I am a great, great admirer of yours," Liu Bang said. "Ten years ago, when the tyrannical First Emperor was at the zenith of his power, you alone had the courage to challenge him!"

"Thank you very much, Lord of Pei. Come to think of it, that was a rash move. There was little chance of killing him. The assassin I hired did hit the carriage, but it was a double. It was drawn by six horses all right. However, oftentimes, the First Emperor traveled in a carriage drawn by *four* horses in spite of the etiquette. And he changed carriages frequently."

"The cunning old fox!" commented Liu Bang. Switching subjects, he said, "Well, now that serving King Jingju is no longer feasible, would you consider joining me? Both Xiao He and Cao Shen recommend you in the strongest of terms."

Zhang Liang made a deep obeisance, and said, "Thank you for your trust, Lord of Pei. But..."

"Well, if you can't make up your mind yet, that's fine. Let me be frank with you. I am not a man of superhuman strength like Xiang Yu. Nor do I possess great wisdom like you. In fact, I am a man of mediocre ability. But I surpass everyone else in one respect: I am a *great* listener and readily take the advice of others."

"That's really great!" exclaimed Zhang, who, after a long pause, continued, "Now, I cannot make a commitment yet. As a descendant of a Hann family that had provided chancellors to the state of Hann for generations, I was thoroughly devastated when it was crushed by the Qin army. I made a solemn pledge to revive Hann. And I still intend to fulfill it. At some point in the future, I will have to go back to the Hann area and re-found the state."

"Of course, loyalty is one of the great virtues I cherish."

Aloof Sovereign (208 BCE)

TO THE HEAD EUNUCH OFFICER Zhao Gao, the real purpose of authoritarian rulership proposed by Li Si was not to get the Emperor more actively involved in making policy decisions, but to eclipse his own power. He began to think of ways to guide the Emperor in a different direction. For now, Zhao still enjoyed a great advantage over his rival: easy access to the throne. However, he had to make his move carefully. Otherwise, if the Emperor became annoyed, he himself would be in serious trouble.

An opportunity presented itself when the news of Chen Sheng's death reached Xianyang. The Emperor was so delighted that he held a grand feast in the palace to celebrate. This first rebel leader and self-proclaimed King of Zhang-Chu had not died a hero's death as he had wished but had been stabbed in the back by his coachman when fleeing from the pursuing Qin army.

The next morning, when the Emperor was still euphoric, Zhao Gao submitted a memorial, not to remonstrate against His Majesty's current practice, but to point to a superior way of rulership. It said,

> *What makes a Son of Heaven noble? His aloofness. A truly noble sovereign is someone who is only heard but never seen. Your Majesty is still young,*

and is not necessarily familiar with the ways of government. So when Your Majesty makes an inappropriate decision at today's court, it will become a sign of weakness to the senior officials. It does not accentuate Your Majesty's divine sagacity at all. Here is a far better way, according to which a sovereign should keep himself inside the Forbidden Circle while the court officials and attendant gentlemen attend to government business. This will enable the sovereign to stay invisible and govern like a true sage-ruler.

"How about authoritarian rulership?" the Emperor asked.

"It should not be affected at all. Your Majesty can still practice it through your most trusted deputies, as the late Emperor did. It can only redound to Your Majesty's power."

"I would love to rule like my father," said the Emperor.

"So Your Majesty will try to rule like an 'aloof' sovereign for a change?"

"On condition I continue to exercise authoritarian rulership."

"Absolutely, Your Majesty," answered the head eunuch officer.

Thereafter, the Emperor began to reduce the number of court sessions each month. Noticing that he was in no danger of losing control, he stopped holding court altogether, spending most of his time inside the Forbidden Circle, that is, his residential palace. This new aloofness was achieved at the expense of contact with the outside world. Meanwhile, his intermediary Zhao Gao by dint of access to the throne had become the most powerful executive officer at court.

The Meeting in Xue (208 BCE)

IN THE AUDIENCE HALL of the County Government of Xue (south of Tengzhoushi, Shandong, and northeast of Pei), leaders of various anti-Qin rebel groups gathered for the first time for a meeting on strategy. Apart from the Xiangs, who were the hosts, present at the meeting were Liu Bang lord of Pei and Zhang Liang and the southern warlord Ying Bu, clearly recognizable by the black brand on his forehead. At least nominally, both Liu Bang and Ying Bu (and his father-in-law Wu Rui as well) had joined forces with the Xiangs. Zhang Liang was delighted to reconnect with his old friend Xiang Bo, Xiang Yu's young uncle. Years before, having killed his enemy, Xiang Bo fled to Xiapi as a fugitive, where it was Zhang Liang (himself a fugitive) who provided him with shelter and virtually saved his life.

A commemorative ceremony was held to mourn the death of Chen Sheng, the hero who had started the first anti-Qin rebellion. A shaman priest chanted incantations and performed a ritual, with a sacrificial offering to appease the soul of the fallen hero.

Xiang Liang then rose to introduce his chief counselor Fan Zeng. A short, scrawny old man with sparse white hair and thin white eyebrows stood up to address the meeting in a feeble voice, "I am awfully sorry about Chen Sheng's fall. On the other hand, it was not completely unexpected. Why? Because immediately after he started the uprising, he founded his own kingdom and declared himself king. And that greatly undermined his legitimacy.

"Instead, he should have focused on reviving the Six States destroyed by the Qin. Of these fallen states Chu was the least deserving of its fate. It was mortally weakened when King Huai was kidnapped by Qin (299 BCE) and had gone downhill ever since until it was brutally crushed by the Qin army. No wonder the Chu people harbor an intense hatred against the Qin. An elderly gentleman from the south once said, 'So long as Chu has three households, it will be the destroyer of Qin.' And I totally agree. In my view, to succeed, one must revive the state of Chu first."

"Great idea!" said Xiang Liang, who then asked all present, "What do you think? Do you agree with Fan Zeng?" All including Liu Bang and Zhang Liang voiced their assent.

***

AFTER THE MEETING WAS OVER, with Xiang Bo's help, a private meeting was arranged between Xiang Liang and Zhang Liang.

Zhang started the conversation with an eloquent analysis of the overall situation before he switched focus to his favorite topic, the revival of Hann. "Now that the state of Chu has been founded," said he, "it could greatly increase its influence just by setting up Hann Cheng as the new King of Hann."

"Who is Hann Cheng?"

"He is not only a direct descendant of the Hann royal family, but also a man of honor."

After a brief consultation with his brother Xiang Bo, Xiang Liang gave his approval.

With 1,000 Chu soldiers supplied by Xiang Liang, Zhang Liang moved west. In a matter of months, he captured a small territory in the south Central Plain where a new state of Hann was set up with Hann Cheng as king and Zhang Liang himself as chief counselor.

Audience in the Forbidden Circle (208 BCE)

REBELLION WAS GETTING INCREASINGLY out of hand. An urgent top-level meeting was held in Xianyang to discuss the situation. The officers and officials present were in agreement that urgent measures should be taken to bring it under control. Faced with a common enemy, rival factions agreed to sink their differences.

After the meeting, Zhao Gao found himself alone with Li Si, and said in a low voice, "I am gravely concerned, Chancellor. Banditry is rampant in the Central Plain and is spreading to Guanzhong. But the Emperor is paying no attention to it at all. Instead, he is using a massive labor force to renovate the Epang Palace while hoarding rare dogs and horses and a host of useless objects. Something should be done about it. Don't you think so?"

"Indeed, something must be done," answered the chancellor.

"I would like to remonstrate with the Emperor," said Zhao Gao. "But as a person of base status, I am not really in a position to do so. This should be done by a normal court leader like you."

"I have been hoping to discuss it with the Emperor. But so far I haven't got a chance. The Emperor has stopped holding court, and is now living behind the tall walls of the Forbidden Circle."

"This shouldn't be a problem," said Zhao Gao. "Let me arrange for an audience."

About one week later, on a bright morning, Li Si was informed by Zhao Gao that the Emperor had some spare time in the evening. After nightfall, Li Si was led into the Forbidden Circle. When he entered the audience hall, the Emperor was feasting while being entertained by a group of skimpily dressed young girls dancing. With a wave of his hand, the Emperor sent the girls away. Li Si then gave a lengthy report on rebellion and urged immediate action. The Emperor listened absentmindedly as he ate.

After the chancellor departed, the Emperor exploded, "What the heck was he doing? I had plenty of free time all day long, and he did not show his face. Why did he choose this time to visit, when I had a private moment eating and watching my favorite dance? Does he think me dumb, or what?"

"Your Majesty, can I say something?" asked Zhao Gao.

"Yes, speak up."

"I think he bears a grudge against Your Majesty. At the Shaqiu Palace, both Your Majesty and the chancellor were in on the plan to seize power. Thereafter, you became emperor, but he remained where he had been. Today he paints a dismal picture of the situation. Apparently, he is not happy. But nothing can make him happy unless he becomes a king with his own feudatory. And there is something else, Your Majesty.... His eldest son Li You is governor of Sanchuan Commandery (in north and northwest Henan, with Luoyang as its seat). After Chen Sheng's rebel forces moved through Sanchuan, the governor refused to fight them. I heard that the chancellor was in correspondence with this son of his and was aware of the situation; but I have not been able to confirm it."

"Why don't you start an investigation of the son, Zhao Gao?"

"Yes, Your Majesty," answered the eunuch.

Xiang Liang in the Battle of Dingtao (208 BCE)

BY MID-SUMMER, Xiang Liang's men, who had been on a mission looking for a royal Chu descendant, had identified a young shepherd called Xiong Xin, allegedly King Huai's grandson.[6] He was promptly brought to Xue, where he was given a wash and a full meal. A few days later, this bony rustic in his early 20s was clothed in embroidered silken royal robes and named King Huai after his grandfather. Pledging his allegiance to the king, Xiang Liang himself took the lesser title of lord of Wuxin.

Soon, on the advice of his close advisers, the shepherd-turned-sovereign began to hold court. Xiang Liang was annoyed, but decided to play along. He came to believe that there was no harm in allowing the puppet king to indulge in his delusions.

At one court session, the king issued a decree to the top generals present, "Anyone who conquers Guanzhong first shall be made its king." Nobody raised a voice against it. However, Xiang Liang was not pleased. Of course, he could overrule the decree. But he chose not to. It was nothing more than a nuisance. At that time, the conquest of Guanzhong in the west, where the capital Xianyang was, was only a remote possibility. Soon Xiang Liang led the Chu forces *north* to confront the main force of the Qin.

Xiang Liang, supported by the troops of Xiang Yu and Liu Bang, scored his first major victory against the Qin general Zhang Han at the town of Dong'e (south of Liaocheng, Shandong). He then marched his main force south to the town of Dingtao (northwest of Dingtao, Shandong) and began to lay siege. As he was taking a rest in his campaign tent in the eastern suburb, he received a message that Xiang Yu and Liu Bang had jointly sacked the town of Yongqiu to the south (in east Henan) and captured and killed the Qin governor Li You (Li Si's son).

Xiang Liang was elated. At a war council he summoned, he announced proudly, "The tide has finally turned against Zhang Han, the 'invincible' Qin

---

[6] More likely Xiong Xin was King Huai's great grandson.

general. We defeated him twice in a matter of days." The audience greeted the good news with thunderous applause and cheers.

A medium-built man with a gray beard in his late 60s stood up and started talking. "That is wonderful news indeed. However, Zhang Han is not crushed yet."

"I know," replied Xiang Liang with confidence. "But it has been raining for weeks, and the muddy roads make it impossible for him to launch a counterattack. In fact, in my view, Zhang Han's forces are seriously decimated, and the days of the Qin are numbered."

"I'm afraid there is an overabundance of confidence among our officers and soldiers," the man with the gray beard said. "Usually that does not end well."

"Don't be afraid, General Song. These troops of ours are not the same as the ones under your command when you were chancellor of Chu."

General Song Yi was at a loss what to say.

"Don't worry. I will address the confidence issue later. Right now, my overriding concern is about the Qi people, our eastern allies. According to our previous agreement, they would coordinate a two-pronged assault with us. So far, they haven't made a move. They'd better keep their promise. Otherwise, after I finish Zhang Han, I will take *them* to task!"

"Have they been notified of your intention yet?"

"Not yet. But I will send an envoy right away."

"A high-level envoy?"

"As a matter of fact, yes."

"Do you mind sending me on that mission?"

"You? Why not? General Song, you can head a Chu embassy to Qi and set off as early as tomorrow."

Song Yi departed soon afterwards. As he and his suite were advancing with celerity towards the city of Linzi (in east <u>Shandong</u>), they crossed paths with the Qi embassy, moving in the opposite direction.

"Do you want to see Xiang Liang, the Chu general?" asked Song Yi on seeing his Qi counterpart.

"That's obvious," answered the Qi envoy.

"Don't if you want to save your skin!" advised the Song Yi.

"Why?!" asked the dumbfounded Qi envoy.

"Mark my words: General Xiang Liang is finished. If you want to avoid certain death, run, and run fast!"

The Qi envoy took Song at his word and returned to Linzi, taking Song Yi and his suite with him.

***

ON THE NIGHT OF Song Yi's departure, the Chu camp at Dingtao was raided by the Qin general Zhang Han, who had received reinforcements from the Emperor Huhai. Xiang Liang, the Chu commanding general and the supreme leader of the anti-Qin cause, put up a heroic fight like his famous father. But, attacked by a vastly more numerous force, he had no chance. After the two dozen or so of his bodyguards were slaughtered to a man, Xiang Liang was hacked to pieces. And his entire army was wiped out.

Xiang Yu was laying siege to Chenliu northwest of the town of Yongqiu (and southeast of Kaifeng, Henan) with the help of Liu Bang's men when the news of his uncle's death hit. The Chu army under his command was so demoralized that he had no choice but to retreat. He and his men marched east as far as the west suburb of the city of Pengcheng (Xuzhou, Jiangsu), where King Huai of Chu had made his home.

Liu Bang and his men also fled, following a different route and ended up in the city of Dang (south of Shangqiu, Henan).

The Fate of Li Si (208 BCE)

ZHAO GAO'S INVESTIGATION OF Li You did not take place after all. Sanchuan had already been overrun by the Chu forces and Governor Li You had been killed.

At court, the Emperor was distracted by something much more serious: an exposé letter from Chancellor Li Si, in which he rebutted all the accusations Zhao Gao had made against him, and denounced Zhao as an avaricious, ambitious, dangerous schemer, and requested his expeditious removal.

But, thought the Emperor, *how did he know that Zhao Gao had badmouthed him? He must have eyes and ears right among the eunuchs working inside the palace!*

The Emperor sent Li Si a reply in which he vigorously defended the head eunuch. As he was about to order an investigation of the leaks in the palace, he received an urgent memorial jointly authored by three of the most powerful court leaders: Co-chancellor Feng, a top general also named Feng, and Li Si himself. The memorial called attention to the fact that, after reinforcements had been sent east to Zhang Han, manpower in Guanzhong was almost exhausted, and entreated the Emperor to put an immediate stop to the practice of forcing male laborers to perform transportation corvée service or frontier garrison duty, or to take part in the horrendously costly renovation project at the Epang Palace.

At Zhao Gao's urging, the Emperor summoned the authors of the memorial for questioning. After the three had taken turns to speak, the Emperor stood up and said sharply, "A true Son of Heaven is someone who can do whatever he wants without having to worry about turmoil. The late Emperor was able to do just that. During my reign, banditry has risen everywhere. You are unable to check it. Now you want to blame it on the palace project started by the late Emperor? This precisely demonstrates that you have betrayed the late Emperor and are disloyal to me."

The remonstrators were used to imperial outbursts, but accusation of "betrayal" and "disloyalty" was something new and ominous. They hastened to defend themselves. However, this incensed the Emperor even more. He regarded their protestations as acts of defiance and ordered their incarceration in the Office of the Censor-in-chief. Forthwith, the three top court leaders were frogmarched out of the audience hall. Zhao Gao was then put in charge of their prosecution.

Soon the co-chancellor and the top general committed suicide. Li Si, who refused to do the same, was thrown into jail. Zhao Gao then charged him with treason, on the evidence that he had colluded with his son Li You, the perfidious governor of Sanchuan. All his male relatives and associates were arrested on grounds of culpability by association. Having been subjected to severe floggings on numerous occasions, Li Si, who had already been in frail health before his arrest, broke and confessed to his crime.

While waiting for his sentence in the prison cell, Li Si wrote on a piece of white silk a letter of appeal addressed to the Emperor. It read,

> *I, your subject, have served as chancellor for more than 30 years. I started working for the court at a time when Qin was a small country with a military force of little more than one hundred thousand men. I did my utmost to help strengthen the military, edify the masses, promote warriors, and honor meritorious officers. Consequently, all of the Six States that rivaled Qin for dominance were conquered, and their kings captured. In the north the Hu (Huns) were dislodged and in the south the Hundred Viets were pacified. The Qin Empire was founded and the Qin sovereign became emperor. The power of the Qin state had become immeasurably stronger.*

> *If all this was a crime, I, your subject, would have died a long time ago. The reason why I survive to this day is that Your Majesty has allowed me to exert myself in serving him. Thus I sincerely wish that Your Majesty will give full consideration to my appeal for mercy.*

But the letter never reached the Emperor. For fear it might arouse in His Majesty a sense of sympathy, Zhao Gao refused to deliver it. Instead, he sent his minions to take turns to interrogate Li Si under torture until the chancellor completely gave up the hope for appeal. On Zhao Gao's recommendation and with the Emperor's full approval, Li Si was sentenced to death together with all male members of his Three Clans (that is, his father's, mother's and wife's clans).

On the day of his execution, Li Si was conducted to Xianyang's marketplace in shackles. As he was led out of his prison cart to the central crossroads, he saw another prisoner in a blood-stained uniform. When Li Si recognized it was his second son, whom he had not seen for months, he was suddenly in tears and said,

"Remember we used to go hare-hunting with our yellow doggy? How I wish I could do that again." Minutes later, father and son were put to death by severing the body at the waist.

Xiongnu and Its Neighbors

THE NEWS THAT a new *chanyu* had ascended the Xiongnu throne did not impress its neighbors, Yuezhi and Donghu. It was Donghu that first tested the resolve of the 26-year-old sovereign. It sent a delegation headed by a high-ranking official. As soon as they arrived at the Xiongnu court, the Donghu emissary and his suite were wined and dined as if they came from the most powerful country.

Then the emissary made an unpleasant request on behalf of his king for the *chanyu*'s famous stallion, who could cover 1,000 *li* in a single day. The top officials were all incensed. One of them said to Modu, "This is our treasured horse. We should never part with him."

"But I think otherwise," said Modu. "To exchange a horse for good relations with a powerful neighbor—it is certainly worth it." So on his orders, his favorite steed was delivered to the emissary.

Not long afterwards another Donghu delegation arrived with a demand that was downright insulting: the *chanyu* give up his pretty consort (*yanzhi*) to the Donghu sovereign as a token of friendship. Modu's senior officials all found the request intolerable. One of them even said, "That is going too far. They have the cheek to request the *yanzhi*! We demand to declare war on the Donghu immediately!"

"She is my beloved consort all right," replied Modu calmly. "But I am willing to give her up for the sake of friendship with our powerful neighbor." In the end, despite the loud protests of his officials, he had her sent to the Donghu emissary as a gift for his sovereign.

Along the ill-defined border between Donghu and Xiongnu there was a stretch of wasteland over 1,000 *li* across. Both sides had set up their watch posts there. Having acquired the stallion and the *yanzhi* from Modu just by asking, the Donghu king sent one more delegation to request this piece of "no-man's land" from the young *chanyu*. The submissive nature of Modu emboldened the Donghu emissary to phrase the request in such a way that it sounded like an order. Modu's senior officials were divided, with some in favor of and others against granting the request.

Finally, Modu broke his silence, saying gravely, "Land is the foundation of a country. We cannot afford to give it away. I am disappointed that some of you even suggested to accept the Donghu demand. That is tantamount to treason." He raised his eyes to stare at the vault of the massive yurt and resumed, "You all know the punishment for treason, don't you? I hereby condemn those of you who want to give up the land...to death."

His hatchet men sprang forward from the crowd and dragged the guilty officials out of the yurt, who were summarily beheaded.

Modu then retained the Donghu emissary and led his entire military force on an all-out campaign against the Donghu. The Donghu, who had taken the *chanyu*'s restraint as a sign of weakness, were caught completely unprepared. Under vicious attack by the Xiongnu cavalry, the Donghu state collapsed.

Ms. Qi

SINCE THE BATTLE OF Dingtao and the death of Xiang Liang, Liu Bang and his troops had taken shelter in a neighboring area. In November, after the main force of Zhang Han pulled out, Liu Bang's men moved north into Dong Commandery and sacked the key town of Chengwu, southeast of Dingtao (in southwest <u>Shandong</u>).

In the evening, a banquet was held, organized by Zhang Liang. The food and wine were by no means sumptuous even by wartime standards. The highlight of the evening, however, were a dozen or so colorfully dressed young female dancers performing their numbers, to the accompaniment of zithers, flutes, pipes, and drums, that showcased their slender waists. As the audience—Liu Bang and his top officers—became intoxicated with wine and enraptured with their seductive dance movements, a petite girl with a shapely figure dressed in red came on the stage, and immediately captured their attention. She swung her long dangling sleeves high into the air and bent her supple, nubile body forward and backward as she cast alluring glances at them.

That night, thoughts of the young dancer in red kept Liu Bang awake. Her mysterious, dark eyes seemed to speak to him, penetrating his soul. He had fallen for at least a dozen women before. Some of them were stunningly beautiful. But he had never been so captivated as he fell helplessly under the spell of her mesmerizing charm.

Late the next morning, while still giddy from the experience the night before, Liu Bang had a scheduled meeting with Zhang Liang. At the end of a long discussion about provisions and military stores, among other things, Liu Bang brought up the subject of the banquet, and thanked Zhang Liang for doing a great job as its organizer. He then asked, "Incidentally, where did you find the dancer?"

"Which one?"

"The one in red with long sleeves."

"You mean Ms. Qi? She is a local of Dingtao (northwest of <u>Dingtao, Shandong</u>)."

"How old is she?"

"She is 13."

"Does she live with her family?"

"No, her family died out two years ago. She has been living alone ever since."

"She is cute, isn't she?"

"Yes, indeed. If you are interested, you can take her in."

"Can I?" asked Liu Bang.

"Absolutely, my lord. You can keep her as a court dancer."

"Court dancer? No, that's not what I mean."

"You want to take her as your secondary wife?"

"Can I do that?"

"I think Ms. Lü, your principal wife, probably would not mind. But as the Lord of Pei, you may want to marry someone with pedigree."

"Pedigree? Nobody around me has pedigree, maybe except you. I was supposed to be the son of the Red Emperor. But in real life, I was just a country bumpkin. Fan Kuai was a dog butcher; Lu Wan and Xiahou Ying were peasants like myself; Xiao He and Cao Shen were petty clerks."

"But she is a professional dancer. Like courtesans, dancers are of extremely low status. Furthermore, she has to rub shoulders with men everyday, and may have gone to bed with some of them."

"Do I care?"

"I guess not," answered Zhang Liang.

Two days later when Zhang Liang informed Ms. Qi of Liu Bang's offer, she accepted it without demur. For her, it was a "no brainer." Although Liu was more than 30 years her senior, he would offer her, so long as he lived, a lifetime of protection and wealth, and save her from a precarious existence which could end any time.

Therewith, Ms. Qi was accepted into Liu Bang's entourage and not long thereafter became Liu's concubine with the title of "Lady Qi." This was not to say that Liu Bang had forgotten his wife Ms. Lü and his children. But they were in Pei, a long distance away. As Liu Bang was setting his sights on the lofty goal of uniting the realm, he had to, he thought, rise above the tender feelings for family. Nevertheless, his strong desire for feminine companionship had to be fulfilled.

Superior General Song Yi (208 BCE)

HAVING DESTROYED XIANG LIANG'S army, General Zhang Han did not march south to finish the remnants of the Chu forces. Instead, he pushed north across the Heshui (<u>Yellow</u> River) into Zhao. The Zhao army still posed a threat, and had to be removed first. Having stormed the ancient city of Handan (in south <u>Hebei</u>), General Zhang Han razed it to the ground. Suddenly, the fall of Zhao (mostly <u>Hebei</u>) was imminent.

The only power that could help defend Zhao was Chu. But Xiang Liang's death had left a power vacuum in the Chu leadership. The king in Pengcheng seemed to have accrued some power by default, but he urgently needed to appoint another powerful figure to command the military. While the obvious choice was Xiang Yu, who was the de facto heir and had proven himself as a great field commander, the king found his overbearing manner and explosive temper unbearable.

It was then that the Qi envoy arrived. At a lavish banquet held in his honor, the king asked his opinion. Without hesitation, the envoy recommended Song Yi, who had accompanied him, on grounds of his pedigree, seniority, and most importantly, prophetic power. In the absence of strong opposition from the other top leaders, the king nodded his approval. So Song Yi, who had not won a single battle for Chu, was promoted to the top job of the military—superior general. Xiang Yu, who considered himself the rightful successor to his uncle, became second in command as full general with "Lord of Lu" as his noble title; and Fan Zeng, the strategist, was appointed lower general below him.

The king summoned a war council, where his three top generals and a number of commanding officers of the Chu forces discussed two pressing military objectives: to push north to save Zhao from attack by the Qin main force under Zhang Han, and to march west to capture the capital Xianyang in Guanzhong. It was subsequently agreed that an overwhelming force should be brought to bear against Zhang Han. A much smaller force was needed to take Guanzhong. Xiang Yu offered to lead the second operation. He was anxious to revenge the destruction of Chu and to strike at the heart of the evil Qin.

The king then solicited the opinion of the generals, but none of them were willing to let Xiang Yu lead the western expedition. They all agreed that Xiang Yu was the greatest general, but he lacked benevolence, a necessary quality if he were to pacify the populace in Guanzhong, who had suffered tremendously under Qin tyranny. A case in point was Xiang Yu's recent sack of Xiangcheng. Not only had he physically destroyed the town but also butchered its inhabitants to a man. Finally, on their recommendation, the king appointed the avuncular, generous, and popular Liu Bang to head the expedition instead.

The main force of the Chu army, now under the command of General Song Yi, with Xiang Yu as his lieutenant, went on the northern expedition.

In early winter, the Chu army reached the city of Anyang (in north <u>Henan</u>), where it set up camp and stayed put for 46 days.

Anxious for battle, Xiang Yu urged General Song Yi to engage the enemy. "The Qin army has Zhao under siege," he said. "We should cross the Heshui (<u>Yellow River</u>) immediately. With us attacking from without and the Zhao resisting from within, the Qin forces will surely be destroyed!"

"Young man," responded Song Yi, "Smashing gadflies on the back of an ox doesn't solve your lice problem. It is much, much more complex. It is true that, right now, the Qin forces are attacking Zhao. But if we wait a bit longer and they lose, we can surround and destroy them. Even if they win, they will be exhausted. We can then attack and defeat them easily. In fighting the enemy with a sword, I am not as good as you. But when it comes to planning strategies, you are not as good as I." With a smile on his face, Song Yi patted Xiang Yu on the shoulder.

Xiang Yu bit his lower lip and fell silent, his hands shaking. Momentarily, he left in a huff.

By December Song Yi had shown no intention to engage the enemy any time soon. Instead, he accompanied his son on a trip east for days. When told that the son was to serve as Chu envoy to Qi, Xiang Yu was irate. To him, the Qi were no friends. It was their refusal to fulfill their promise that had caused his uncle's death.

That evening, when Xiang Yu received word that Song Yi's son would actually take up position as chancellor of Qi, his anger boiled over. He uttered through clenched teeth, "That is treason!"

Later that night Song Yi came back, entered his campaign tent, went to bed, and immediately fell asleep. By daybreak the next morning, Xiang Yu, fully armed and armored, appeared at the flap of the tent demanding to see the superior general with urgent military intelligence. The guard on duty told him that the general was not awake yet, and asked Xiang Yu to come back later. Xiang Xu turned to leave. After a few steps, he stopped and turned around. Suddenly, he made for the flap again, sword drawn, and struck down the guard with a single blow. He lifted the flap and entered. As his eyes were getting adjusted to the semi-darkness of the tent's interior, he descried an old man sleeping on a pallet. With a sweep of his sword, Xiang Yu lopped off the general's head. With the sword back in its leather scabbard, Xiang Yu reemerged from the tent's flap, his armor and hands bespattered with the blood of the two victims.

"Song Yi was a traitor. He was in secret liaison with Qi in a plot against the throne," Xiang Yu addressed the crowd that had gathered, his hand firmly clutching the hilt of his sword. "He was killed on the king's orders."

All present, generals and common soldiers alike, were too shocked to speak a word for several minutes. Then one of the leading officers said, "It was the Xiangs who revived the state of Chu in the first place. It is only proper that you, General Xiang Yu, should smash this plot. I would like to propose that General Xiang from this point forward serve as *ad hoc* superior general." The crowd was silent for a brief moment before it burst into uproarious cheers.

A special messenger was sent posthaste to Pengcheng to report on what had happened. A few days later, the man returned with the king's decree that confirmed Xiang's promotion as superior general.

Meanwhile, on Xiang Yu's orders, a team of commandos was on the move. They went east and caught up with Song Yi's son in Qi before he reached his destination, and dispatched him on the spot.

Zhang Er and Chen Yu in the Zhao Campaign (208–207 BCE)

NOT LONG AFTER ITS destruction by Zhang Han, the city of Handan (in south Hebei) gradually came back to life. Wu Chen, the self-proclaimed King of Zhao, chose it as his capital. But with its makeshift houses and pallet walls, Handan was more like an army camp than a city. It could, however, serve as a base from which to expand.

On the advice of his two top advisers, Chancellor Zhang Er and General-in-chief Chen Yu, King Wu Chen moved to consolidate the territory Zhang and Chen had captured. Two senior officers were sent on two separate strategic missions. The first was to invade Yan to the north. The second was to set up a defense line against the Qin forces in the south. General Hann Guang soon accomplished the first mission by capturing Yan, only to go it alone with himself as king.

The general on the second mission deployed his troops outside the capital as planned, but was soon suborned by Qin agents. He launched a sneak attack on Handan. King Wu Chen was caught off guard, captured, and killed. Zhang Er and Chen Yu made a narrow escape north with only the clothes on their backs.

***

IN JULU (EAST OF <u>Xingtai</u>, <u>Hebei</u>), a city northeast of Handan, Zhang Er settled down and put Zhao Xie, a member of the Zhao royal family, on the throne. With the Heshui (<u>Yellow</u> <u>River</u>) to its east, Julu had been a major urban center in Warring States times and the seat of Julu Commandery under the Qin.[7] Now it was still a sizeable city. Its defense almost entirely depended on Chen Yu, who commanded tens of thousands of Zhao troops, who had been encamped in the northern suburb.

In early 207 BCE, a massive Qin army was spotted marching toward Julu. For some unexplained reason, Chen Yu's Zhao army did not attempt to intercept it. Soon Julu was under siege. Alarmed, Zhang Er hastily dispatched two of his favorite generals, Zhang Yan and Chen Ze, as envoys to Chen Yu, bearing a personal letter that reprimanded him for failing to come to the rescue and urged him to take prompt action.

"But," responded Chen Yu, upon reading the letter, "my army is way too small to take on the mighty Qin."

"Aren't you and Zhang Er great friends?" asked Zhang Yan.

"Yes, we are friends. But I can't just throw my soldiers to the wolves."

"Still, you must save Julu right now," urged Chen Ze.

After the two envoys took turns to goad him to take action, Chen Yu relented and placed 5,000 of his men under their command. The two envoys then launched a brave attack on the enemy's flank, in a desperate attempt to thwart their assault on the city. Overwhelmed by a vastly more numerous battle-tested army, the Zhao troops under Zhang Yan and Chen Ze were either killed, captured, or scattered.

Outside Julu there were more than a dozen rescue armies sent by various local lords. But there was no unified command to coordinate their operations. Individually, none of them was strong enough to confront the Qin army.

The city defenders led by Zhang Er put up a frantic resistance. But great odds were stacked against them. As the days wore on, they exhausted their food supply

---

[7] In antiquity, the mighty Heshui (present-day <u>Yellow</u> <u>River</u>) turned northeast north of <u>Zhengzhou</u>. Today, it runs east past <u>Zhengzhou</u> and <u>Kaifeng</u> before it turns northeast.

and were reduced to cannibalism. In the meantime, the enemy forces were able to maintain the siege, well provisioned as they were by a long corridor built by Zhang Han, linking the Qin camp to the Heshui (Yellow River) to the east. Julu was expected to fall any moment.

***

HAVING ELIMINATED HIS RIVAL General Song Yi and arrogated the title of superior general, Xiang Yu moved swiftly north with an army of 20,000 men. As soon as the last unit crossed the Heshui (Yellow River), Xiang gave an order whereby all pottery cauldrons and rice-steamers were smashed, all boats were gutted, and all tents were torched; and each person was given three days' provisions. The message to the officers and men was clear: *If you want to avoid death by starvation you have to get your food from the Qin camp.*

Since the enemy had a clear numerical superiority and the armed forces under the local lords were unlikely to join the fight, Xiang Yu decided to hold off on attacking the Qin camp for a while. Instead, he ordered his commandos into action. Within hours, the long corridor was seriously sabotaged and the vital supply line of the Qin army was cut off. Meanwhile Xiang Yu had received several messages from Chen Yu that urged him to assault the Qin positions immediately. But Xiang Yu stayed put.

Soon the Qin camp began to suffer severe food shortages, as the morale of the Qin soldiers plummeted. It was then that Xiang Yu gave the order to pounce with full force.

The commanders of the various local lords' armies, too cowed to venture out of their stockaded camps, were watching from a safe distance while the Chu officers and men fought with exceptional bravery against the Qin forces, and soon bested them. Only then did the local lords' armies join the fray, finishing off whatever was left of the Qin camp.

The next morning, Xiang Yu, basking in military glory, held a rally to review the troops and parade prisoners of war. The local lords all fell on their knees and crawled through the main camp gate as a way to show their respect for and submission to Xiang Yu; with one voice, they all claimed him as the superior general of *all* the armies.

Chaperoned by Chancellor Zhang Er, the young Zhao king, dressed in his best ritual robes, came out of the city to pay homage to Xiang Yu, the savior of Julu, and to give thanks to the local lords who had taken part in the battle (even though belatedly). Zhang Er lost no time in spotting the boyish face of Chen Yu.

"Why didn't you come to the rescue when Julu was under attack?" Zhang Er asked Chen Yu in a censorious tone.

"My army was grossly outnumbered," answered Chen Yu. "Besides, after your envoys contacted me, I gave them 5,000 of my men to engage the enemy."

"Speaking of the envoys, what happened to them?" Zhang Er asked again, menacingly.

"They perished in action," Chen answered.

"How could they?"

"Well, they led my men into battle and were overwhelmed by the enemy."

"How come you are still here? Aren't you the general-in-chief of the Zhao army?"

"I didn't go on the suicide mission."

"What is a general-in-chief for if he is not willing to save his king?"

"Hey, do you think I love to have this post? If you want it you can have it." Chen Yu produced his general's bronze seal with its decorative ribbons and thrust it into Zhang Er's hands.

"Hell no, I don't want it!" shouted Zhang as if bitten by a snake.

Chen Yu let go of the seal, and it fell to the ground. With anger on his face, Chen Yu stomped off.

The famous friendship between Zhang and Chen was irrevocably broken.

"Madman" Li Yiji (207 BCE)

Hannibal's brother Hasdrubal Barca was killed in battle in central Italy. Hannibal's plan to conquer Italy was now a lost cause.

BY SPRING, LIU BANG lord of Pei had made limited headway on his western expedition. In the township of Gaoyang (southwest of Qixian, Henan), east of Daliang (northwest of Kaifeng), he stopped for a respite.

Inside the township, a destitute scholar in his late 60s called Li Yiji felt inspired by the visit. He saw in Liu Bang an enlightened leader who could recognize his own talent as a strategist even though people around him called him "madman." For years, Li had been working as a gatekeeper in the ward (neighborhood) he lived in.

Li met an old neighbor of his, who was now Liu Bang's chevalier, and said, "I heard that the Lord of Pei is not only a kindly person, but a great visionary. I want to see him."

"I have to warn you, Madman," said the chevalier, "Liu Bang despises Confucian scholars like you. Once, a gentleman came to see him, wearing a scholar's robe, complete with cap and sash. Liu Bang snatched the cap off his head and pissed into it! Still want to see him?"

"Yes," answered Li Yiji, undaunted. "Could you arrange for an audience?"

So with the help of the chevalier, Li Yiji was admitted into Liu Bang's residence the following evening. As Li was led into a spacious room he saw his host sitting on the edge of a large canopy bed with his legs spread apart. Two maids in their teens were busy washing his feet.

The visitor, without making an obeisance, began with a question, "Sir, do you want to help the Qin fight the local lords? Or do you want to help the local lords destroy the Qin?"

"You stupid bookworm!" shouted Liu Bang. "The world has suffered terribly under the Qin. That's why the local lords have risen against them. How can you even suggest 'helping the Qin fight the local lords?'"

"Well, my point is if you want to fight the local lords, I don't have anything to say to you; if you want to fight the Qin, I have got a plan that can probably help."

"What plan?" said Liu Bang, who had now stopped washing his feet and dismissed the two maids with a wave of his hand as he looked curiously at this grey-haired and grey-bearded visitor, whose voice, without pretentiousness or fear, seemed to exude authority and wisdom.

"But, for the sake of common decency, don't you think I, an old man, deserve to be treated with more respect?"

Suddenly, Liu stood up to invite the visitor to the seat of honor, saying, "I sincerely apologize for my most improper behavior."

Li Yiji then launched into a long talk about how Liu Bang might unite the local lords and eventually become the overlord of the realm. Liu Bang listened attentively, but not without a tinge of suspicion. However, Li's eloquence and analytical brilliance fascinated Liu Bang so much that when the time came for dinner, he invited the old man to join him. Li, who had been semi-starved for months, gladly accepted the invitation. And the talk continued.

Over several goblets of wine, Li finally divulged his plan: "With an army of barely 10,000 men, it is suicidal for you to march on the capital of the mighty Qin. What you should do instead is capture the town of Chenliu (southeast of Kaifeng) first. It is a transportation hub with a plentiful supply of grain. The magistrate is an old acquaintance of mine. I have a one-in-two chance of winning him over with a decent offer. If he refuses it, you can then attack. Even then I can probably help you from within." Liu Bang liked the idea and therewith sent Li on this mission.

When the magistrate saw Li Yiji, his first reaction was to treat him to a meal and send him away. However, he soon realized the man standing in front of him was no longer the impoverished gatekeeper, but Liu Bang's adviser. He changed his mind and invited him to a private dinner. It did not take long before Li Yiji's eloquence and Liu Bang's generous terms convinced the magistrate to submit.

A couple of days later, Li Yiji persuaded his brother, Li Shang, with 4,000 troops under his command, to join Liu Bang. Liu Bang was so elated that he raised Li Yiji to lord of Guangye. As Liu Bang's ambassador-at-large, Li would deal with the various local lords. Li's change of fortune was nothing short of extraordinary. In a matter of days, the gatekeeper everybody dubbed "madman" morphed into Liu Bang's senior counselor and top diplomat.

***

SINCE HE LEFT XUE, Zhang Liang had been working hard to rebuild the state of Hann in Yingchuan and surrounding areas. But the new regime he had helped set up was soon under threat by the Qin army.

It was about this time that Liu Bang's expedition army marched into the commandery. After capturing a number of small towns, Liu Bang laid siege to Yangdi, the commandery seat. The defenders offered a stubborn resistance that cost Liu Bang dearly. Upon sacking the city, Liu Bang, perhaps giving in to pressure from his generals, ordered a massacre of its inhabitants, which was contrary to his usual practice. But nobody knows exactly why it happened.

Zhang Liang, who had been frustrated by his inability to expand the territory for Hann, was only too pleased to join forces with Liu Bang. By then he had begun to suspect that Liu Bang was the prophesied son of a dragon.

To Liu Bang's delight, Zhang brought with him a group of battle-hardened Hann officers.

Not long afterwards, Hannwang Xin, a descendant of the Hann kings, also came over to Liu's camp. A middle-aged man of extraordinary height, Hannwang had proven his military talent in the recent struggle for the revival of Hann.

From Yingchuan, Liu's army turned southwest and headed for Nanyang Commandery. Soon it reached the outskirts of the city of Yuan (<u>Nanyang</u>, <u>Henan</u>), the commandery seat. This was a well-fortified city surrounded by a deep fosse filled with water and protected by a strong garrison. Considering how many of his men had lost their lives in the recent battle for Yangdi (the seat of Yingchuan), a much less defensible city, Liu Bang decided to bypass Yuan and proceed west in pursuit of his main goal, the capture of Guanzhong.

But Zhang Liang begged to differ, saying, "The Qin army is still numerous. And the Qin capital Xianyang is protected by natural barriers. So it is dangerous to leave a hostile Yuan in our rear."

That made Liu Bang change his mind. Instead of marching his troops west, he ordered them to envelope Yuan in three rings. As a general assault was imminent, the commandery governor's envoy arrived in Liu's campaign tent for negotiation. Liu Bang's terms for surrender were so generous that the envoy accepted them as soon as they were offered. Thus Liu Bang took another major city without an arrow being shot. In exchange, the city and its populace were spared the ravages of war, the governor was enfeoffed as marquis of Yin, and the Qin garrison troops were either let go or incorporated into Liu Bang's army on a voluntary basis (see Map 1).

Liu Bang's treatment of Yuan followed the example of Chenliu on a larger scale. That would become a pattern to be repeated over and over again, which stood in sharp contrast with the indiscriminate butchering of the inhabitants of conquered cities by Xiang Yu.

In the wake of the victory at Yuan, a string of Qin cities and towns opened their gates to Liu Bang's army.

Zhang Han King of Yong (207 BCE)

AFTER THE BATTLE OF Julu (in south Hebei) the Qin army under General Zhang Han had clearly lost its numerical superiority and a stalemate had prevailed between the Qin and Chu camps separated by the Zhang River. Unhappy with the situation, the Qin Emperor Huhai sent an envoy to excoriate Zhang Han for his failure. Zhang responded by sending his lieutenant Sima Xin to Xianyang to offer an explanation for the situation and request more reinforcements.

Upon arrival in Xianyang, General Sima Xin was promptly received by Zhao Gao, the new chancellor. Like most people in the military, Sima Xin was contemptuous of castrated men, and had a hard time concealing his real feelings. Feeling offended by Sima's lack of deference, Zhao deliberately kept him waiting. Three days later, the hot-tempered general left empty-handed.

Upon return Sima Xin gave his boss an unflattering portrayal of the court in Xianyang. "Zhao Gao, a despicable mean fellow, now dominates the court," he said. "The other officials are useless. If you fight the Chu forces and win, Zhao Gao will go after you out of jealousy. If you don't win, he will have you executed for losing the battle. Either way, you are doomed!"

Zhang Han was bitterly disappointed. *How can I*, he thought, *make the elusive and distrustful Emperor understand the mounting challenges I have to face in fighting the rebels? How can I persuade His Majesty to send additional military stores and reinforcements? How can I protest my loyalty?*

After spending a long time agonizing over how to address the court's concerns, he sat down to write a letter to the Emperor. But the writing was interrupted by an adjutant, who came in with a bamboo message container. Zhang Han was intrigued by the unfamiliar shape of the red seal on it. As soon as the adjutant left, he broke the seal, took out a letter on silk, and started reading.

It began with a sharp reminder of the fate of the great Qin generals of the recent past, Bai Qi and Meng Tian. Both had great victories under their belt, and both were forced to die by their own hand. "You, on the other hand," the letter continued, "despite early victories, have recently lost more than one hundred thousand troops. All over the realm, rebellion is getting out of control. At court, Zhao Gao has never stopped slandering you. Worried about being executed by the Emperor, Zhao will surely make a scapegoat out of you. So for your own sake, you should join the local lords in a common struggle agsint the Qin."

Zhang Han shifted his eyes to the last line of the letter and saw the sender's name "Chen Yu." After he had broken up with his mentor Zhang Er, Chen Yu had become an independent warlord. Maybe he had an ulterior motive in writing this letter, but what he said was by and large true and it was unlikely that he was doing Xiang Yu's bidding.

Although Chen Yu's letter was not enough to sway Zhang, it, together with Sima Xin's report, made him painfully aware of the precariousness of his own position. He took one more look at his unfinished letter on bamboo, wrapped it up and put it away on a long table where dozens of bamboo documents lay, documents that did not need immediate attention.

While Zhang Han remained indecisive over his next move, an unexpected turn of events finally forced him to make up his mind.

Suddenly his troops were attacked and bested by Xiang Yu's superior army on three consecutive occasions. Despairing of further help from Xianyang, Zhang surrendered with his massive army, which effectively brought an end to Xiang Yu's war against the Qin in the north. An ecstatic Xiang Yu raised Zhang Han to king of Yong with Guanzhong as his feudatory.

Palace Coup (207 BCE)

AS CHANCELLOR, ZHAO GAO was *de jure* the leader of the bureaucracy, the most powerful man at court. However, as someone who had lost his sex organs under the knife in childhood, he had been plagued by an overwhelming sense of insecurity all his life and was always looking for ways to assert his power. On one rare ceremonial occasion when the Emperor met with the court officials, a deer was brought into the audience hall at Zhao's request.

"I would like to present to Your Majesty this auspicious *horse* on behalf of the entire court," Zhao Gao said.

"That's not a horse," the Emperor said, laughing. "That's a deer!"

"Your Majesty," said Zhao Gao reverently but firmly, pointing at the deer, "A horse." He then turned to the officials present, and asked, "Don't you agree?"

"Yes, a horse," most of them echoed. Only a few murmured, "A deer," instead.

In the weeks that followed, all those who had agreed with the Emperor and said, "A deer," were thrown into jail.

Zhao Gao knew fully well that, for all the power he had amassed at court, he could never become a sovereign himself, being a castrated man. The best he could do was exercise power in the name of a gullible figurehead such as Huhai. Still, when Liu Bang's rebel army was bearing down on Guanzhong, the Emperor Huhai became antsy and his unpredictable outbreaks grew more frequent, which often threatened the lives of the eunuchs around him.

In September, Liu Bang leading an army of several tens of thousands strong stormed the Wu Pass (in the southeast corner of <u>Shaanxi</u>), and started the final march on the capital. The news sent the entire court into a panic.

One morning, Zhao Gao was absent at court because of an illness. The Emperor felt absolutely grouchy, having just woken up from a nightmare in which a white tiger had bitten and killed one of his carriage horses. A court diviner was summoned to perform a divination, which identified the Jing River to the north as the source of trouble. The next morning, the Emperor with his entourage made a trip to the Wangyi Palace on the Jing River in the northwestern suburb. There a sacrificial ceremony was conducted, in which four slaughtered white horses were sunk into the river.

Having thus appeased the river god, the Emperor sent an envoy to Xianyang to summon Zhao Gao and returned to a basilica in the suburban palace for lunch and a siesta.

***

IN LATE AFTERNOON, the Emperor woke up to the sound of screaming and swords clanging. He shouted for his eunuch attendants, and an old domestic came in.

"What's going on?" asked the Emperor.

"There is a palace coup," answered the eunuch.

"Why didn't you let me know earlier?"

"I could have been killed if I did."

A fully armored man in his 30s broke into the spacious room, sword in hand, followed by a group of armed soldiers, and made for the Emperor.

"You arrogant, murderous tyrant!" shouted the man sharply to the Emperor.

"Where are my eunuch officers, attendants, and guards?"

"They were either cut down or arrested."

"Who are you?"

"Yan Le, magistrate of Xianyang County."

"The husband of Zhao Gao's adopted daughter?"

"Yes."

"Can I see him?"

"The chancellor? No."

The Emperor fell silent, his face the color of a corpse.

"Can I quit and live as a prince in a commandery?" the Emperor continued.

Yan Le shook his head.

"A marquis of 10,000 households?"

Yan Le shook his head again.

"Can I live out the rest of my life with my wife as a commoner?"

"No, no, no!" Yan Le said emphatically. "In fact, this is what I have for you." He waved his hand, and a soldier walked up to the Emperor with an oblong black lacquer tray on which was placed a sword.

"Is that the chancellor's order?" asked the Emperor.

"Yes."

The Emperor picked up the sword, struck his neck, and fell.

***

AT COURT, ZHAO GAO held an emergency meeting at which he announced the execution of Huhai, the enthronement of his uncle Ziying, and the demotion of the country from empire to kingdom, in the hope of appeasing the wrath of the rebels. Ziying, known for his humaneness, was the perfect stooge Zhao had been looking for.

According to state ritual, Ziying was to go to the Palace of Fasting to purify himself for the ceremony to be held at the Ancestral Temple, where as new king, he was to receive the imperial jade seal. When the new king failed to appear at the temple at the specified time, Zhao Gao became worried, and came to the Palace to look for him. It was there that by order of King Ziying another eunuch officer sprang on the eunuch chancellor and hacked him down. Zhao Gao had thought of Ziying as a weakling, and could never imagine that he had harbored an intense hatred for him all along. Completely taken by surprise, the eunuch chancellor finally fell victim to his own machinations.

Liu Bang in Guanzhong (207 BCE)

ON A BRIGHT NOVEMBER morning,[8] escorted by his top generals and thousands of officers and men, Liu Bang lord of Pei, armored cap-a-pie, ambled on a bay horse out of his camp in Bashang in the eastern suburb of Xianyang. He stopped on the dirt road and looked ahead.

In the distance, along the road that led from the eastern entrance of the capital, a long procession was moving slowly towards him. At its head was Ziying clad in white, riding in a white open carriage drawn by four white horses. As the carriage pulled up in front of Liu Bang, the King of Qin with a silk string on his neck descended from it; he knelt down, holding up in his hands the imperial seal, the tiger tally, and the scepter. Liu Bang dismounted to receive the imperial objects. From that moment on, the mighty Qin ceased to exist.

After his advance troops occupied Xianyang, Liu Bang under heavy armed escort entered the city. Accompanied by Xiao He, Zhang Liang, Fan Kuai, and other senior officials and officers, he went directly to the palace, which was in complete disarray—most of the basilicas were in disrepair, and some lay in ruin. Still, the opulence of the imperial residence was very much evident.

The palatial edifices, with their imposing height, majestic façades, and richly furnished interiors, were at once awe-inspiring and extravagant. Ornately decorated tents were seen everywhere in the basilica courtyards. The Palace Stable and Palace Kennels were still holding countless thoroughbred horses and exotic pet dogs and watchdogs.

And there were beautiful palace ladies—thousands of them! It was such a contrast to what Liu Bang had been used to as a peasant who could hardly make ends meet, as a forest outlaw, and as a rebel leader. Overcome by a sense of awe and wonder, Liu Bang remained speechless for quite some time. In the end, he murmured to his attendant gentlemen, "I want to move into the palace tomorrow."

Fan Kuai responded, "Please don't, my lord. Do you still want to be the lord of the world? If you do, you'd better stay away from these things. They were the reason

---

[8] The Han followed the Qin in starting the year with the 10th month (November to December). of the Chinese calendar. Liu Bang entered Guanzhong in the 10th month of the first year of Gaodi 高帝, which falls in 207 BCE instead of 206 BCE.

why Qin fell in the first place. I beg you: at the end of the day, please return to the camp in Bashang!"

To Liu Bang this giant of a man with a swarthy complexion was a fierce warrior and a loyal follower, but his ideas, especially those on strategy, should not be taken too seriously.

"Thanks, Fan Kuai," said Liu Bang. "However, King Huai decreed that whoever conquers Guanzhong first shall be its king. That has become the King's Covenant with all the lords. Now that I've done it, why shouldn't I rule over Guanzhong from Xianyang?"

"In my opinion, Lord of Pei," said Zhang Liang, "Fan Kuai has a point. Undoubtedly, you have taken on the tyrannical Qin successfully. But much has yet to be done to eliminate the bandits and unify all under Heaven. To achieve that, you must adopt a policy of simplicity and frugality. If, as soon as you enter the capital, you begin to seek pleasure and comfort, you can only add to the suffering of the people. Before long, you too will become a hated tyrant."

Liu Bang listened quietly, his face turning crimson. Then he asked petulantly, "Don't I deserve to be the King of Guanzhong?"

"Of course you do. But your enthronement has to be put off. You must have heard that Xiang Yu just named Zhang Han as king of Yong with his fief in Guanzhong. Clearly he wants to use Zhang as his vassal to control the area. If you declare yourself king of Guanzhong now, you will surely incur the wrath of Xiang Yu."

Liu Bang fell silent as his face darkened. He waved his hand to dismiss his advisers and spent the night in the palace. The following morning, except for a small force to guard the palace and government quarters, granaries, and marketplaces, he ordered his army to withdraw to Bashang. Meanwhile he deployed some of his units to garrison the newly conquered territory. One detachment went east to the Hangu Pass to protect his flank. The pass was the most important strategic point that linked the Central Plain to Guanzhong, vital for the defense of Xianyang and its environs.

***

BY EARLY DECEMBER, it was getting very cold at night. Liu Bang and his men still camped out outside the city. In the capital and its suburbs, after the tumultuous initial phase of military occupation, things began to quiet down. However, because the legal system of the previous regime had broken down, too many crimes were committed everyday.

To bring peace and order to the capital area, Liu Bang summoned elders and magnates from various counties for a meeting to make a major policy announcement.

"Folks," said Liu Bang, addressing the whole crowd. "Not long ago, the local lords and the Chu king entered into this Covenant. That is, whoever takes Guanzhong first shall be its king. I took Guanzhong before anyone else. But I won't assume the title of king now, because I am still waiting for confirmation by the local lords. For the moment, I am taking on the duties of the provisional leader of Guanzhong.

"By that authority, I request your cooperation in keeping the order so that officials and civilians can live in their homes peacefully. By that authority again, I hereby proclaim the Three Article Code. That is, firstly, whoever kills shall be killed; secondly, whoever maims another person shall be punished accordingly; thirdly, whoever robs or steals shall also be punished accordingly. That's all." The audience cheered.

"Under the harsh Qin laws," Liu continued, "if you are labeled a libeler, you would be punished by the extermination of your entire clan; you could be executed in the marketplace simply for gossiping. Not any more. I will free you from those harsh laws and give you a break. From this point on, I will govern with benevolence."

The audience roared with excitement; someone shouted, "The Lord of Pei, we are with you!" Many murmured their assent.

Following the meeting, Liu Bang sent former Qin officials to various counties, townships, and settlements to spread the message. The contrast between the oppressive rule of the Qin and benevolent government of Liu Bang seemed like night and day. The ecstatic locals thronged the army camp, bringing with them pigs, oxen, and sheep as gifts. They set up tables with wine and food to feast Liu Bang's men. To the surprise of everyone, Liu's men would neither accept the gifts nor touch the wine and food, because, they said, their leader had warned them: "Under no circumstances should we allow the civilians to spend their own money for us!"

Hongmen Banquet (206 BCE)

Scipio Africanus soundly defeated the Carthaginians in Spain; Spain was now a Roman province, and Scipio was elected consul.

AFTER HIS CONQUEST OF the Julu-Handan area (south Hebei), Xiang Yu marched the main force of the Chu army west. Its ranks had been swollen by the surrendered Qin troops. Problems soon arose. Xiang Yu could not bring himself to trust these men, most of whom hailed from Guanzhong, the heartland of the Qin. When a rumor was bruited about that some disgruntled former Qin officers were planning a revolt, acting on his impulse, Xiang Yu had all the former Qin army men, totaling 200,000, surrounded, and then killed en mass, with the exception of a few top generals. But that still left Xiang in charge of the largest army in the realm, over 400,000, a number often exaggerated to be one million.

In January, Xiang Yu's army arrived at the Hangu Pass, the famous landmark in the west Central Plain (Henan) near the Heshui (Yellow River). But Liu Bang's troops had closed the pass and blocked the passage of the Chu army. This seemed to confirm an earlier report that Liu Bang wanted to make himself king of Guanzhong with Ziying (the ex-king) as his chancellor. In a fit of fury, Xiang Yu issued an attack order. Ying Bu, now one of Xiang's leading generals, stormed the pass in short order, and subsequently all the captured defenders were butchered (see Map 1).

The westward advance of Xiang Yu's army continued until it reached Hongmen, where it encamped. It was just about 20 *li* from Liu Bang's camp in Bashang.

At a war council held in a campaign tent, Fan Zeng, now Xiang Yu's top adviser, observed, "We all know that Liu Bang was an avaricious amasser of wealth and a notorious philanderer. After he entered Guanzhong, however, something weird has happened; he has taken neither treasure nor women. Does that mean the old lecher suddenly had a change of heart? No! This only shows that he harbors hidden ambitions. Yesterday, an aeromancer informed me that there is a five-color aura above Xianyang in the shape of a dragon or tiger. The dragon, as you all know, is a symbol of imperial authority. Clearly, it shows that someone is coveting the throne. And the person can only be Liu Bang. We must attack him forthwith to counteract this prophetic omen before it is too late!"

After a few murmurs of approval, the campaign tent fell quiet. Fan Zeng went on to lay out a foolproof plan for action. First, an invitation would be sent, asking Liu Bang to attend a banquet at Hongmen. At the banquet, Fan Zeng would drop a hint by holding up his jade pendant, and the bodyguards of General Xiang Yu would kill Liu on the spot. If he refused to come, however, the king would have the moral authority to attack him for insubordination.

***

THAT NIGHT, A MAN in his early 50s, clad in coarse hemp garments, appeared at the gate of Liu Bang's camp, asking to see Zhang Liang, whom he claimed to be his friend. Momentarily, Zhang Liang came out, and was startled to see the Chu general Xiang Bo, Xiang Yu's uncle, in a peasant's outfit.

As soon as Zhang Liang and his guest were inside the camp, the latter said, "You saved my life before, it is time I saved yours."

"What?!" Zhang Liang was completely clueless.

"You must flee right now when there is still time," urged Xiang Bo. "Liu Bang will have to attend a banquet at Hongmen tomorrow. If you go with him, and I am sure you will, your life will be in great danger."

"But," answered Zhang Liang, "to abandon the Lord of Pei at this most dangerous moment is an act of betrayal. I wouldn't do it even if I could. In fact, I must go warn him right now, if you would excuse me."

Zhang Liang left, only to return in about ten minutes.

"The lord wants to see you," said Zhang Liang urgently.

"But if I am late, I will be in serious trouble," answered Xiang Bo.

"I promise it won't be long," said Zhang Liang as he dragged his friend along.

When Xiang Bo entered Liu Bang's campaign tent, he was greeted by a very appreciative host, who insisted on addressing him as "elder brother" and poured wine for him.

As Xiang Bo started sipping his goblet, Liu Bang said with a sigh, "Some people said that I want to be king and rebel against General Xiang Yu. That cannot be further from the truth. After I took Guanzhong, I imposed strict discipline upon my troops, forbidding them on pain of death to harm the masses. On my orders, officials and commoners were registered, and government storehouses were sealed and placed under heavy guard. Why? Because I have been waiting for the arrival of General Xiang Yu so as to personally deliver Guanzhong into his hands."

"I understand that, my lord," answered Xiang Bo. "How about the troops you posted at the Hangu Pass."

"I posted a garrison there to keep bandits and other hostile forces at bay and to keep Guanzhong safe. Anyone in my shoes would have done the same. The fact is I have neither the intention nor the temerity to challenge the authority of the general."

"I see," said Xiang Bo as he took another gulp of wine.

Liu Bang went on to talk fondly about a ceremony that had taken place a few years back where Xiang Yu and he had taken a solemn oath together to be sworn brothers for life. He then asserted emotionally that he would never break that oath.

Eventually, Xiang Bo rose to leave, promising to bring Liu Bang's message to his nephew Xiang Yu.

***

THE FOLLOWING AFTERNOON, Liu Bang, Zhang Liang, and Fan Kuai, escorted by about one hundred cavalry, arrived at Xiang Yu's camp at Hongmen. Liu Bang and Zhang Liang were led into Xiang Yu's massive tent, where a banquet was prepared for them.

About a dozen guests and hosts were seated around a rectangular space. Each had his own low table for food and wine. Liu Bang found himself seated at the center of the south side facing north, in a position that symbolized vassalage and submission. Facing him on the north side was Fan Zeng, the "Second Father" (as he was called by Xiang Yu), in the seat of honor. Xiang Yu and his uncle Xiang Bo sat on the west side while Zhang Liang sat on the east side.

After a three-course meal, wine was served and hosts and guests began drinking. Momentarily, Fan Zeng stood up and proposed a toast to the distinguished guests, downing the wine in his goblet in one swallow. He then winked at Xiang Yu while holding up his white jade pendant. Xiang Yu seemed to take no notice, and the party continued. Fan Zeng held up the jade pendant two more times, but received no response on either occasion. Perplexed, he rose to exit the tent. Presently, Fan Zeng came back, bringing with him a stout man in his early 30s.

At the strike of a gong, the tent fell silent, and Fan Zeng introduced Xiang Zhuang, Xiang Yu's cousin, who went into the central space to offer belated birthday felicitations to Xiang Yu. Then Fan Zeng said, "On this festive occasion, I would like to invite Xiang Zhuang to stage a performance to entertain our guests."

Addressing Xiang Yu, Fan Zeng continued, "General, would you please allow your cousin to perform a sword dance?"

Laughing, Xiang Yu said, "Of course!"

When two attendant gentlemen standing behind Xiang Yu began beating drums, the "dance" was underway. Xiang Zhuang moved rhythmically up and down the central space, flourishing his sword in the air to strike and parry, amid intermittent cheers from the spectators. Suddenly he jumped in front of Liu Bang's table, his sword raised high above his head, and struck. There was a loud clanging sound of two swords clashing—Xiang Bo had joined him for a duo dance.

Zhang Liang, who had watched all this with horror, quietly left the tent and rushed to the camp's gate where he found Fan Kuai.

"The lord is in danger!" said Zhang. "Xiang Zhuang is doing a sword dance, but his real intention is to kill the Lord of Pei!"

"Son of a bitch," shouted Fan Kuai as he went rushing toward the tent, shield and sword in hand.

Outside the entrance to the tent, Fan Kuai saw this muscle-bound, tall soldier armed with a halberd standing guard. Fan knocked him down with his shield and barged in. Rushing to the front of Xiang Yu, Fan Kuai stared at him with unblinking angry eyes, his hair bristling. By then the dancing and drumming had stopped.

Xiang Yu knelt up swiftly on one knee. He clasped his hand around the hilt of his sword and asked, "Who are you?"

Zhang Liang hurriedly announced, "Carriage Gentleman Fan Kuai."

"Brave man!" exclaimed Xiang Yu. "Wine!"

An attendant brought a large stoup of wine. Fan Kuai threw down his shield and sword, held the stoup high with both hands, and poured the wine down his throat.

"Bravo!" shouted Xiang Yu. "Give him a pork shoulder."

The attendant brought Fan Kuai a large chunk of raw meat, dripping blood. Fan Kuai placed it on the shield, chopped it up with the sword, and swallowed the meat piece by piece.

"Brave man!" shouted Xiang Yu. "Join us!"

After Fan Kuai was seated beside Zhang Liang, more wine was served. The feast continued for another half hour. Xiang Yu, somewhat intoxicated, stood up to propose a toast to Liu Bang. But Liu was nowhere to be found.

Zhang Liang rose and said, "Liu Bang felt indisposed and left about 20 minutes ago. He had drunk too much and thrown up. In fact, he was in such a terrible mess that he was not able to bid good-bye in person. But he has left some gifts: a pair of white jade *bi*-discs for General Xiang Yu, and a pair of jade cups for the Second Father Fan Zeng." As he said so, Zhang presented the precious objects.

Xiang Yu placed the jade discs on his seat. Fan Zeng put the jade cups on the floor. Suddenly, he unsheathed his sword and slashed them into pieces, saying with a sigh, "The churl doesnot deserve my advice. Mark my words: it is Liu Bang who will conquer all under Heaven!"

To Hanzhong (206 BCE)

WHEN LIU BANG was back in his camp in Bashang, it was well past midnight. His narrow escape from Hongmen left him feeling thoroughly exhausted. He crawled into bed and instantly fell asleep, only to be awoken a few moments later by a bunch of anxious senior officials led by Xiao He and Cao Shen. Having learned what had happened at Hongmen, they were worried that the cunning old fox Fan Zeng could make Xiang Yu change his mind at any moment. Liu Bang had no choice but to issue an urgent order for departure. His army then struck camp and set off into the dark night.

After marching hastily westward for about 200 *li*, Liu Bang and his army turned south as a massive mountain of the Nanshan Range came into view. A narrow road wound upwards until it disappeared into the woods. Protected by a small troop of cavalry in front and behind, Liu Bang rode up to a mountaintop. From there he began a slow descent into a small dale. About 500 paces on, he arrived at the foot of a gigantic rock mountain with steep sides. Bald-headed vultures, perched on cliff tops or circling in the air, gave out shrieking cries. The road ahead had imperceptibly morphed into a cliff-hugging plank path (*zhandao*). The planks were resting on wooden supports wedged into the cliff face. The path was not steep, but was in serious disrepair because of warfare in recent years. Dozens of vanguard troops were dispatched to repair it to make it travel-worthy, securing loose planks and replacing missing and rotten ones. Liu Bang and his army had set up camp in the rocky bottom of the dale and waited. They did not resume the trek until the following morning, after an "all clear" signal had been given.

The path only allowed the passage of a single person at a time. Everybody, including Liu Bang himself, had to dismount and walk on foot. Along the path stretched long ropes that served as handrails. Below was a ravine up to hundreds of feet deep. Occasionally, when an unlucky person or horse slipped and fell off the path, plunging into the abyss, vultures would swoop down in search of their prey.

Liu Bang and his army struggled along the path for the greater part of a day. As the sun was setting, the path dipped sharply before it came to an abrupt end.

Suddenly, they found themselves moving along the Baoye Vale, which marked the beginning of a new territory, Hanzhong. The treacherous crossing was finally over, and Liu Bang was riding his horse again.

After the march continued for about half an hour, Liu Bang's heart sank when he heard a series of crackling sounds. He turned his head and saw a massive fire in the distance, consuming the plank path along the cliffs and sending palls of smoke spiraling upwards. The rearguard units were carrying out his orders. The destructive measure proposed by Zhang Liang was necessary to keep Liu's potential enemies at bay, because it announced to the world that Liu Bang was determined to stay in Hanzhong and Ba-Shu (Sichuan) to the southwest for good.

***

AFTER DARK, A STARRY sky imperceptibly spread overhead. As Liu Bang trotted along the rugged path on horseback, his spirits sank. The rough, craggy landscape seemed to suggest that he was destined to live out the rest of his life in a remote, god-forsaken place.

Someone approaching from behind addressed him, "Your Highness."

"Yes, Zhang Liang?" answered Liu Bang.

"There is a rare phenomenon in the sky."

"What it is?"

"Look," Zhang Liang said as he pointed a finger to the east. "The conjunction of the Five Planets in the stellar lodge Well (Jing)."

"What the fuck does that have to do with anything?" asked Liu Bang impatiently.

"A Five Planet conjunction is an auspicious omen. It is especially meaningful when it occurs in the lodge Well, the allotted field of Qin, that is, Guanzhong, on earth. You just took Guanzhong and should be its king according to the Covenant. This phenomenon shows that divine power supports you when you pursue earthly power and you will eventually be the sovereign of all under Heaven."

"That seems unlikely to me."

"Trust me: the astrological sign points to your return to Guanzhong before long."

"Is that right?" asked Liu Bang, and his spirits somewhat lifted.

Part II.

The Chu-Han War

Kings and Marquises under Xiang Yu (206 BCE)

WHEN XIANG YU and his massive army were marching through Liu Bang's abandoned camp in Bashang, it was already broad daylight. Hundreds of ash piles were scattered across the campsite. Some of them were still smoldering. It seemed that Liu Bang and his men had just decamped in a great hurry. Fan Zeng urged that a large force be dispatched immediately to chase after Liu Bang while there was still time. Xiang Yu ruled against it and marched his army into the Qin capital, Xianyang, instead. As the new master of Guanzhong, he sent a report to King Huai, seeking his endorsement.

Outside the main palace gate, Xiang Yu was greeted by Ziying, the dethroned last sovereign of the Qin, accompanied by a dozen or so attendant gentlemen.

Without dismounting, Xiang Yu ordered to have the former king taken into custody and turned his battle-hardened troops loose on the neighborhoods and markets. They pillaged and plundered; carried out the wholesale killing of male residents regardless of age; and ravaged young women before forcing them into slavery.

Fan Zeng was horrified. He made a desperate attempt to stop the mayhem. "If you abuse the people like the First Emperor," he argued, "you will lose the hearts and minds of the people and never gain all under Heaven. Furthermore, Xianyang should be preserved as the new Chu capital to keep an eye on Liu Bang and his men in Hanzhong and Ba-Shu."

Xiang Yu responded, "The reason my uncle and I raised the standard of rebellion was to revive the state of Chu and destroy the state of Qin. The hatred against Qin and its evil people is visceral. When I was barely nine years old, a Qin army of 600,000 under General Wang Jian defeated the Chu army, and caused the death of its commanding officer, Xiang Yan my grandfather. They went on to butcher the Chu officers and men by the hundreds of thousands and wipe out the state of Chu. Every day I am consumed by a strong desire for revenge. I am sorry, Second Father. I simply can't help it!"

"But you can't kill off all the people in Qin."

"I am not going to kill them all. As for Xianyang, I don't need to move my capital there just because Liu Bang is nearby in Hanzhong. In fact, Second Father, your worries about Liu Bang and company are way overblown. Now confined to a sparsely populated, semi-barbarian area, they have little chance of threatening our mighty Chu. On the other hand, it is an indisputable fact that Xianyang was the evil capital where the First Emperor called home. I have to level it to the ground to avenge the death of my grandfather, my uncle, and my fellow countrymen."

"Don't you know, in so doing, you will create hundreds of thousands of enemies in Qin."

"You know what, Second Father, I really don't give a damn."

"It's insane!" Fan Zeng shouted.

***

AFTER SEVERAL DAYS OF wanton slaughter of the local residents, the Chu soldiers set public structures in and around Xianyang ablaze, including the lavishly built Epang Palace, the Mausoleum at Mount Li, and hundreds of palatial halls in the suburbs.

All this did not prevent a brave adviser called Mr. Hann from attempting to stop the violence and arguing in favor of making Xianyang the capital. He believed that because of its geographical isolation and fertile land, Xianyang was the ideal place from which to dominate the realm.

"Well, Mr. Hann," said Xiang Yu facetiously. "Too bad Xianyang is gone. You should have told me earlier. Now I will have to make my capital in Pengcheng instead."

Frustrated with Xiang Yu's lack of vision, Mr. Hann commented to his friends, "A monkey in man's clothing."

When Xiang Yu heard of the insult, he ordered to have the adviser thrown into a boiling cauldron and cooked alive.

By then King Huai's reply had arrived, which ordered Xiang Yu "to act according to the Covenant." Xiang Yu was furious. *That would mean that Liu Bang would be crowned king of Guanzhong*, he thought. *But the reality is, Liu yielded Guanzhong to me. He did not even take the title!*

***

WHILE THE CONFLAGRATION OF Xianyang was still raging, Xiang Yu had Ziying executed, in spite of the vehement protest of Fan Zeng. He then marched with his troops back east across the Central Plain to take up residence in Pengcheng.

Acknowledged as the *primus inter pares* by the various local lords, Xiang Yu took for himself the title of "Hegemonic King of West Chu," which was a notch higher than that of other kings.

He also gave King Huai of Chu, that apology for a sovereign, a grand title, the "righteous emperor," before transferring him to Chen County (<u>Chenzhou</u>, south <u>Hunan</u>) down south, which was virtually in the middle of nowhere.

Upon the more powerful lords Xiang Yu bestowed kingly titles and territories. Most notably, Liu Bang was raised to king of Han with Hanzhong (south of the Wei River) and Ba-Shu (mostly <u>Sichuan</u>) as his fief. Wu Rui, who had joined the Xiangs with his son-in-law Ying Bu, was raised to king of Hengshan. Ying Bu himself was raised to king of Jiujiang. Both had their fiefs in the central Jiangshui (the <u>Yangzi</u> east of <u>Wuhan</u>) valley.

The old state of Yan in the northeast was enfeoffed to a certain General Zang Tu. Hann Guang, formerly Wu Chen's general who had declared himself king of Yan, was enfeoffed in Liaodong further to the north.

The core area of Guanzhong, however, was divided up among the ex-Qin generals Zhang Han, Sima Xin, and Dong Yi, all raised to kings (see Map 2).

Annoyed by Zhang Liang's "defection" to Liu Bang's camp, Xiang Yu penalized Hann Cheng king of Hann by demoting him to a marquis, and then had him secretly killed. Someone called Zheng Chang, a former county magistrate from the Wu area and Xiang Yu's friend, was then enfeoffed as the new king of Hann.

Suddenly, peace broke out all over the realm. But it was founded on political marriages of convenience and on the unreliable allegiance of the newly enfeoffed local lords to Xiang Yu. It could not last unless Xiang Yu moved fast to integrate the feudatories held by the lords into a viable state. However, Xiang Yu, the general *par excellence*, was apparently content with the pseudo-feudal system he had helped create, and was in no hurry to change it.

The Checkered Life of Hann Xin

LIU BANG KING OF Han settled in Nanzheng (in south <u>Shaanxi</u>), the seat of Hanzhong Commandery. This city was known for its association with a tragedy that had happened in 771 BCE. In that year, the Rong barbarians from the west had invaded and sacked the capital Hao (<u>Xi'an</u>, <u>Shaanxi</u>), and captured the Duke of Zheng, a Zhou royal, and the Zhou sovereign King You, both of whom later died in exile. Some of the duke's subjects in Zheng (based in central <u>Henan</u>), on hearing the unlucky news, fled south to a settlement in Hanzhong, which was then named Nanzheng ("south Zheng"). Liu Bang, like most people, considered the tragic association bad luck, and did not feel at home in the new environment. Enveloped by mountainous and rugged terrain, Nanzheng did not have at its disposal a large swath of fertile land that could produce enough grain to support a growing population.

With the cliff-side plank path destroyed, Hanzhong no longer had direct access to Guanzhong to the north. Still, Liu Bang could not get Guanzhong off his mind. When Xiang Yu's decree of enfeoffment arrived that conferred upon him the title of King of Han but kept Guanzhong out of his reach, Liu Bang was furious. For a while he even seriously considered the idea of launching a war on Xiang Yu to retake Guanzhong. But in the end he had to give it up—persistent remonstrances by his associates such as Fan Kuai, and particularly Xiao He, convinced him that in order to recapture Guanzhong he had to build a firm foundation in Hanzhong and Ba-Shu first.

It was about that time that Xiao He, now chancellor, became acquainted with a talented young officer and recommended him for promotion. In Xiao's view, this young man could play a crucial role in the re-conquest of Guanzhong. The man was the legendary Hann Xin, later regarded as the greatest military genius of the age.

Growing up in abject poverty in the town of Huaiyin (east of <u>Qingjiang</u>, <u>Jiangsu</u>), Hann Xin taught himself to read and became well versed in the classics and books on strategies and the art of war. As a young adult, he tried his hand at business and attempted to get recommended for some low-level official posts, but failed in both endeavors. He was so poor that when his mother died he could not even afford to give her a proper burial. For quite some time, he was a drifter, relying on the largesse of acquaintances and strangers for subsistence. He would visit the home of a community head on a regular basis. He always arrived at breakfast time and stayed for food. Hann Xin charmed this man with engaging conversations on strategy and military tactics. But, eventually, the charm wore off. On one visit, Hann Xin was left alone to wait in the hall for hours while the couple ate their breakfast in the bedroom. Hungry and angry, Hann Xin left never to return.

On another occasion, having gone without food for two days, he sat down on the bank of the moat that ringed the city to try his luck at fishing. A middle-aged laundry woman was washing silk flosses nearby. When she saw the emaciated, desperate countenance of the young man, she gave him a bowl of rice. Hann Xin devoured it with gusto. In the next 20 days and more, Hann came to the same spot every day. Each time the woman fed him. At their last meeting, Hann Xin said, "Madam, I just can't tell you how grateful I am to you. I'll repay you for your kindness, I promise."

"Shut up, you moron," said the woman angrily. "I did it out of pity. I did not expect a return from someone like you, who can't support himself!" Hann left the scene, humiliated.

As he wandered about in the marketplace, Hann wore a sword across his back, like someone aspiring to be a warrior. But his white smooth skin, gentle manner, and soft voice seemed to suggest that he was a bookworm.

Once a young butcher accosted him and shouted to passersby, "This tall man wearing a long sword looks like a brave man. But, I dare say, at heart, he is a coward." Turning to Hann, he continued, "If you are a man, stab me in the chest! If not, crawl through between my legs!"

Hann Xin looked down with his bright eyes at this burly man half a head shorter than he for a few seconds and got down to his hands and knees and crawled through, much to the hilarious amusement of the spectators.

Hann got his first break when the Chu army under Xiang Liang arrived in his home area and was recruited as his personal guard. After Xiang Liang's death, he joined Xiang Yu, who promoted him to halberd-holding gentleman. Although his was a lowly position, it gave him direct access to the top leadership. It was then that he befriended Zhongli Mo. Several years Hann Xin's senior, Zhongli was already a top general under Xiang Yu. He saw in Hann Xin a great military strategist, and recommended him to Xiang Yu for promotion to general-in-chief. Xiang Yu invited Hann to offer his views on strategy several times, but failed to adopt any of them, nor did he give Hann a promotion.

After Liu Bang took over Shu as king of Han, Hann Xin left Xiang Yu to join him. Soon he was implicated in a conspiracy and slated for execution. After 13 of his confederates had been beheaded, his turn came. When Xiahou Ying, the general in charge of the case, came to see him for the last time, he was impressed with Hann's great looks. So Xiahou set him free on the spot, and recommended him to Liu Bang, who then promoted him to commandant.

Through several long talks with Hann Xin, Chancellor Xiao He became convinced that he was the greatest military genius alive. Repeatedly, Xiao recommended him to Liu Bang for a higher post, but Liu Bang saw no reason to promote him any further before he proved himself in the battlefield.

Several months later, a disillusioned Hann Xin fled. At that time, many officers and men in the Han army were from the east and were often homesick. Among them desertions were fairly common. But to Xiao He, Hann Xin was different. He might be able to help Liu Bang conquer all under Heaven, or just as easily help Liu Bang's rival to crush him. Without hesitation, Xiao He went chasing after Hann Xin.

When told of Xiao He's disappearance, Liu Bang let out a primal cry that was at once terrifying and painful, as if he had lost his two hands.

Two days later Xiao He reappeared, much to the relief of Liu Bang, who greeted him with a mixture of joy and anger, asking, "What the fuck did you run away for?"

"I didn't," answered Xiao He reverently. "I just chased after a runagate."

"Who?"

"Hann Xin."

"A bunch of crap! That lousy drifter who crawled between the legs of a butcher? More than ten generals have given me the slip recently, and you did not chase after any of them. Do you think I believe your stupid story about Hann Xin?"

"Please trust me," said Xiao He sincerely. "Those generals are easy to come by, but there is only one Hann Xin. If you, Great King, want to stay in Hanzhong forever, Hann Xin is of little use. But if you want to conquer the world, he is the only one who can help you accomplish that goal."

"Of course, I am not going to stay in this hellhole of a place forever," answered Liu Bang. "In fact, I would like to retake Guanzhong as soon as tomorrow."

"Then you must use him. Otherwise, he will run again."

"All right, for your sake, I am going to name that son of a bitch general."

"Even as general, he probably will not stay."

"How about making that son of a bitch general-in-chief?"

"Great! I am sure that would be satisfactory to Hann Xin."

As Liu Bang was about to summon Hann Xin for the appointment, Xiao He stopped him and said, "You cannot just order him around like a child. This appointment is serious business. May I suggest that it be made on a propitious day with proper ritual?"

"You know what you are, Xiao He? You are fussy as hell!" shouted Liu Bang impatiently.

"Are you going to do it, Great King?" asked Xiao He insistently.

"Yes, I'll do it," acquiesced Liu Bang grudgingly. "But you are fussy as hell!"

General-In-Chief (206 BCE)

TWO MONTHS AFTER a public announcement on the search for the general-in-chief, the date of the appointment arrived. To the surprise and disappointment of most, Hann Xin was offered the most coveted post in the military with much fanfare. At the conclusion of the ceremony, Liu Bang king of Han invited his newly appointed top general for a drink.

"How can you help me, General-in-chief?" asked Liu Bang.

"Your Highness, your goal is to conquer the entire realm, and the only man standing in your way is Xiang Yu, is he not?" asked Hann Xin

"Without a shadow of a doubt."

"I was his guard until recently and I know a thing or two about him. Xiang Yu is brave, fierce, benevolent, and powerful. Great King, you cannot compare with him in all four areas, can you?"

After a brief pause, Liu Bang said, "I'm afraid I can't."

"That is what I think. But let me give you a closer analysis of his character. In combat, he can scare away a crowd of one thousand simply by roaring. But he cannot promote talented officers to high posts. So his bravery is that of an ordinary commoner. To people around him, he is respectful, affable. If one of them falls ill, he will even weep and share his food and drink with him. But when his meritorious generals are desirous of the noble titles they deserve, he simply cannot part with them. So his benevolence is that of a petty-minded woman. No doubt, Xiang Yu is the overlord to whom all the local lords have submitted themselves. But, instead of basing himself in Guanzhong, he moved to Pengcheng, a city of little importance for conquering the realm. He awarded kingly titles to his favorites, forced the Emperor to move south of the Jiangshui (Yangzi), and laid waste to many of the cities he conquered after butchering their inhabitants. People under his rule obey his orders. But they do so not out of respect and love, but out of fear. He is the hegemon all right, but he has lost the hearts and minds of the people. So his strength can easily be turned into weakness."

Hann Xin stopped to take a sip of wine.

"What you, Great King, need to do," continued Hann, "is just the opposite. Appoint the brave and reward them well, and there will be no one you cannot conquer; enfeoff your meritorious subjects with cities and towns, and there will be no one who will not submit; use those officers and men homesick for the east to conquer the Central Plain, and you will scatter any enemies.

"As for the Guanzhong area, the Three Qins, it is now divided among those three ex-Qin generals—Zhang Han, Sima Xin, and Dong Yi. But when they were in the service of the Qin, many Guanzhong soldiers lost their lives. Zhang Han, in particular, tricked his army into surrendering to Chu. Later, Xiang Yu butchered all 200,000 of them, with the exception of those three. No wonder they are absolutely hated by the locals. You, on the other hand, eliminated the harsh Qin laws, and enforced the Three Article Code among your troops. When you were forced out of Guanzhong, the locals were heart-broken. They now are all hankering to have you as their king. With a bit of preparation, you can start moving east and eventually retake Guanzhong. There you will be welcomed with open arms."

"Excellent!" exclaimed Liu Bang.

After the meeting, Liu Bang king of Han started planning his next strategic move: the re-conquest of Guanzhong.

***

AT THE CENTER OF Ba-Shu to the southwest of Hanzhong was the Chengdu Plain, an extensive area drained by the Min River, a major tributary of the Jiangshui (<u>Yangzi</u>). During the Warring States period, Governor Li Bing of Qin had constructed an irrigation system (the Dujiang Weir) along the Min, which had turned the plain into the granary of the southwest. For Liu Bang, it was vital that a steady flow of grain was maintained from Ba-Shu to feed his expeditionary army. He had assigned this crucial task to Xiao He, his most trusted administrator. Most of Liu Bang's men, however, remained in Hanzhong, going through training for the invasion.

Two months into the preparation, Liu Bang realized that it was not possible to keep it a secret forever. Sooner or later, something would leak out. He began to have doubt about the soundness of his plan. Hann Xin then tried to reassure him, arguing that with the rising tensions in the east, Xiang Yu would not have the time and energy to confront him in the west. Instead, Liu was more likely to deal with Zhang Han, Sima Xin, and Dong Yi—the kings of Three Qins—as his primary enemies. Fortunately, they were much weaker adversaries than Xiang Yu himself.

Liu Bang found the argument convincing, but he still had doubts. "How can we," asked he, "prevent our troop movements from being detected when we eventually launch the invasion?"

"Your Highness, leave that to me," answered Hann Xin.

Hann Xin then sent hundreds of soldiers into the western section of the South Mountains south of Guanzhong. There, their task was to rebuild the plank path along the cliff-side. But judging by the slow progress of the project, it would take a long, long time, perhaps many years, before Liu Bang's men could make passage through the path possible.

In response, Zhang Han beefed up the defenses at the north end of the path along the northern slopes of the South Mountains.

In September, not long after the summer was over, Zhang Han received an urgent report that a numerous Han army led by Hann Xin had debouched into Guanzhong from Chencang further to the west. Zhang Han king of Young rushed to intercept the invading army, only to be worsted. The Han army went on to encircle troops under the other two Guanzhong kings, Sima Xin (King of Sai) and Dong Yi (King of Di), forcing them to surrender.

***

XIANG YU WAS ALARMED at Liu Bang's victory in Guanzhong and but took a little comfort in the fact the commanding general of Liu's army was that former guard of his Hann Xin. Admittedly, what Hann Xin did—throwing Zhang Han off the trail with the repair of the plank path and taking an abandoned route at Chencang to surreptitiously enter Guanzhong—was brilliant. But it precisely revealed Hann as someone only capable of skulduggery. Hann's victory, Xiang determined, could only be a one-off event, a lucky hit.

Furthermore, having the Huai and Jiangshui (Yangzi) valleys under his control, where he was more at home, Xiang Yu felt very secure and was not terribly interested in another western expedition.

Then he received a letter from Zhang Liang, which claimed that Liu Bang's occupation of Guanzhong was justified by the Covenant with the Righteous Emperor, and that Liu had no desire to move further east. Xiang Yu found the rationale unconvincing. But he decided to focus on the east, where places like Qi (Shandong) worried him even more.

***

ONE NOVEMBER EVENING, the Righteous Emperor was drinking with his companions in the audience hall of his "palace," a spacious structure converted from the Chen County Office building. Since his settlement in the new domain (Chenzhou, Hunan), he had been very unhappy. When Xiang Yu had first ordered him to move, he had resisted, backed as he was by Fan Zeng and his own advisers, who considered the new domain a place of banishment in a semi-civilized area down south. The Emperor, though a ceremonial sovereign, had done nothing to deserve such a treatment. However, Xiang Yu, who never forgot the trouble caused by the Covenant, had threatened to remove the Emperor by force. Begrudgingly, the Emperor had left Pengcheng to settle in Chen County.

That evening, the Emperor was throwing a drinking party as he had done many times since his arrival. As he was getting a bit tipsy, a troop of masked warriors crashed into the hall, weapons drawn. Three intruders wrestled the Emperor to the ground, while others chased after his companions, making short work of them.

One tall man motioned to have the Emperor dragged to his feet, and pulled down his black mask to reveal a beautiful face marked by a black scar in the center of his forehead.

"Have I ever done you wrong, King of Jiujiang?" asked the badly shaken Emperor.

"No," answered Ying Bu, while an underling brought a pot of wine to the Emperor.

"Why?" asked the Emperor.

"Well..."

"This is by order of the hegemonic king?"

"You know why. You were nothing but a shepherd from Chu. You should know your place, not order people around."

"I didn't."

"How about this decree on who should be the King of Guanzhong?"

The Emperor, in tears, started gulping down the wine, and murmured, "I wish I never left the country."

The Emperor fell; on Ying Bu's orders, his minions lifted the limp body and hauled it away.

Chen Ping (205 BCE)

EARLY IN THE YEAR, as Xiang Yu was busy fighting the Tians in the Qi area (Shandong), Liu Bang made a "perfidious move," as Xiang Yu called it, and ventured out of Guanzhong into Shaan County (west of Sanmenxia, Henan). This was tantamount to breaking the promise Zhang Liang had made on his behalf only recently and declaring total war on Xiang Yu. The Campaign of the Central Plain was underway.

As the Han army marched through the Central Plain, the cities and towns threw their gates open or offered very little resistance. Thanks to Liu Bang's generous policy on deserters from Xiang Yu's camp, Chu officers and men began to switch allegiance in increasing numbers.

In early spring, while in the town of Xiuwu (west of Xinxiang, north Henan), Liu Bang hosted a night banquet in his campaign tent to honor some of the key Chu officers who had recently joined the Han camp.

As the banquet drew to a close, Liu Bang stood up and said smilingly, "Now my adjutants will take you to your dormitories. Welcome home!"

The officers also stood up and applauded. They all made for the tent flap except for a tall man in his early 40s, who walked toward Liu Bang.

"Your Highness, can you spare a moment of your time?" asked the man.

"Oh?" responded Liu Bang. "Have we met before?"

"Yes, Your Highness. At the Hongmen banquet."

"You are?"

"Chen Ping."

"Yes, of course. I just received a memorial from Wei Wuzhi, recommending you for high office. Wei, I have to add, is one of our most respected counselors."

As they sat down by a small table, Chen Ping, by the king's leave, gave his take of the current situation. The Han army, accordingly to him, would conquer the Central Plain soon, and would then move east to fall on Pengcheng where Xiang Yu was headquartered. Pengcheng, which had few natural barriers, could be an easy target so long as the Chu main force under Xiang Yu was bogged down in Qi.

"After Pengcheng?" asked Liu Bang.

"To tell the truth, Great King, I can't see that far into the future."

"Of course, perhaps nobody can," concurred Liu Bang, who, by now, had been impressed with Chen's knowledge and wisdom, and above all, extraordinary physiognomy. When he learned that he had served as commandant under Xiang Yu, Liu Bang appointed him to the same rank. Chen would work directly under the king as his carriage gentleman with the duty of supervising the army generals.

The next morning, Chen, while in his new residence, received a "first-meeting present" of 200 catties of gold, courtesy of the king.

After a few days' rest, Chen went to work as the king's man, inspecting the barracks. Wherever he went, he would be wined and dined and oftentimes loaded with gifts by the generals. But beneath this façade of friendliness, widespread resentment brewed. They abhorred the fact that an outsider had been given a key post on account of his soft, white skin and good looks. Some of those who had risen from the ranks openly questioned his qualifications. "How many troops has he commanded?" "How many battles has he fought and won?" "Could he have gotten this post without his good looks?"

These questions, which Liu Bang dismissed as petty jealousies, only deepened his trust of Chen Ping.

Then, Generals Guan Ying and Zhou Bo submitted a joint memorial in which they detailed the treacherous acts Chen Ping had committed—sleeping with his sister-in-law, abandoning his former masters, and taking bribes, among others. They demanded in unequivocal terms for his removal. To this Liu Bang had to respond. Guan Ying and Zhou Bo were his top commanders, who had never collaborated on anything, let alone a memorial, before. Liu Bang called Chen Ping into his tent and showed him the nasty document.

Chen Ping responded, his face turning red with anger, "Adultery with my own sister-in-law? Well, it is nothing but baseless gossip. When I was a young man I lived with my elder brother, who worked the five acres of land we had then while I studied fulltime the ideas of the Yellow Emperor and Laozi and the art of war. My sister-in-law did not like it a bit. So she pestered my brother with complaints. My brother was so annoyed that he expulsed her. While she was there, I never once had improper contact with her. If I did, my brother would not have allowed me to stay for so long.

"Why I left my former masters? It is a complex story. But I promise I can explain it to your satisfaction. Not long after the Chen Sheng Rebellion erupted, I entered into the service of Wei Jiu (Wei Bao's brother), who had been raised to king of Wei by Chen Sheng. But it did not work out. Not only was I maligned at the Wei court, my advice went unheeded. And I saw no point in staying with the king. So I left to join Xiang Yu. There I was admitted into his inner circle. But soon I found it hard to work for him. He got an explosive temper, and was pusillanimous when it came to rewarding his subordinates. Besides, when he had to make a crucial decision, he was often hesitant.

"Recently, Sima Ang, head of the minor kingdom of Yin, rebelled against Xiang Yu, and I was tasked to fight him. Subsequently, I attacked and conquered the kingdom, only to lose it again to Your Highness' army. Xiang Yu was furious beyond control, threatening to kill me. That was the key reason why I left Chu for Han. I had no choice if I wanted to live. Moreover, I was drawn to Your Highness' reputation as a wise leader and great listener."

"I see," said Liu Bang. "How about 'taking bribes from the generals?'"

"Well, it is true that when I visited the barracks, the generals treated me very well, and even on some occasions heaped gifts upon me. But they have never influenced my judgments. Your Highness can check my reports. I think they can stand up to scrutiny. As for the gifts including the 200 catties of gold given by Your Highness, they are still there. If Your Highness suspects me of doing anything wrong, I will give back the gifts, resign the post, and leave."

"All right, I'll make a decision soon," said Liu Bang.

A few days later, Liu Bang summoned Wei Wuzhi for questioning. To the memorial by Guan Ying and Zhou Bo Wei Wuzhi responded, "When I recommended Chen Ping I thought that he had this rare talent for strategic thinking that can help Your Highness win the war against Chu. I still think so today. Sleeping with his sister-in-law and taking money from the officers—these are character issues. Even if they were true, which are quite unlikely, they would have nothing to do with warfare and the fate of Han. As for why he left Wei for Chu, then Chu for Han, I think his explanation is quite reasonable."

After seeing off his guest, Liu Bang issued an order to gift Chen Ping with 500 catties of gold and promote him to the prestigious post of "army protector of the center" (*hujun zhongwei*).

The Pengcheng Campaign (205 BCE)

IN THE MONTHS FOLLOWING Liu Bang's departure from Guanzhong, his Han army had tipped the balance of power in his favor. One of his most formidable generals, Hannwang Xin, had sacked more than a dozen Hann cities, eventually forcing its king, Zheng Chang, to surrender. In acknowledgement of Hannwang's merit, Liu Bang raised him to king of Hann.

In May, with much of the Central Plain already under his control, Liu Bang king of Han led his gargantuan army, numbering 560,000 men, in a decisive move east to invade the home territory of his archrival Xiang Yu.

Several independent warlords had contributed troops to the campaign. General Peng Yue, a native of Changyi (south of Juye, Shandong), alone sent no less than 30,000 of his men. Active in the Central Plain and Qi (Henan and Shandong), Peng was a tall man of great charisma with broad shoulders and an angular face.

When the Chen Sheng Rebellion broke out, Peng only had under him a few hundred footloose soldiers. Once he issued an order to his men to gather for an operation at sunrise the following morning, a few of them arrived late. He ordered the last arrival executed. He then sacrificed his head to the gods at a makeshift altar. That unhappy event marked the beginning of a long, distinguished military career. Before long, the rabble of outlaws under his command was turned into a disciplined loyal army.

Pleased with Peng Yue's generous gesture, Liu Bang raised him to chancellor of Liang (Wei) under King Wei Bao.

***

AFTER A SHORT RESPITE at the town of Waihuang (northwest of Minquan, Henan), Liu Bang's expeditionary army began the final leg of the long march. In less than a week, it reached the suburbs of Pengcheng. On Liu's orders, the Han troops fanned out to environ the Chu capital.

As we have noticed, Pengcheng was not an ideal city for someone interested in conquering and dominating all under Heaven. It did not have the geographical advantages of Guanzhong or Qi, nor did it have the cultural and political dominance of the Central Plain. But, situated at the confluence of the Si and Gu Rivers, it was a vital transportation hub between east and west and north and south. Thus the region was absolutely essential for control of the Huai and Jiangshui (Yangzi) valleys. For Liu Bang, Pengcheng had an added level of importance: it was the place where Xiang Yu called home.

The terrain of Pengcheng was essentially flat and smooth with low-lying hills scattered in the suburbs. The city was surrounded by the two great rivers hugging its north and west walls and by a moat protecting its south and east walls. Because of the wide expanse of the waterways encircling the city, fixed bridges instead of drawbridges were built across them.

From reports sent by his agents planted inside the city, Liu Bang learned that Xiang Yu had left only 10,000 men as its garrison force. Incredibly, most of them were posted near or on the north and west walls, leaving the south and east sides vulnerable.

After an emergency war council, where Liu Bang gained the unanimous support of his top generals with his battle plans, he issued an order for the general assault.

Early the next morning, with great fanfare, the Han army started storming the city walls and gates on all four sides. Heavy siege engines and specially trained wall-storming commandos were deployed in attacking the south and east gates and walls. Before the Chu commanding officers could rush reinforcements to where they were most needed, the south gatetower had fallen, and the gate was thrown open from within. Led by its forward troops, the Han army poured in like water gushing through a breached dam. By dusk, Pengcheng, the capital of Chu, had given up fighting.

Liu Bang's men soon moved into the palace. They took captive of more than a thousand palace personnel including hundreds of court ladies from the basilicas, and seized hold of a large hoard of gold, silver, jade, and other precious objects from the state storehouses. On Liu's orders, half of the treasure was set aside to support future military operations; the rest would be used to reward the officers and men.

As the Han soldiers were taking over the marketplaces and neighborhoods of the city, some behaved like a typical occupying army, brawling, looting, and ravaging local women. Alarmed, Liu Bang re-issued the Three Article Code, as a stern warning against harassing local businesses and residents. After a number of severe punishments including beheadings were carried out, order returned to the city.

Liu Bang then announced a general amnesty and an unprecedented ten-day grand celebration. All the troops, except for those on garrison duty, were given a time-off. They spent days and nights, feasting, drinking, and merry-making. In the main basilica of the palace, Liu Bang hosted nightly parties for meritorious officers. They were wined and dined and entertained by acrobatic shows and musical performances. About two dozen stunningly beautiful Chu girls who danced for the parties were eventually admitted into the service of the king.

At these parties, the officers never failed to shower Liu Bang with praises for his brilliant execution of the war. Far from sounding sycophantic, the praises were actually rooted in reality. Finally, it began to dawn on him that the victory he had won afforded him the prospect of becoming the overlord of the realm, and that his own military talent was proven to be superior to that of Xiang Yu, or anyone else for that matter. In fact, deprived of his home base, Xiang Yu was clearly on his way out.

∗∗∗

HUNDREDS OF *LI* AWAY in the north, Xiang Yu had been campaigning against the Qi forces under the Tian clan (in <u>Shandong</u>). As he was laying siege to Linzi he received intelligence from his agents that, leading a mammoth army, Liu Bang was heading east for Pengcheng.

"That churlish clown should never be allowed to lay his hands on Pengcheng!" exclaimed Xiang Yu.

"It is intolerable, Great King," echoed Zhongli Mo.

"I must set off immediately. Pengcheng is in danger."

"How about the rest of the army?"

"I am deputizing you and General Long Ju to take over command. During my absence, I want you to avoid battle with the Qi forces. Wait until I come back!"

Leading an elite force of 30,000 cavalry, Xiang Yu moved south with celerity. When he was about 70 *li* north of his destination, he received an intelligence report marked "urgent." Upon opening the bamboo container, he retrieved a piece of silk. The moment he glimpsed at the message, his face darkened.

"We have to pitch camp," he said to his adjutant.

"Where?"

"Here in Xiao County."

"But if we make a final push, we can reach our destination before dark."

"I know that. But there is no more point in trying to make a surprise attack in the Han army's rear. Pengcheng has been taken!"

Stunned by the sad news, one of his top commanders asked, "What are we going to do, Great King?"

"Revise the battle plan and get ready to sack the city."

"Wouldn't it be better to request reinforcements from Zhongli Mo and wait until they arrive?"

"I don't think so. If we wait, the Han scouts will find out about us. That will jeopardize the entire campaign. To win a battle, size matters. But what matters more is the element of surprise."

The next morning, a team of unarmed Chu commandos dressed as peasants and vendors headed for Pengcheng and entered the city through the north gate before dark. At night, after all the gates had been closed, they attacked and strangled the gate guards with bare hands and seized control of the gatetower after disarming or dispatching the soldiers posted there. Quietly descending from the gatetower's steps, two commandoes rushed into the gate archway and unbarred the gate. The others lit up a small fire behind an embrasure on the second floor of the gatetower.

After the sack of Pengcheng by Liu Bang, most of the troops sent by the local lords had withdrawn, and some of Liu Bang's own forces had moved back to the Central Plain. Still there remained a formidable army in excess of 200,000 in the area. However, only a small force was left to defend the walls and gates, and most of the Han troops were billeted in the barracks and civilian houses in and around the city. They were resting or partaking in the festivities.

As soon as Xiang Yu saw the signal from the north gatetower, he issued an attack order. After the Chu commandos seized control of the bridge on the Si River, Chu riders galloped swiftly across and charged through the open gate into the urban area. Xiang Yu who knew every street and alley like the back of his hand led a troop of 500 on horseback, making a beeline for the palace. After breaking into the palace, they headed for the main basilica.

By then, the Han officers and men were thrown into total consternation and took flight before any meaningful resistance was organized. Those going north found themselves trapped near the confluence of the Gu and Si Rivers. Attacked by Xiang Yu's vanguard, more than 100,000 of the Han troops lost their lives: either drowned in water, killed by arrows, or trampled by both horses and men.

The remnants fled south in the opposite direction and were forced to stop at the Sui River beyond the southern suburb. In complete disarray, they milled around, pushing against one another this way and that. So many of them fell into the river that the water stopped flowing. The Chu forces waiting in ambush chose this moment to strike and, in the ensuing chaos, wiped out more than 100,000.

***

SINCE HER HUSBAND LIU BANG became an outlaw in the Mangdang Mountains, Ms. Lü had continued to live in Pei, his adopted hometown. She had been the de facto head of the Liu household, consisting of herself, two young children, and an old man, Liu Bang's father. She had to work in the field, gather wood, do the cooking and the dishes, and take care of the kids and her grumpy father-in-law. Every now and then, when stragglers or tramps showed up at the gate, she had to coax them away. Although previously her husband had hardly helped with household chores or work in the field, without him, the household became much harder to manage. The weight and care of life took its toll; and the smooth face of this small-town beauty became lined with wrinkles around the eyes and mouth, although it still possessed some charm. Oddly, however, over the years, the hardship had only strengthened her character. Having overcome the initial feelings of despair and abandonment, she was more determined than ever to pull through.

Following the Chen Sheng Rebellion, things had begun to take a turn for the better, as Liu Bang had become, by turns, a rebel leader, the Lord of Pei, and the King of Han. With the help of some Han officers, they had moved into a much bigger house. At Liu Bang's request, Shen Yiji, a baby-faced local man in his 30s, moved in to help manage the household. He was very handy inside and outside the house and soon Ms. Lü took a liking to him. But at best, Mr. Shen was a smart butler, and no substitute for the kids' father. His presence only sharpened her longing for reunion with her husband in spite of his blemishes. Then she heard of Liu Bang's marriage with Ms. Qi. Even though taking a concubine was socially acceptable, and her status as the matriarch of the Liu household was by no means compromised, she experienced a terrible feeling of being let down. That night, after the kids and the old man had gone to sleep, she slipped into a room in the east wing, and crawled into bed with her butler.

As Liu Bang was on his way to Pengcheng, he sent her a letter delivered by his personal messenger, which did not reveal his military plan but suggested that he would lead his troops into Pei soon and told her how much he missed her, his father, and the kids.

About two weeks later, everything changed. Suddenly, Pei, the adopted hometown of Liu Bang, was in danger of being overrun by Xiang Yu's ruthless army. Thousands of local residents, many of whom had close ties with Liu Bang and his followers, poured into the streets of the city and its suburbs as they attempted to flee war and avoid retribution.

Ms. Lü would have joined the exodus a few days before, had it not been for the stubborn resistance of her father-in-law. The old man just wanted to be left alone in the last years of his life and die in familiar surroundings. Eventually, she decided to evacuate the entire family no matter what, and requested the butler Shen Yiji to hustle him into the horse-drawn carriage, in which she and her two children were seated waiting. Shen jumped into the dickey, and off the carriage went into the semi-darkness of the early evening. Thus Ms. Lü and her household embarked on a westward journey in search of Liu Bang.

About an hour into the journey, the carriage stopped in a village, where she left her children in the care of her parents and sister. And the journey continued.

***

HAVING NARROWLY SURVIVED the Pengcheng debacle, Liu Bang and his party turned north and then west to head for the Central Plain. Under the escort of a few dozen cavalry, Liu Bang galloped desperately for about two hours until his Chu chasers faded into the distance. He then stopped to take a rest by the roadside. As he lay down under a tree, Liu felt overwhelmed by a sense of physical and emotional exhaustion, having experienced the most exhilarating victory and the most devastating defeat in his entire life within the short space of a week.

About an hour later, Liu rose to his feet, but found himself unable to ride his horse, even after two attendant gentlemen had helped him into the saddle. From that point on, he had to continue his journey on a horse-drawn cart commandeered by his soldiers, with one of his trusted associates, Xiahou Ying lord of Teng, as his coachman.

Liu Bang was pleasantly surprised when he was reunited with his eleven-year-old daughter, Yuanyuan, and four-year-old son, Yingying. The team he had sent to rescue his family had found the two kids in his father-in-law's home outside Pei. But the rest of his family were missing.

No doubt, Liu Bang welcomed his children to his "royal cart." But before long he began to have doubts. The two kids, although small, added to the weight of the cart, and slowed down the speed. Speed was everything when traveling down this treacherous road infested with robbers, bandits, and hostile forces.

Yingying the boy at first did not recognize his father at all, and kept crying out of fright, in spite of his sister's effort to calm him. Eventually, he quieted down somewhat, only to start whining about wanting to eat rice.

Yuanyuan herself had no trouble calling Liu Bang "daddy," but requested breaks to relieve herself a bit too often. Each time, she would go behind a tree or into the millet field to do her business while hidden from view. One break took more than ten minutes, and the father, growing impatient, shouted, "Hurry up, stupid ass! We'll leave without you." When the daughter came rushing back to the cart, Liu Bang had already shifted his attention to her brother, threatening to beat the crap out of the little brat, who had started crying again.

As soon as the caravan arrived in a large village to get food and water, Liu Bang boiled over. Preoccupied with how to defeat his rival Xiang Yu, he had no time for nor interest in learning how to bond with his children. He violently pushed the two poor kids, kicking and screaming, off the cart. Only a vigorous argument by the coachman, who reminded him that the next town was only 20 *li* away, saved the terrified children from abandonment.

Liu Bang in Xingyang (205 BCE)

FINALLY, AT XIAYI (Dangshan, Anhui), Liu Bang and his party were able to stop for a much-needed respite. Liu held a special meeting to assess the overall situation. After the Pengcheng fiasco, Sima Xin king of Sai and Dong Yi king of Di, both vassals to Liu Bang in Guanzhong, had defected back to Chu; and the kingdoms of Qi (Shandong), Zhao-Dai (Hebei and northeast Shanxi) under Chen Yu, and Wei (Henan), all allies with Liu Bang at the time of the Pengcheng Campaign, had broken away.

Having been thoroughly defeated at Pengcheng, Liu Bang had to settle for something less ambitious. He said to his counselors and generals, "I am now willing to share power with those who can help me turn the tables on Xiang Yu. Who would you recommend?"

Fan Kuai, Chen Ping, and other top officers suggested about half a dozen names. A raucous discussion followed. In the end, Liu Bang fixed his gaze on Zhang Liang, who had been unusually quiet, asking, "How about you?"

"Well, because of poor health," said Zhang, "I have not been able to keep abreast of things. But if you insist, this is my view. In the long run, you only have to ally yourselves with a triad of powerful players, that is, the Three Heroes. They will help you defeat Xiang Yu in the shortest possible time. The first hero is Ying Bu, now king of Jiujiang. He is the most redoubtable general under Xiang Yu. Recently, he was the one who carried out Xiang's order to assassinate the Righteous Emperor. But he and Xiang Yu do not get along well. The second hero is Peng Yue, who is active in the Wei area and rendered us much help in the Pengcheng Campaign. As chancellor of Wei, he is on friendly terms with us, even though his king is not. But the Wei king does not call the shots there. Peng does. The third hero is Hann Xin. Among your generals, Hann is the only one who can hold his own against Xiang Yu. But his loyalty has yet to be tested."

"Excellent!" exclaimed Liu Bang.

For Liu Bang, Hann Xin, the most powerful of the three, was also the easiest to deal with, because unlike the other two heroes, who were independent local lords, Hann was the Han general-in-chief based in Guanzhong. On Liu Bang's orders communicated through Xiao He, Hann Xin began to march his massive army east toward the junction of the Wei and the Heshui (Yellow River), in preparation for a possible attack against the kingdom of Wei.

In the meantime, Liu Bang dispatched two separate missions to Ying Bu and Peng Yue, in the hope of winning over the former and securing the loyalty of the latter.

***

AT XINGYANG, Liu's new base in the Central Plain, a standoff ensued. Every now and then, Xiang Yu's Chu army would send a contingent to harass Han troops in the southern suburb. After a brief engagement, the Chu men would pull out, even when victorious. Neither side had made much headway. But Liu Bang was growing anxious. Because of the civil war between Chu and Han, large swathes of arable land in the Central Plain were abandoned. A widespread famine hit many rural communities and cities and towns. A *hu* (bushel) of rice fetched as much as 10,000 cash. A growing number of peasants resorted to cannibalism to stay alive. It was impossible for Liu Bang to sustain his ambitious undertaking in the Central Plain if the situation continued.

Guanzhong with its vast riches could help. However, Zhang Han, who had survived the disastrous defeat by the Han army, still posed a threat there. Liu Bang had to take a break from his campaign in the Central Plain and return west to deal with him. In July, commanding a large expeditionary force, Liu Bang caught up with Zhang as he and his troops were immured within the walls of a small riverine town west of Xianyang. Liu Bang had an upstream dam breached, unleashing a torrent of water that crashed through the tightly shut gates and destroyed the bulk of Zhang Han's army. In despair, Zhang Han fell on his own sword.

In the end, under Xiao He's able management, the backyard of Liu Bang—Guanzhong, together with Hanzhong and Shu—began to take shape like a self-sufficient state. Reasonable laws had been promulgated (in addition to the Three Article Code) and local inhabitants registered. The Ancestral Temple and the Altar of State (or the Altars of the Soil and Grain) had been set up in the Han capital Yueyang (northeast of Lintong, Shaanxi). A constant flow of military stores and army recruits to the east was maintained and relief grain was sometimes shipped to the Central Plain to feed the starving masses.

Wei Bao King of Wei (205 BCE)

THE KINGDOM OF WEI did not have famous urban centers with the exception of Anyi the capital, but the land was fertile. Its primary importance, however, was strategic. Coterminous with both Guanzhong and the Central Plain, it could be used as a base against both areas. It occupied only a small part of what had been the state of Wei in the Warring States period, corresponding to Han Hedong Commandery (southwest Shanxi).

When Wei Bao was raised to king of Wei by Liu Bang, he had been expected to play the role of a figurehead. Real power had been in the hands of Chancellor Peng Yue. Recently, while Peng Yue was away, campaigning in the Central Plain, Wei Bao began to assert his power and distance himself from Liu Bang.

***

IN THE WEI PALACE in Anyi (northwest of <u>Xiaxian</u>, southwest <u>Shanxi</u>), a young lady called Xu Fu was studying the facial features of Madam Bo, a beautiful woman in her early 20s. Sitting next to her was her husband Wei Bao, watching with fascination. About a quarter of an hour later, Xu Fu finished her examination, and said, addressing Wei Bao, "Congratulations, King of Wei. Your wife has the look of a great noblewoman. I can assure you, she will give birth to a son, who will one day be the Son of Heaven."

Wei Bao beamed with a wide smile. He knew that, in spite of her young age, Xu Fu was a famed physiognomist, whose service was greatly sought after. Her talent had been recognized when she was only a teenager. She had even received an endorsement from the First Emperor.

"Give my regards to your father," said the king as Xu Fu departed.

***

A FEW DAYS LATER, the Han envoy Li Yiji came for a visit and was received by Wei Bao in the audience hall of the principal basilica.

As Wei Bao settled down in the seat of honor, Li said, "Great King, the King of Han greatly prizes your friendship, and hopes the cooperation can continue."

"Thank the King of Han for me, please. But the way he sometimes treats the local lords and his subordinates is abusive. He curses them as if they were his slaves."

"I am awfully sorry on behalf of the king. But it will not happen to you, I promise."

"I am a descendant of the royal Zhou house and a Wei noble. The King of Han is a down-to-earth man who has risen from the ranks. Although we are fundamentally different, we could still work together for our own mutual benefit. However, his vulgarities I find very hard to stand. For now, I am reluctant to enter into a long-term alliance with him or anyone else."

"But in this world of Chu-Han rivalry, it is hard not to take sides," said Li Yiji.

"The least I can do is this: I will mind my own business so long as the King of Han minds his," the King of Wei answered.

In the end, in spite of his slick tongue, Li Yiji failed to get Wei Bao to accept Liu Bang's offer.

After Li Yiji returned from the Wei mission, the Wei King's secret military alliance with Chu was revealed. It turned out that the commanding officers of the Wei army and the officers in charge of defending the capital were all Chu generals.

Having exhausted every possible avenue to win over Wei Bao, Liu Bang ordered Hann Xin to march a sizeable army to the front, in preparation for an invasion.

With Cao Shen and Guan Ying as his lieutenants, Hann deployed his army along the west bank of the Heshui (Yellow River). On the east bank near Puban was arrayed Wei's main force. The two sides were about equal in strength. But Hann was at a disadvantage because his troops had to cross the treacherous waters of the Heshui and make a forced landing on the east bank. Hann Xin ordered his men to set up camp near the river while he figured out a solution. For three days and nights, all was quiet on the front except for the drills held during the day, and the faint glow of campfires at night. The Han army under Hann Xin did not make a single attempt at crossing.

The next morning, King Wei Bao was horrified to find Anyi tightly encircled by the enemy forces. Soon they started storming the city gates. Cut off from the main force of the Wei army still at Puban and from outside logistical support, the Wei capital surrendered, and the king, together with his beautiful wife and attendant gentlemen, were taken captive.

Only later did the Wei king learn what had happened. After his troops had encamped near the Heshui, Hann Xin had secretly led an attack force north to Xiayang. From there his troops, using rafts buoyed up by sealed jars, crossed the river at night, and turned east to march on Anyi.

Hann Xin and the Battle of the Jingxing Pass (205 BCE)

FOLLOWING THE CONQUEST OF Wei, Hann Xin submitted an ambitious plan to annex Yan (north Hebei) and Zhao (south Hebei) in the north, to attack Qi (Shandong) in the east, and to cut off the grain supply route to Chu in the south. Impressed with Hann's depth of vision, scope of knowledge, and meticulous attention to detail, Liu Bang gave the plan his approval.

Hann Xin's first move was to bring Zhao and the small kingdom of Dai into the fold. Commanding a force of 30,000 and with General Zhang Er as his lieutenant, Hann Xin was soon on his way.

On the Zhao-Dai side, the central figure was Chen Yu. Although king of Dai in name, Chen Yu resided in the kingdom of Zhao to the south where he was the de facto regent of Zhao Xie king of Zhao. After his unpleasant meeting with Zhang Er following the siege of Julu in early 207 BCE, Chen Yu had a falling-out with his best friend and mentor. Later that year, Xiang Yu raised Zhang Er to king of Changshan (Zhao), and Chen Yu to marquis. And that was the last straw!

"Zhang Er and I were of the same rank and similar merit. Why is he a king and I am only a marquis?" asked Chen Yu. From then on, Chen was obsessed with how to destroy Zhang Er. With a small army he borrowed from Qi, Chen Yu fell on Changshan without provocation, forcing Zhang Er to scuttle away and join Liu Bang.

At the time of the Pengcheng Campaign, Liu Bang had made a request to the local lords to contribute troops. Chen Yu had responded, "King of Han, I would love to send my troops to fight with you. However, I want you to do something for me first: kill Zhang Er."

In a matter of days, a severed head was delivered to the Zhao court, and Chen Yu, upon identifying the head as that of his sworn enemy, sent a significant force to join Liu Bang. But the campaign soon collapsed, and Liu Bang himself fled west. As Chen Yu began to ponder whether he should remain Liu's ally, he found out about the true identity of the head: it had belonged to a Zhang Er look-alike. Thereupon, Chen Yu cut his ties with Liu Bang.

Liu Bang was enraged by Chen's change of allegiance, and found intolerable the presence of Chen's sizeable army in his rear, allegedly 200,000 strong, most of whom were deployed near the Jingxing Pass (west of <u>Shijiazhuang</u>, <u>Hebei</u>). The pass was a vital passage through the Taihang Mountains, which were a massive barrier between the Jizhou and Bingzhou (<u>Hebei</u> and <u>Shanxi</u>) areas of the Han dynasty. If Liu Bang wanted to launch a campaign against Chu, Chen Yu had to be removed (see Map 3).

However, Chen Yu had a much larger force, and was advised by the talented strategist Li Zuoche lord of Guangwu. At a war council, Li laid out his plan for fighting Hann Xin. He said, "General Hann Xin has recently crossed the Heshui (<u>Yellow</u> <u>River</u>) and captured the King of Wei. Now he is leading a large army, aided by Zhang Er, to fall on Zhao. The momentum seems unstoppable.

"But they still have to go through the narrow Jingxing Road. It does not allow two carriages to travel abreast, nor does it allow cavalry to ride in formation. Their army will spread out for miles and miles with grain wagons in the rear. If Your Lordship would allow me to lead a force of 30,000 to launch a surprise attack and cut off its logistical supply, within 10 days the Han army will be defeated and the heads of Generals Hann Xin and Zhang Er will be delivered to your court. Meanwhile all you need to do is stay behind the tall city walls and refuse battle."

Chen Yu was well read in military strategy and did not like the use of trickery or deceit in war, so he said, "The *Art of War* says, 'When you are 10 times the strength of your enemy, encircle them; when you are twice the strength, fight them.' Hann Xin's army of several thousand men is not only many times smaller than ours, it must have been exhausted, having covered more than one thousand *li*. If we don't fight it today, how are we going to deal with it when it grows into a much larger army in the future? Besides, if we don't fight, the local lords will regard us as cowards and invade Zhao." So he ignored Li Zuoche's advice, and ordered his massive army to stay where it was, getting ready for an enemy attack.

In fact, Hann Xin took Li Zuoche very seriously and was worried about falling into a trap set by him. In November, Hann encamped his army about 30 *li* from the Jingxing Pass, and waited. He made his move only after he received confirmation from his spies that Li Zuoche's plan had been rejected.

On the day of the attack, Hann Xin sent out 2,000 light troops at midnight, each carrying with him a red-colored Han flag. They were to hide themselves in the mountain overlooking the Zhao camp.

Hann Xin's subaltern officers then handed out a small meal to the troops that remained with a message from the general-in-chief, "There will be a feast after the battle."

After the meal, Hann Xin and his army marched forward. As soon as they went past the Jingxing Pass, they encountered a river. The army crossed over to the east side without incident. Hann arrayed 10,000 of his men along the east bank, and marched the rest further east to get closer to the enemy line.

At dawn, Hann Xin and Zhang Er ordered the main force of their army to launch a forward attack. The Zhao army rushed out of its camp to engage them. Hann and Zhang feigned defeat and pulled back to join forces with the 10,000 troops deployed along the river bank. As the Zhao army chased after them, its movement was hampered by many of the drums and flags deliberately left behind by the Han troops in flight.

By this time, the Zhao camp was all but empty. The 2,000 Han light troops came out of hiding in the mountain and stormed the camp, pulling out all the Zhao flags and planting 2,000 red flags of Han.

Near the river, the officers and men of the Han army engaged the Zhao troops fearlessly and drove them into retreat. In the commotion that ensued, Chen Yu was captured and delivered to Zhang Er, who personally lopped off his head.

When the remnants of the Zhao army were approaching their camp, they were horrified to see a sea of red flags. This could only happen if their commanding general had either been killed or captured. Suddenly, the Zhao army broke in rout as soldiers and officers alike took to flight. In desperation, the commanding general, who was still alive, shouted orders to stop the stampede, while brandishing a sword to strike at anyone who refused to listen. But it was no use. The morale of the army was completely shattered.[9]

---

[9] This event happened in the 10th month of the third year of Gaodi and falls in 205 BCE.

***

ON THE MORROW, feasts were held throughout Hann Xin's camp. One was given in the largest tent, in which Hann Xin and Zhang Er were sitting in the seats of honor in the company of about 20 senior officers. Standing up, Hann addressed them, "We defeated Zhao-Dai, killed Chen Yu, and captured Zhao Xie king of Zhao and his adviser Li Zouche. It would not have been possible had it not been for your death-defying courage, superb combat skills, discipline, and resourcefulness. Let me propose a toast to all the officers and men." He raised his goblet and emptied it in a single gulp amid a chorus of cheers and sat down. The officers in turn toasted their commander-in-chief. As the dishes were being served, one of them stood up and said to Hann, "The *Art of War* says, 'Troops should only be positioned with a river or a body of water in front and a hill in the rear.' But you arrayed the troops east of the bank with their backs to the river. We all thought it was a deadly mistake. Surprisingly, the troops fought valiantly and won the battle. What kind of tactic is that?"

"This," answered Hann, "is actually inspired by another teaching in the *Art of War,* 'Those who are placed in a position of death shall live.' That is, if they know the only way to survive is to fight, they will fight to the death. If instead there are escape routes readily available, everyone will fight for himself and flee at the earliest opportunity."

"Brilliant!" said the officer.

The feast continued.

Li Zuoche (205 BCE)

AFTER A VISIT TO the barracks, Hann Xin rode back to his campaign tent and saw a man in his 40s sitting on the ground, with hands bound behind his back. One of the two soldiers standing guard bowed to Hann.

Hann Xin jumped off his horse, stepped towards the captive, and helped him to his feet. Having untied him, Hann brought the captive into his campaign tent and sat him down in the seat of honor.

"Li Zuoche lord of Guangwu," began Hann, "it is a great honor to make your acquaintance." Pouring out two goblets of wine and setting them down on a small table in front of them, Hann continued, "I need your advice for my next campaign, against Yan."

"Great General," Li answered, "as a subject of a fallen country, I am thankful to be alive, and in no position to give advice."

"Well, Lord, I do hope you'll change your mind. Just imagine yourself as Baili Xi, the Qin chancellor who made that state great. He was serving Yu when that small state fell. But as a subject of a fallen country he went to work for Qin, and Qin thrived and became a hegemon. So it does not matter whether you come from a fallen country or not. It is your advice itself that matters. Had Chen Yu listened to it, I would have been taken prisoner. That is precisely the reason why I seek your advice. Please don't turn me down."

"Well," said Li Zuoche, "I heard that a fool will hit upon a good idea once in a blue moon. Let me try to offer my humble view. You have scored two brilliant victories in a row. As a result, the King of Wei was captured and Chen Yu was killed. All the local lords are shaken and your fame has spread far and wide. Everyone in your camp is geared up for more victories. But, the reality is, after a major campaign, your troops are seriously fatigued. If you use them to attack Yan, you will exhaust your grain supply long before you sack its well-fortified cities. By then, Qi to the south will have moved against you. A drawn-out stalemate will follow. The only one that will benefit from all this is not Han, Qi, or Yan, but your archenemy Chu. In my opinion, that is not a most desirable position to be in."

"I completely agree," said Hann Xin. "What is your solution?"

"Well, I think the best way is to make no move at all, for now. Send an envoy to Zang Tu, the King of Yan, laying out your terms for submission. Because of your reputation as a great general and your numerical superiority, he will give them very careful consideration. With Yan subdued, you will have an easy time dealing with Qi."

"Excellent!" exclaimed Hann, who raised his goblet to toast his guest.

By the time Li Zuoche had left the tent, he was not only a free man, but a senior adviser on Hann Xin's staff.

***

FOLLOWING LI'S ADVICE, Hann sent a senior envoy to deliver his personal letter to Zang Tu king of Yan, who had recently annexed the kingdom of Liaodong under Hann Guang (with a territory extending from north Hebei to Liaoning).

The silk letter bearing the seal of Hann Xin set off a debate between the king's hawkish and dovish advisers. The hawks argued: Yan can reject Hann Xin's request to be its "friend." Yan's large army can effectively resist Hann's invasion. Yan can also link up with the Xiongnu to the north and the Qi to the south. That will keep Yan going for a long, long time to come.

The doves countered: however, Hann Xin is not just another commander. He is a military genius. The gods seem to be always on his side. Just look at how he fooled Zhang Han and retook Guanzhong, and how he captured Wei Bao and killed Chen Yu, Yan's next-door neighbor. If Yan submits now, the king will continue to rule. But if Yan resists and loses, the outcome will be unthinkable.

At length it was the prospect of subjugation after defeat that prompted Zang Tu to side with the doves and send a letter of submission.

Hann Xin was delighted with the victory over Yan. It could be regarded as the best kind, according to the *Art of War*, because it was won not on the battlefield but through negotiation and diplomacy. But he also knew that much remained to be done. This victory only neutralized Zang Tu, and did not bring his war-like people and vast territory into the fold. To keep an eye on him, Hann Xin, with Liu Bang's blessing, installed Zhang Er as king in the kingdom of Zhao next door.

Envoy Sui He and Ying Bu (205 BCE)

ONE DAY IN LATE 205 BCE, the Han envoy Sui He arrived at the palace in the town of Lù (north of Lu'anshi, Anhui), the capital of the kingdom of Jiujiang. He was surprised to see the seneschal at the gate to greet him. Even though he was only a Han herald (*yezhe*), he had been handpicked by King Liu Bang to negotiate with the King of Jiujiang. As such he expected to be received at least by the chancellor, if not King Ying Bu himself, one of the Three Heroes. Since Ying Bu's decision would likely influence the outcome of the civil war, Sui He's mission was of vital importance.

As Sui He placed Liu Bang's personal letter in the hands of the seneschal, he demanded to see the king at the earliest possible time. The seneschal promised to deliver the letter promptly, but asked the envoy to be patient and wait in his inn. The so-called inn turned out to be an ordinary posthouse, where the rooms, though not small, were sparsely furnished, with hardly any amenities. Sui He had to rub shoulders with common travelers like muleteers, coachmen, and lowly traders.

On the morning of the fourth day, Sui lost his patience, and said frankly to the seneschal, "It is obvious that your king does not want to see me. I know why. He thinks Han is weak and Chu is strong. But how does the king know what we have to offer without seeing us? Why don't you do this: let me see the king and present my view. I am sure he will like it. If not, he can then have our heads chopped off with axes in the marketplace to show his solidarity with Chu."

"Don't say that, Mr. Envoy!" reacted the seneschal, who was a bit ruffled by the strong talk. "Of course, the king wants to see you. I will take care of that."

The next day, Ying Bu, at the urging of the seneschal, granted an audience in the palace. Still furious with his treatment, Sui He said with a cold smile, "I find it curious indeed that I, on behalf of Liu Bang, the King of Han, had to deliver his personal letter to your butler. I suppose that shows your close relations with Xiang Yu of Chu?"

"Well, to be frank with you, I regard him as my sovereign," answered Ying Bu.

"Is that right? When Xiang Yu launched the war against Qi, he led the charge, putting himself in harm's way. You, Great King, as his so-called 'subject,' should lead the main force of the Jiujiang army to fight as his vanguard. But what did you do? Sending a paltry 4,000 men instead. When the King of Han was attacking Pengcheng, you, Great King, should have led an army to cross the Huai River to defend it. What did you do? In spite of the multitude of your army, you did not send a single soldier to the rescue. Is that how one serves a sovereign?"

"I was sick at the time," said Ying Bu, his face flushing with embarrassment.

Taking a sip of wine, Sui He continued in an agitated voice, "Perhaps. But I don't think so. The true reason is that you were sitting on the fence. Is it not? What I want to do is convince you to stop doing that and join us, for your benefit. You may think that Han is weak and Chu is strong. But that is not necessarily the case. Militarily, Chu may be a strong country, but it is a country devoid of justice and righteousness. It not only disregarded the famous decree issued by the Emperor, but also cowardly assassinated him. Han, in contrast, has allied itself with the local lords, using Xingyang and other cities as strongholds in the Central Plain. Supported by grain from Shu and Hanzhong, its troops are protected in trenches and fortifications.

"Admittedly, right now, Han is not strong enough to defeat Chu. But, if you open another front against Chu, Xiang Yu will have no choice but to stay behind. Then, in several months' time, Han will conquer all under Heaven."

"But I am already a king under Chu."

"Han will give you a larger feudatory."

At this point, Ying Bu waved his hand to dismiss all the attendant gentlemen present, and said in a low voice, "Mr. Sui, can we make a deal?"

"Yes, of course, Great King."

"I promise I will eventually join you. But there are still a few issues I have to deal with. So keep it a secret for the time being, will you?"

"Sure, I can wait for your official response," said Sui He, his earlier ire now gone.

After the talk, Sui He and his suite of 20 men moved into the state guesthouse, where they were assigned more spacious rooms with more comfortable furniture and better room service. He had been upgraded to the status of a distinguished guest, with the special privilege of having access to the king in the palace without appointment.

However, for two days, Ying Bu did not make a formal commitment. Sui He then learned that a Chu envoy was also present at Ying Bu's court. *That must have been the main reason why Ying was reluctant to see me in the first place*, he figured.

The next morning, as soon as breakfast was over, Sui He made directly for the palace. Having passed through the gate guards, he walked up to the door of the audience hall. He shoved aside the attendant gentleman and barged into the room, where he caught sight of a stranger in his 50s, who was urging Ying Bu to commit his troops to help Chu right away.

Ignoring Sui He's presence, the man continued, "This is the only way to show your sincerity."

"I don't think so," Sui He interrupted. "The King of Jiujiang doesn't need to send troops at all."

"Who are you?" asked the Chu envoy curtly.

"The Han envoy Sui He. And you must be the Chu envoy."

"That's correct," answered the man in a dignified voice.

"Jiujiang has already submitted to Han. It is no longer obligated to help Chu," said Sui He.

"What?" the Chu envoy asked in disbelief.

Ying Bu did not answer. After a while, the Chu envoy walked off.

This left Ying Bu no choice but to throw in his lot with Liu Bang. Half a dozen of his men then caught up with the Chu envoy when he was half way to the guesthouse. They hacked him to death and disposed of his corpse in a nearby river.

A week later, Ying Bu led the bulk of his army to invade Chu to the north. However, the Chu army under the command of General Long Ju was too strong for Ying Bu's ill-prepared troops, who were thoroughly defeated within two months.

On Sui He's advice, Ying Bu created a plan to bring the remnants of his troops north to join Liu Bang. But its execution turned out to be very difficult, if not impossible. He managed to gather several thousand men, but they moved too slowly and became an easy target for the enemies. In the end, Ying Bu had to flee incognito with Sui He to the city of Xingyang (in Henan). In the meantime, the Chu general Xiang Bo had wiped out what remained of Ying Bu's army and in the process killed his wife and children.

Ying Bu's Meeting with Liu Bang (204 BCE)

ONE MORNING IN JANUARY, Ying Bu and Sui He arrived on horseback at a palatial mansion in Xingyang, where Liu Bang, the King of Han, had been residing after returning from his victorious campaign against Zhang Han in Guanzhong.

Having passed through three sets of armed guards, they were ushered into an audience hall, where they waited for about half an hour sipping rice wine before they were called into an adjoining room. Upon entering, Ying Bu saw Liu Bang, his host, sitting on the edge of an expansive bed topped by a yellow brocade canopy with orange hanging tassels. Liu, in his sleeping robe, was washing his feet in a silver basin while two pretty teenage housemaids were attending him.

Sui He announced the name of the guest. Liu Bang nodded coldly to Ying Bu's humble salutations while wiping his feet fastidiously with a white silk cloth.

It took about five minutes before Liu Bang motioned to his visitors to sit down.

"Well, what's happened down there, King of Jiujiang?" asked Liu Bang casually, who was now in bed with his head propped up by three embroidered silk pillows. Ying Bu proceeded to report on the war he had waged against Chu. When he described how he had lost his country, army, and wife and children, he struggled to hold back his tears. With a sullen look on his face, Liu Bang listened quietly.

When the report was over, Liu Bang waved his hand, and two attendant gentlemen came over and led Ying Bu and Sui He away.

After they had passed through the outer gate, Ying Bu suddenly turned to Sui He and said, "To be frank with you, I regret my decision."

"Why?" asked Sui He in astonishment.

"He treats me like a beggar."

"Don't take it to heart. He does it to everybody. The first meeting with Li Yiji took place under exactly the same circumstances. Li is now his top adviser."

"I've lost everything," Ying Bu murmured to himself. "Now I'm nothing but a homeless dog. What's the point of going on living?" As he said so, he unsheathed his sword.

"Stop!" shouted Sui He as he struggled to seize the sword from his hand. "If you kill yourself, you can only make Xiang Yu happy. May I advise you to do this: stay as Liu Bang's guest at least for a while to see if he really trusts you. If not, you can then leave or take your life."

"We'll see," said Ying Bu absentmindedly.

After mounting their horses, they rode for about ten minutes and arrived at another mansion. It was similar in size to Liu Bang's, but seemed more richly ornamented. Sui He introduced Ying Bu to the gatekeeper and left. A few moments later, two dozen servants, both men and women, led by a butler, came out to greet him.

At the conclusion of a gratifying dinner, prepared by one of the two chefs of the mansion and served with tasty wine, Ying Bu withdrew into the main residential house, and entered his bedchamber through the audience hall. A large charcoal burner kept the spacious room warm and cozy. He took off his outer garment, kicked off his boots, and jumped into the luxurious canopy bed. Slipping under a thick, down-filled silk quilt, he fell asleep instantly.

The next morning, two commandants came to report for duty as Ying's adjutants, who had under them a staff of about 20 men, including clerks and scribes. Obviously, Ying Bu was treated in the same way as the King of Han himself.

Gradually, as he pushed the unpleasant meeting with the King of Han to the back of his mind, Ying Bu began to rebuild his army. He moved his headquarters to the town of Chenggao (west of Xingyang, Henan), and sent some of his loyal followers south to Jiujiang. In a matter of weeks, they raised an army of several thousands by using his old friends, underlings, and acquaintances to recruit from their hometowns and home villages. The new recruits were transported to Chenggao. Within months, Ying Bu's new Jiujiang army, bolstered by the units assigned to him by Liu Bang, had grown to several tens of thousands.

Li Yiji's Proposal (204 BCE)

THE CIVIL WAR BETWEEN Han and Chu eventually settled into a prolonged stalemate. While Liu Bang was not able to launch another southern expedition to conquer Chu, Xiang Yu had failed to dislodge the Han army from the Central Plain. However, Liu Bang's base in the Central Plain, Xingyang, was much more vulnerable than Xiang Yu's capital, Pengcheng. It depended upon the regular shipment of grain through the Heshui (<u>Yellow</u> <u>River</u>) for survival. Since Xingyang was some distance away from the Heshui, a long corridor had been built linking the city to the river. It had been used exclusively for the transportation of grain. But recently it had been seriously damaged by enemy attacks, and become impassable.

An anxious Liu Bang asked the counselor Li Yiji for a long-term solution. Li said, "After the fall of the Qin, the world has reverted to the ways of the past."

"What do you mean?"

"It is kind of reminiscent of the Warring States era when the Seven States contended for dominance. In the end, it was Qin that destroyed the other six, which sowed the seeds of ruin for Qin itself. I believe that a winning strategy has to follow an ancient practice, according to which victorious sovereigns, in the name of virtue and righteousness, enfeoffed the descendants of the vanquished."

"Give me some examples," requested Liu Bang.

"King Tang of Shang was a good sovereign," replied Li Yiji, "he enfeoffed the offspring of King Jie of Xia, a bad ruler, in Qǐ; and King Wu of Zhou, another good sovereign, enfeoffed the offspring of King Zhòu of Shang, another bad ruler, in Song.[10]

"The Qin, however, abandoned virtue and righteousness. They destroyed the lords of the Six States, leaving their descendants with no lands of their own at all. If you, Great King, set up the descendants of the lords of the Six States as kings, their subjects will be grateful to Your Highness for your virtuous decision. Out of their admiration for your righteousness, they will of their own accord submit to your authority. Even Chu will have to bow to your power. You will then be able to dominate the realm as hegemon."

---

[10] King Jie of Xia was the last ruler of the Xia. Qǐ was a small state in the Central Plain. King Wu of Zhou was the founder of the Zhou dynasty. King Zhòu of Shang was the last ruler of the Shang.

After a long pause, Liu Bang responded, "Suppose you are right, how can we persuade the folks in the Six States?"

"If you, Great King, have no objection, I am willing to serve as your ambassador."

"All right, I am now appointing you to that post," said Liu Bang.

About one week later, the special ambassador's seal was delivered to Li Yiji's home.

***

AS SOON AS ZHANG LIANG returned from an official mission, he was summoned to Liu Bang's residence, where he joined the king for lunch.

"Someone has provided me with a plan to weaken Chu without using the army," Liu Bang said to his guest, smiling, and went on to explain what Li Yiji had proposed.

"In my view," answered Zhang Liang, "if you, Great King, carry out this plan, your great cause will be in mortal danger."

"How so?" Liu Bang asked, the smile on his face disappearing.

"It is true that, in the past, King Tang and King Wu enfeoffed the descendants of King Jie and King Zhòu. But Tang and Wu had the power to make them live or die. Do you have the power to make the descendants of the local lords live or die?"

"No."

"When King Wu conquered the Shang, he rehabilitated the Shang loyal officials who had been persecuted by the Shang king. Can you do something like that?" Liu Bang shook his head.

"He also," continued Zhang Liang, "opened the granaries and storehouses to give out millet to the starving and money to the poor. Can you do that?" Again Liu Bang shook his head.

"In today's world, no one can subdue Chu. If the Six States were revived, they would be so weak that they would have no choice but to submit to Xiang Yu. Would you then expect to be their leader?"

"Damn!" shouted Liu Bang, who had stopped eating. "That stupid bookworm has almost screwed things up for me!" Thereupon, he issued an order to cancel Li's trip and take back the seal for the special ambassador, which was later destroyed.

Advice by Fan Zeng (204 BCE)

IN MAY, ON THE advice of Fan Zeng, the "Second Father," Xiang Yu led a massive army to lay siege to Xingyang. Liu Bang became seriously worried for the first time since he had set up his Central Plain headquarters in this city. His troops were outmatched at least six to one. His orders to Hann Xin and Peng Yue (who had submitted not long before) to come to the rescue seemed to have fallen on deaf ears, while the grain supply in the city was running extremely low. Liu had no choice but to sue for peace, offering, among other things, to give up all the territory east of Xingyang.

***

FOR HIS PART, XIANG YU was inclined to give Liu Bang's offer serious consideration, but Fan Zeng would have none of it.

"You can't trust Liu Bang at all," said Fan Zeng at a war council. "In the recent past, when dealing with him, we have committed two monumental errors. First, we let him escape at the Hongmen banquet. We should have finished him then, or immediately thereafter. Second, we did not set up our capital in Guanzhong to prevent him from making a comeback. Look at what has happened. He has broken every promise he made. He retook Guanzhong, invaded the Central Plain, and even sacked Pengcheng!"

Xiang Yu remained silent.

"Liu Bang is the only one who could hold the coalition against Chu together. Without Liu, Chu can easily subdue the other lords one by one. So you must attack the city of Xingyang as soon as possible."

Obviously, Xiang Yu could not gainsay Fan's argument. But his gut feeling told him to act against it. *I respect the old man for old time's sake,* he thought. *But he is not supposed to embarrass me like that in front my own officers time and again. Although I am calling the shots here, the way he treats me clearly undermines my authority. I simply can't afford to let him get his way. Yes, I might have the ability to sack the city with wall-storming commandos, but the cost could be too high. Besides, my troops are seriously fatigued.*

In the end, Xiang Yu accepted Liu Bang's offer and dispatched troops to take over the area east of Xingyang. That left Fan Zeng disconsolate.

***

LIU BANG GOT THE much-needed break. Meanwhile his search for a long-term solution for his problem continued. He consulted his close adviser Chen Ping, and said "I agree with Zhang Liang (who was now away on a mission) that reviving the Six States won't do it for me. But does it mean there is nothing I can do but wait?"

"I don't think so, Your Highness," answered Chen Ping. "There is something we can do. You see, Great King, Xiang Yu is the greatest warrior—nobody in the world can beat him in combat. But he is a mediocre leader at best. He depends on his closest advisers for strategy. What we should do is to drive a wedge between him and his advisers, especially Fan Zeng. We can start with sowing discord amongst them. Since Xiang Yu is suspicious of everyone, this strategy may indeed work. Should that happen, Han can attack and trounce Chu in a matter of months."

"Brilliant," Liu Bang said.

***

SOON THE CHU ENVOY arrived with his suite for the peace talk. Chen Ping made sure he received a warm welcome. In the courtyard of the main hall of the government compound, 12 bronze quadripods (*ding*) containing cooked ox and sheep heads were set up for the Grand Sacrificial Rite, a ceremony befitting a Son of

Heaven. On behalf of the King of Han, Chen Ping said, "Our king has been looking forward to your visit. Since you and your party were sent by the Second Father, he insisted that you be put up in the Guesthouse for Distinguished Visitors. He always holds the Second Father in highest esteem."

"I would like to thank the king for his hospitality and kindness," the envoy answered. "But I am not sent by Fan Zeng. I am sent by Xiang Yu, the hegemonic king of Chu himself!"

"Is that so?" asked Chen Ping, with a startled look on his face. "I have been under the impression that since the death of Xiang Liang, Fan Zeng was the visionary leader who directed the Chu state. He was like a father to the hegemonic king of Chu, and that is why he is called the 'Second Father.'"

"Not really. The King of Chu respects the Second Father tremendously, but it is King Xiang Yu not the Second Father who is the man of authority," the Chu envoy answered unequivocally.

Chen Ping then led the envoy and his entourage into a waiting room in the main office building, sat them down, and left.

About half an hour later, one attendant gentleman came to bring them back into the courtyard for the ceremony. The envoy was surprised to find the 12 ritual bronzes set up for the occasion were gone, replaced by half a dozen pottery vessels. The sacrificial rite that followed was brief and simple and was presided over by a middle-ranking official. Chen Ping himself was nowhere to be found.

The negotiation did not go very well. The envoy made a request that Liu Bang be present at the formal ceremony that finalized the agreement. It was rejected by the Han chief negotiator Chen Ping out of hand. Neither was the envoy pleased with the posthouse where he and his party were put up. Obviously, it was not the upscale Guesthouse for Distinguished Visitors Chen Ping had promised. The rooms were small with simple furniture and the fare was plain. Not a single banquet was held in their honor. Neither was there entertainment at night.

Upon return, the Chu envoy briefed Xiang Yu on his humiliating experience. Puzzled by Liu Bang's obvious reluctance to conclude a deal, Xiang Yu asked the envoy to give his opinion.

The envoy, after some hesitation, said, "Well, if you want me to take a guess, Great King, it is because I was sent by the wrong person."

"What do you mean?"

"Well, when I first arrived Chen Ping greeted me in person, and I saw with my own eyes that 12 bronze quadripods were set up for the welcoming ceremony. That is the standard for kings. I was really impressed. But later, when the ritual ceremony was held, the bronze vessels were replaced by six cheap pottery pots. Nor was Chen Ping present. We were then housed in this uninspiring posthouse, instead of the lush government guesthouse they had promised. I notice that things began to go wrong after I clarified that I was not sent by the Second Father."

Xiang Yu was not pleased. "The Second Father is the top adviser, but I am the man in charge!"

"Yes, indeed. But so long as the Han consider Fan Zeng the man of authority, they are not going to take us seriously."

"In your opinion, what should we do? Should we act on Fan Zeng's advice and launch an attack?"

"No. We should stay the course. If we maintain the siege for a while, the city's grain supply will be exhausted. By then, they will have no choice but to come to the negotiating table."

"I think so too," Xiang Yu said.

***

THAT AFTERNOON FAN ZENG came to visit Xiang Yu. Well over 70, he was wan and frail. As he shuffled forward with a cane, Xiang Yu came up to greet him.

"Second Father!" Xiang Yu exclaimed with tears in his eyes as he stared at the old man's snow-white thin hair and beard. "You don't have to come. I can pay you a visit anytime!"

"Great King, I have to come because the matter in question is urgent," said Fan.

Xiang Yu helped him to a seat, and Fan continued, "Liu Bang isn't serious about negotiating with us at all. It is obvious that he is stalling for time. North of the Heshui (<u>Yellow</u> <u>River</u>) is Hann Xin's army, and to our south is Peng Yue's. If these two hostile forces converge on Xingyang, we will be in trouble."

"What do you think we should do, Second Father?"

"Launch an attack on Xingyang with full force immediately."

Staring at the gaunt face of Fan Zeng pensively, Xiang Yu said, "With due respect, Second Father, I would like to exercise restraint for the moment. Peng Yue is not really posing a serious threat. We have enough troops to keep him at bay. Hann Xin, together with Zhang Er, is a different matter. He should have made a move by now. The fact he hasn't probably suggests that he is not keen on coming to the rescue of Xingyang. For now we should give negotiation a chance."

"In my humble view, you should attack now when enemy reinforcements are nowhere in sight. This is your last chance to win the war, Great King! If we don't do it, we will probably die without even a burial place!"

Xiang Yu responded, "You have blown it way out of proportion!"

After some heated back-and-forths, Fan Zeng left, angry and bitter.

The next morning, Fan handed in his resignation letter, in which he said, "Since you are no longer willing to take my advice, Great King, I ask your permission to spend the rest of my years in retirement in the countryside."

For Xiang Yu the letter brought back a flood of memories of the Second Father: his debut as Uncle Xiang Liang's strategist in Xue, his scheme to kill Liu Bang at the Hongmen banquet, and his role in bringing about the siege of Xingyang. It seemed that he possessed a strong sense of vision and an uncanny ability to see into the future. Recently, however, Fan had become unusually irascible, cantankerous. Xiang Yu was not sure if he could maintain a cordial relationship with him any more, which was absolutely essential for his role as the top strategic adviser. He then reminded himself of this ancient maxim, "There is not enough room for two tigers in the same mountain," and granted the request.

To show his appreciation for Fan's past service, Xiang Yu provided him with a horse-drawn carriage and a coachman in addition to a generous sum of money.

Fan Zeng departed soon afterwards for Pengcheng. On his way, his poor health caught up with him. Falling seriously ill with a festering sore on his back, Fan Zeng succumbed in a roadside inn a few weeks later.

The Siege of Xingyang (204 BCE)

LIU BANG HAD FELT ambivalent about Fan Zeng. While his advice to Xiang Yu had nearly cost him his life, he had always been a worthy opponent. Now that he had departed from the scene, Xiang Yu would be, Liu Bang believed, more prone to bad decisions. When Xiang Yu requested that the negotiation be renewed, Liu Bang stalled for time and refused to make a commitment, hoping that Hann Xin's reinforcements would eventually lift the siege. By June, Hann Xin had not sent a single soldier. Meanwhile, Xiang Yu had lost patience. He put his troops laying siege to the city on high alert in preparation for an assault.

Liu Bang mounted the east city wall and saw from the battlements the Chu troops in the distance. He could vaguely make out the yellow-brownish sackcloth tunics of the soldiers and the black suits of armor of their officers. Their dispositions seemed to suggest an attack was imminent.

Descending from the wall, Liu Bang made directly for his residence inside the government compound where he summoned an emergency war council with his top generals—Hannwang Xin, Chen Ping, and Wei Bao. Of these, Hannwang Xin was by far the most accomplished military leader. Descendant of the old Hann royalty, this man of extraordinary height had recently been raised to king of Hann, thanks to his success in capturing territories and cities in the Central Plain. His original name was Hann Xin, the same as that of the general-in-chief. To avoid confusion, history refers to him as "Hannwang Xin," which means "Xin, king of Hann." Chen Ping was present as Liu Bang's high-ranking adjutant, companion, and confidant. Wei Bao had been the King of Wei. After the sack of Anyi, he had been captured by Liu Bang's general-in-chief Hann Xin. Well treated by his captors, he had willingly switched allegiance to Liu Bang.

In addition, there were three more senior officers: Zhou Ke, General Cong, and Ji Xin. Zhou Ke came from Pei, Liu Bang's adopted hometown. He and his paternal cousin, Zhou Chang, were among Liu's earliest followers. Recently he had been promoted to censor-in-chief. General Cong was of rather obscure origin. We know practically nothing about his background. But one thing we know for sure. Like Zhou Ke, General Cong was a diehard loyalist to Liu Bang. The last one, Ji Xin, had joined the cause early as well. He had been present at the Hongmen banquet when Liu Bang's life was hanging in the balance.

"Give me an honest assessment of the situation: can we or can we not hold the city?" Liu Bang asked.

"We are outnumbered six to one," said Chen Ping. "Although we have enough manpower to man the walls and gatetowers, before very long we will run out of provisions."

"May I say something?" asked Hannwang Xin.

"Yes, go ahead," said Liu Bang.

"The main reason Xiang Yu is besieging the city is the presence of Your Highness. If you leave, he will probably leave it alone."

All present echoed the sentiment.

"All right, then, I'll leave the city. I will get Hann Xin to move his troops across the river soon. Hannwang Xin, you shall take over command of the troops in Xingyang during my absence."

"Yes, Great King," answered Hannwang. "One of us has to go with you."

"How about you, Chen Ping?" Liu Bang asked.

"Yes, Great King," replied Chen. "But there has to be a decoy before we can make it safely out of the city."

"I can do it," said Ji Xin, raising his hand.

"You?" asked Liu Bang. As he looked at this middle-aged man of medium build, he suddenly saw a mirror image of himself. "Don't you realize how dangerous it is?"

"Yes, Great King," Ji Xin said chokingly. "For your sake and for the sake of the great cause, it is worth it."

"Brave man. I hope you will come back from this mission safely. But in case you don't, we will take good care of your family," Liu Bang said as he hugged Ji Xin.

Later that day after dark, 2,000 women were let out of the east gate. Chu soldiers surrounded and detained them. Then a two-horse-drawn carriage flying a white flag with a yellow top and a feather canopy trundled out of the same gate. Sitting inside the closed carriage was a man wearing a king's crown. Two Chu soldiers stopped the vehicle. A commandant came up and asked the coachman, "Who is inside?"

The coachman answered, "This is the King of Han."

The officer opened the door, identified the man, and asked, "Why now?"

The man answered, "We have run out of food."

As the news of Liu Bang's capture began to spread, the Chu troops were overjoyed.

The captive was brought into Xiang Yu's campaign tent. Xiang Yu approached him to have a closer look under the light of torches. Suddenly, he snatched off the man's crown and shouted, "This is not Liu Bang!"

A furious Xiang Yu struck the man across the face, asking, "Who are you?"

"Ji Xin, a Han general," answered the man.

"Where is Liu Bang?"

"He is gone."

Thereupon, on Xiang Yu's orders, a pyre was set up and Ji Xin, trussed up, was thrown upon it. Xiang Yu then asked, "Are you going to submit to me?"

"No. I am proud to be the servant of the King of Han."

Xiang Yu waved his hand, and a torch was hurled into the pyre.

By then several dozen Han light cavalrymen had stormed out of the western gate, broken through the encirclement, and vanished into the darkness. Among them were two armored riders, Liu Bang and Chen Ping.

***

WITH HIS QUARRY GONE, Xiang Yu put off the attack on Xingyang. While the hunt for Liu Bang was still in progress, Xiang Yu was soon distracted by Peng Yue, who had started fighting a guerrilla war and caused serious disruption of Chu's grain supply. Xiang Yu had to lead an army to confront him.

This afforded the Han leaders—Hannwang Xin, Zhou Ke, General Cong, and Wei Bao—a great opportunity to strengthen Xingyang's defenses while their troops took a respite. But unexpectedly dissension among these leaders came to the surface. Both Zhou Ke and General Cong had nothing but hatred for Wei Bao, the former king of Wei.

"That bastard stubbornly opposed the King of Han. Even Li Yiji failed to change his mind," commented Zhou Ke to General Cong.

"He also cursed the king with foul language," said General Cong.

"It is a shame that I have to work with him now," said Zhou Ke.

"Tell me about it!" said General Cong.

Both of them agreed that they would be better off without Wei.

At a war council attended by the top leaders, Zhou Ke and Wei Bao got into an argument. When Wei Bao rose to leave, Zhou Ke unsheathed his sword and shouted in anger, "You dirty traitor!" The moment Wei turned around Zhou struck him down. Hannwang Xin immediately took Zhou Ke into custody. As acting commander-in-chief of the garrison, he was obligated to penalize Zhou's murderous act. Then he learned, to his surprise, that Xiang Yu had defeated Peng Yue's army and returned. Hannwang Xin had no choice but to release Zhou Ke.

Soon a general assault on Xingyang was underway. Now that both Ji Xin and Wei Bao were dead and Liu Bang and Chen Ping had left, only three top officers—Hannwang Xin, Zhou Ke, and General Cong—were left to defend the city. The north wall, which had been defended by Wei Bao, was now in the hands of an inexperienced officer. After two day's intense fighting, the Chu army stormed the north gate and went on to sack the entire city.

All three top commanders were captured, tied up, and hauled in front of Xiang Yu for an interrogation.

"I don't understand it: why do you want to serve Liu Bang?" asked Xiang Yu. "If you agree to work for me, I will promote you to higher positions."

The three men gave no response. Xiang Yu moved closer to Zhou Ke and asked, "What's your position under Liu Bang?"

"Censor-in-chief."

"Not bad! But I'll make you superior general with a fief of 30,000 households."

"Pah!" shouted Zhou Ke. "Why don't you surrender to Han before it is too late? You are a no match for the King of Han."

An infuriated Xiang Yu had a cauldron of fuming oil prepared. On his orders, six of his men lifted Zhou Ke and hurled him into the oil. Zhou Ke kept screaming and cursing until his last breath.

The killing of Zhou did not seem to have an effect on General Cong, who refused to submit, and was put to the sword.

Xiang Yu now turned his fierce gaze to Hannwang Xin. His face pale as if drained of blood, Hannwang mumbled a few confused utterances. Xiang Yu motioned to have him unbound and sent into house arrest. Several days later, the brilliant Han general accepted Xiang Yu's offer and switched allegiance.

Hann Xin's Camp (204 BCE)

SINCE HIS NARROW ESCAPE from Xingyang, Liu Bang had been staying in Chenggao, a small walled town to the west. With Xingyang's fall, suddenly Chenggao became vulnerable.

Liu Bang had sent out more requests to Hann Xin for reinforcements and still received no response.

"Why the hell does it take so long for Hann Xin to make a move?" Liu asked his close associate Xiahou Ying, who had replaced Chen Ping as his companion.

"Indeed, General Hann is just north of the Heshui."

"I suspect he is sitting on the fence."

"That would be too bad, Great King."

Pausing briefly, Liu Bang continued, "I wonder how long Chenggao can hold out like this. It is much smaller than Xingyang, and much less defensible. We can't just sit here, waiting to die."

"Where do you want us to go?"

"North. Cross the river and join Hann Xin."

"Is he still loyal to you, Great King?"

"I suppose so. But he is calculating. I think it is time to teach him a lesson."

That evening, before Xiang Yu tightened the noose on Chenggao, Liu Bang and Xiahou Ying slipped out of the Jade Gate (in the north) in a horse-drawn carriage, and hurtled north until they came to the south bank of the Heshui (<u>Yellow River</u>). They boarded a ferry that took them and their carriage across to the north side. From there they went further north and reached the camp of Hann Xin and Zhang Er early the next morning. As the carriage came to a halt at the camp gate, a sentry on duty shouted, "Password."

"The King of Han is here to inspect the camp. Call your commandant," ordered Xiahou Ying sitting in the dickey.

An officer came up, opened the carriage door, and saw Liu Bang holding up his royal jade seal.

"My apologies, Your Highness," said the officer as he made obeisance. "Shall I notify Generals Hann and Zhang?"

"Where are they now?"

"Both are asleep."

"Don't wake them up, Commandant. I command you to take me to the main campaign tent." As he said so, Liu Bang stepped out of the carriage.

About ten minutes later, Liu Bang and Xiahou Ying arrived at the largest tent of the camp. The commandant ordered the guard at the tent flap to step aside. Liu Bang raised the flap and went in. Hann Xin was sleeping, his lanky body wrapped in two blankets lying motionless in the shadows. Liu Bang stepped stealthily toward the head of his bed, picked up the seal and tiger tally lying next to his pillow, and came out.

Thereupon, the King of Han summoned a meeting with the generals. It was then that Hann Xin came rushing, his hair unkempt, followed by a distraught Zhang Er. Both of them dropped on their knees to beg for the king's forgiveness.

"King of Zhao," Liu Bang said to Zhang Er, "you can sit down."

Turning to Hann Xin, Liu shouted sharply, "Who are you? If you are my general-in-chief, why did you ignore my orders to move south? Or are you the fucking coward from Huaiyin? "

With sweat beading on his forehead and his face scarlet red, Hann Xin did not say a word.

"What do you want to say?"

"I...I," finally Hann Xin stammered. "Great King, you are absolutely right. I, your guilty subject, am awfully sorry to have let you down, and deserve to be punished."

"As your punishment, I've taken back your general-in-chief's seal and tally. I will keep them for you for a while. Meanwhile, I'll give you an opportunity to make amends." Liu Bang paused, then said in a loud voice:

"I, the King of Han, am appointing you as chancellor of the kingdom of Zhao. You will work under King Zhang Er."

Hann Xin accepted the new appointment with a profusion of thanks.

"General Hann Xin," Liu Bang continued, "I hereby order you to command 30,000 men of this army on a campaign against Qi in the east."

"Yes, Your Highness," answered Hann Xin meekly.

Envoy to Qi (204 BCE)

WITH THE MAIN FORCE of Hann Xin's army under his command, Liu Bang was getting ready to cross the Heshui (Yellow River) back into the Central Plain. But an astrological event got him deeply worried. In July, a comet with a large tail made its appearance in the sky and stayed in the Great Horn area (Arcturus in the constellation Boötes) for two weeks before it vanished. Great Horn was the principal star of the stellar lodge Horn (Jiao; mainly in Virgo). Its allotted field was mainly in Qi (Shandong).

"I don't like this 'cometary apparition' at all. Is it going to bring disaster to my campaign?" Liu Bang asked his personal astrologer.

"The comet, the so-called 'broom-star,' is ominous because of its tail, which is destructive as it sweeps across the sky. In this case, the affected area is in Horn in heaven, which governs Qi (<u>Shandong</u>) on earth. For now, the northern part of it is controlled by the Tians and the southern part by Xiang Yu. In my humble opinion, it is an indication that Xiang Yu will be swept away. So it is a disaster to Chu but a boon to Han."

Greatly relieved, Liu Bang ordered his army to cross the river.

***

LIU BANG WAS PLEASED to find that the situation in the Central Plain had greatly improved during his absence. Peng Yue had launched a series of counterattacks and seized several cities and towns back from Xiang Yu. This allowed Liu Bang to lay siege to Xingyang, his erstwhile capital in the Central Plain, and Chenggao, its satellite town to the west. He then made a few attempts to sack both, but all failed.

These failures caused him to consider his next strategic move: withdrawing his troops west to Gong and Luoyang for a long rest before a possible comeback. In response to that, his adviser Li Yiji said, "I don't think you should do it, Great King. I heard that 'he who knows what Heaven's Heaven is can rule as king.' A kingly ruler regards the people as Heaven, and the people regard food as Heaven. As it happens, northeast of Xingyang, there is the famous Ao Granary. With its huge storage of millet, the granary has long served as the hub of grain shipments. Whoever controls it holds in his hands a vital supply of food, a 'people's Heaven.' With that, he can easily win over multitudes of people. If you, Great King, seize control of the Ao Granary and the key strategic points such as the White Horse Crossing, you will show to the world you are the dominant force in the Central Plain. All under Heaven will flock to you."

"Is that all?"

"Not yet. Please hear me out, Great King. Having subdued Zhao and Yan to the north you will soon dominate the Central Plain. What vital area is still beyond your control? Qi! The Tians of Qi have in their domain the Heshui (<u>Yellow</u> River), the Ji River, the Eastern Sea, and Mount Tai. Their territory is bordered by Chu on the south. Their people are notoriously cunning and fickle. Months ago you sent an army, tens of thousands strong, to conquer them. So far it has not made any progress at all. Xiang Yu campaigned against them, but failed to win a decisive victory. However, they know very well, in the long run, they cannot survive without joining Chu or Han. Their overriding concern is how they will be treated after submission. I think if I lay out the facts, I can allay their fears and persuade them to join Han. Anyway, once the Ao Granary and Qi are under your control, you can easily force Xingyang and Chenggao into submission."

"Excellent!" said Liu Bang. "Do go to Qi as my envoy. As for the Ao Granary, I'll send an army to take it tomorrow."

The Tians of Qi (204 BCE)

THE TIANS HAD DOMINATED QI for generations during the Warring States period until their state was destroyed by Qin. After the fall of the Qin, they were once more in ascendency. When Xiang Liang faced off with the Qin general Zhang Han, the Tians threw their support behind the former. Following the death of Xiang Liang, the Tians became Xiang Yu's enemies, because Xiang Yu blamed his uncle's death on their failure to send the reinforcements they promised. They allied themselves with Liu Bang at the time of the Pengcheng Campaign, only to break away when it failed. Recently, they had attempted to remain an independent force, but could not afford to offend either Chu or Han, especially the latter.

Now Hann Xin's expeditionary army was moving east, Tian Guang, the King of Qi, became alarmed. He put his troops on high alert, especially those guarding the western border, and beefed up the defenses of his capital Linzi.

Unexpectedly, the Han envoy, Li Yiji, came on a state mission. The King of Qi was delighted and welcomed him as a distinguished guest of state.

The son of the powerful Qi general Tian Rong, who had perished recently in fighting Xiang Yu, the young king Tian Guang was barely 20 years old. Even though he was not officially under the tutelage of a regent, he relied on his uncle, Chancellor Tian Heng, for every major policy decision. Not only was Tian Heng the younger brother of Tian Rong (the king's father), but also the king-maker who had placed Tian Guang on the throne. Like most Tians, Uncle Tian Heng, now in his mid-30s, was tall with broad shoulders. His angular face, dusky red and weather-beaten, was marked by sharp, piercing eyes.

At Li Yiji's first meeting with the King of Qi, not surprisingly, the uncle was also present.

"Do you know who will eventually reign over all under Heaven?" Li Yiji asked.

"I don't know," the king answered, shaking his head.

"Liu Bang king of Han. Why? He was the first to enter Xianyang and should be made king of Guanzhong according to the Covenant. But Xiang Yu forced him to leave for Hanzhong. From there, he raised an army, conquered the Three Qins, and crossed the Hangu Pass into the Central Plain to assume power on behalf of the Righteous Emperor. He granted titles to descendants of the old local lords and generals. Those who surrendered a city were made marquis and were given lands as their fiefs. Because of this willingness to share wealth, heroes, magnates, worthies, and talents all flock to him.

"Now, what is his opponent Xiang Yu like? Not only did he violate the Covenant, he was behind the killing of the Righteous Emperor. While he never misses an opportunity to brag about his merit, he refuses to acknowledge the merit of others. Under him, one cannot get rewarded for winning a victory, nor can one get enfeoffed for sacking a city. One is never promoted to an important post unless one is a Xiang or a close friend. No wonder people everywhere have abandoned him. That's why I say, 'All under Heaven will come under the King of Han's rule.' The King of Han has already controlled Shu, Hanzhong, Guanzhong, Wei, Yan, and Zhao. Clearly, in his endeavor to coqnuer the realm, he has been aided by Heaven. Recently, he captured the Ao Granary. That has made him invincible. If you submit to the King of Han now, the state of Qi will remain. If you do not, Qi will be attacked and destroyed."

"Is that why Hann Xin's army is marching east?" Uncle Tian Heng asked.

"Well, as soon as he learns of your decision to join Han, he will desist from hostilities."

"How can you make sure that the King of Han will make good on what you promised?" asked the King of Qi, who still had some lingering doubts.

"To prove our sincerity, I will stay here until you receive a confirmation from the King of Han himself. Is there anything else, the King of Qi?"

The king was silent for a while. He then shifted his eyes from the Han envoy to his uncle, who inclined his head slightly. The king continued, "What can I say? You have covered everything, Yiji. We'll join Han and avoid a disastrous war."

The Qi, from the sovereign down to common soldiers, breathed a collective sigh of relief. Garrison forces in the west subsequently relaxed their guard.

The king and his uncle spent the next few days feasting and drinking in the company of Li Yiji.

Hann Xin and the Qi Campaign (204 BCE)

BY EARLY NOVEMBER, about 100 *li* east of Julu, on the bank of the mighty Heshui (Yellow River), Hann Xin's army had made camp. While Hann Xin was discussing with Kuai Che, an elderly counselor in his 70s, ways to ferry his massive army across the river to reach the town of Pingyuan (south of Pingyuan, Shandong), he received news of Qi's surrender.

"Well, we probably don't need to cross the river after all," murmured Hann Xin.

"With due respect, General," said Kuai Che, "the order you received from the King of Han is to attack Qi. Unless you receive a countermand, you are obligated to proceed."

"Am I?" asked Hann as he fell to thinking.

"Moreover, Li Yiji, a bookworm armed with nothing but a glib tongue, is now bringing more than 70 Qi cities and towns into the fold. By comparison, you, a great general, commanding an army of tens of thousands of men, conquered Zhao with its 50-odd cities and towns, only after campaigning for more than a year. That does not make you look very good."

"But if I follow your advice, I'm afraid the King of Han will fault me for spoiling his plan."

"I have to disagree. So long as you conquer Qi, nobody will question how you did it. Besides, we can halt the attack as soon as we receive an order to do so."

Thus Hann Xin's march to the east continued.

***

NO SOONER HAD HANN Xin's army crossed over into Qi territory did it begin to move swiftly southeast. A couple of days later, it reached the suburbs of Licheng (Jinan, Shandong), catching the Qi garrison forces off guard. Without much effort, Hann sacked the city and began to move toward Linzi, the Qi capital (north of Linzi, Shandong).

When the King of Qi learned of the invasion led by Hann Xin, he was livid with rage and fear. With his uncle Tian Heng's approval, he ordered Li Yiji's incarceration. The hope that the invasion would be halted in the eleventh hour by an order from the King of Han finally evaporated when the Hann Xin's advance troops were sighted near Linzi. Turning down Li Yiji's repeated requests for an audience, the King of Qi, at the urging of his uncle, had the old man plunged into a cauldron of fuming oil. Before the fall of the city, the king, under the escort of a small troop of soldiers, fled to Gaomi to the southeast, while dispatching an envoy to Chu with a plea for help.

The Battle of Chenggao (204 BCE)

BEFORE HE WENT EAST to chase after Peng Yue in the east Central Plain (east Henan), Xiang Yu had charged Zhongli Mo and Cao Jiu with the defense of Xingyang and Chenggao. Neither was given a large garrison force. Xiang Yu had instructed both to stay inside the protective city walls and wait for his return in about two weeks.

A few days later, the Han army environed the town of Chenggao. Outside the eastern gate, some Han soldiers, with drums beating, demanded battle. The Chu commanding officer Cao Jiu, following Xiang Yu's order, declined the request. The next day, the Han soldiers were at it again, hurling invectives at the Chu defenders. Cao Jiu mounted the gatetower of the eastern entrance to monitor the situation several times, but did nothing. On the morning of the third day, some of the Han soldiers stooped to a new low when they shouted, "Bastard Cao, I fuck your mother!" It was accompanied by salacious laughter. Repeatedly subjected to this kind of obscene insult, Cao Jiu lost his composure and ordered a quick assault out of the gate. The Han troops beat a hasty retreat east. The Chu troops, led by Cao Jiu and his lieutenant Sima Xin, gave chase as far as the Si River, a tributary of the Heshui (Yellow River). On Cao's orders, the troops made a forced crossing. Surprised by a sudden Han counterattack, most of the Chu troops perished midstream. Having watched the debacle unfold, the despondent Cao and Sima took their own lives on the west bank of the river.

The Han army went on to sack Chenggao and now had direct access to the Ao Granary to the northeast. It then pitched camp at Guangwu (west of the Ao Granary), and started laying siege to Xingyang. This seriously alarmed Zhongli Mo, the Chu commanding officer in charge of defending the city. Greatly outnumbered, the Chu defenders could hold out for less than a week. While preparing the city for an attack, General Zhongli sent out three urgent messages to Xiang Yu to request reinforcements (see Map 3).

Xiang Yu was somewhere in the east Central Plain, hot on the tail of Peng Yue, when he received Zhongli Mo's messages. He turned around and headed for Xingyang with a few thousands of his men. It was in the southern suburb of Xingyang that they encountered the Han siege troops. Xiang Yu attacked and scattered them, pushing through the siege line. The junction of the two Chu forces made it impossible for Liu Bang to maintain the siege. So he retreated to the Ao Granary area where his field headquarters had been set up.

Xiang Yu moved north as well, and encamped most of his troops in Guangwu to the west of the Han camp. A tedious standoff followed that lasted several months. Neither side could gain the upper hand. However, the Han army enjoyed a long-term advantage. Its control of the Ao Granary allowed their officers and men to have access to a virtually endless supply of grain. In contrast, the Chu troops were gradually reduced to starvation.

The Meeting in Guangwu (204 BCE)

SINCE CHEN SHENG and Wu Guang started their famous rebellion in Daze Township five years before, the entire realm had been embroiled in endless warfare. Three years later, the end-of-dynasty turmoil had given way to the civil war between two rival camps: the Han camp led by Liu Bang and the Chu camp led by Xiang Yu. By now people on both sides had grown war-weary. When a Chu envoy proposed on behalf of Xiang Yu a summit to resolve the stalemate, Liu Bang jumped at the chance.

One bright morning in late November,[11] Xiang Yu and Liu Bang made their appearance on horseback to face each other in a large stretch of flatland denuded of anything green that separated the two camps at Guangwu. Each side was escorted by a significant cavalry force.

As Liu Bang, accompanied by his entourage, rode up to the front to meet his archrival, he was startled by the furious barrage of Chu drums. The rhythmic beating suddenly crescendoed into a chaotic cacophony as the Han drummers joined the fray. Liu Bang saw in the distance Xiang Yu's men wheel to the front a flatbed cart on which a gagged old man in his late 70s was tied to a tall table.

The drumming died down. Xiang Yu roared to the Han side, "Liu Bang! I demand your immediate surrender! If you refuse, I will have no choice but to cook this old man alive!"

"Xiang Yu!" answered Liu Bang, overcoming his fear that something awful would happen to his aging father, showed no sign of losing his composure. "When you and I received our mandate from King Huai, we took an oath together and became sworn brothers. So my father is your father. If you want to cook him, go ahead. But don't forget to give me a cup of the soup!"

[11] The event took place in the 10th month of the fourth year of Gaodi and falls in 204 BCE.

"This heartless bastard! I am going to chop off his father's head right now!" an infuriated Xiang Yu growled as he flourished his sword. Xiang Bo rushed forward to stop him, saying, "It does not help matters if you kill him. It will probably make things much, much worse. Besides, does Liu really care about his family? No! We have his wife in custody as well. Has he ever attempted to rescue either? No!"

Xiang Yu was silent, his eyes red with rage.

"If we keep these two hostages, in the future, we may be able to exchange them for something big. You'll never know." As he said so, Xiang Bo helped his nephew put the sword back into the sheath.

Xiang Yu trotted a few paces forward, and shouted, "Liu Bang! The world has been in turmoil for the last two years, all because of you and me. I want to spare millions of innocent people the pain and suffering of war and challenge you to a one-on-one combat to settle our old scores once and for all."

"No way," said Liu Bang smilingly. "I would rather engage you in a battle of wits, not a battle of strength."

Xiang Yu waved his hand and a Chu general on horseback galloped forward to demand battle, only to be unhorsed by an arrow shot by Loufan, Liu Bang's Xiongnu sharpshooter.

Two more Chu generals rode to the front one after another, and both met the same fate.

In a fit of fury, Xiang Yu, fully armored, rode his famous warhorse Dapple (Zhui)—a silky black stallion with white markings—into the clearing and roared out his demand for battle, his eyes glowering fiercely. Terrified, the Xiongnu archer disappeared into the Han camp, never to show his face again.

Finally, tempers cooled down. Both sides came to an agreement that they should hear out each other's grievances and seek to reach a middle ground if possible.

Xiang Yu was the first to speak. He accused Liu Bang of violating the deal between Chu and Han at Hongmen by leaving Hanzhong to enter Guanzhong, capturing Xianyang, and invading the Central Plain and the Huai valley.

Liu Bang responded with a laundry list of ten crimes against Xiang Yu, including violating the Convenant; killing General Song Yi, the ex-king Ziying, and the Righteous Emperor; torching the Qin palaces; raiding the Mausoleum of the First Emperor; and massacring 200,000 of surrendered Qin troops.

Flying into a towering rage, Xiang Yu howled, "Cut the nonsense, you churl! I dare you to fight me alone!" Neighing and snorting, Dapple kicked his forelegs into the air.

Liu responded, "Fight you alone? Hell, no! The local lords and I are joined together in a common struggle against you, the ruthless robber. Just by using our ex-inmates we can attack and kill you. Why do I need to fight you alone?"

Suddenly, Xiang Yu roared out a blood-curdling threat, and Liu tumbled off the horse. With his hand holding his left foot, Liu shouted, "A hooligan has hit my toe." Two attendant gentlemen whisked him into a carriage, which swiftly pulled away.

Inside the carriage, the gentlemen found that Liu Bang had actually been wounded in the chest and the wound was much more serious than Liu Bang had made it out to be. At times, it even caused him to have difficulty breathing.

In the Han camp a troop rally was planned for that evening. At Zhang Liang's urging, Liu Bang attended the event, even though he looked pallid and wan. Zhang was afraid morale would plummet if Liu did not make the scheduled appearance. Later that night, however, the wound worsened, and Liu Bang was rushed to Chenggao for treatment and care.

Hann Xin and the Battle of Gaomi (204 BCE)

AFTER LINZI'S FALL TO Hann Xin, the King of Qi fled south to Gaomi (also in Shandong), where he joined Long Ju, one of Xiang Yu's top generals. General Long, who had recently trounced Ying Bu, was now commanding a massive rescue army (see Map 3).

At a war council Long Ju held, a local counselor offered some practical advice, saying, "The Han army has trekked a long way and won many battles. It has tremendous momentum. To counter that, we should strengthen our defense line.

Right now, the Qi and Chu forces are encamped separately, which makes them vulnerable to attack. I think that they should be concentrated in one well-fortified area instead. For now, we should turn down any requests for battle and wait while the King of Qi sends out his trusted senior officials to various fallen cities and towns to suborn the inhabitants. When they hear that the king is alive and well and is being supported by the Chu army, they will surely rebel against Han. Before long, the Han troops will end up with no food and be forced to surrender."

"What do you think, General?" the King of Qi asked, addressing Long Ju.

Long replied, "I know something about Hann Xin, the commanding officer of the Han invading army. He is a drifter and a coward, begging a laundry woman for food and crawling between the legs of a butcher. There is no need to fear him. Besides, to defeat an enemy like Hann Xin without fighting—that is quite beneath me." Thus the counselor's proposals were rejected.

To the west of Gaomi ran the Wéi River, which constituted a formidable barrier against the invaders. It was along this river that Chu and Han arrayed their troops. Hann Xin, who was on the west side, sent some of his men upriver on a secret night mission. They dumped more than 10,000 bags of soil to create a dam that greatly restricted the flow of water.

The next morning, the Han troops crossed the river to make a feint, only to fall back as soon as the enemies started a counterattack. The Chu soldiers gave chase. As those leading the charge were about to reach the west bank, on Hann Xin's orders, the dam was breached. Suddenly, a torrent of water flooded the riverbed. Many of Long Ju's men were trapped. By then the Han troops had turned around and started falling on them. In a matter of hours, the Chu troops were scattered, taken prisoner, or killed. General Long Ju himself perished in the chaos. The King of Qi made an attempt to flee north, but was soon captured by Hann Xin's men. With the help of other Han generals such as Cao Shen and Guan Ying, who struck out in different directions, Hann Xin finally brought all of Qi under the dominion of Han.[12]

---

[12] This event took place in the 11th month of the fourth year of Gaodi and falls in 204 BCE.

Hann Xin's Request (203 BCE)

AFTER A BRIEF PERIOD of recuperation, Liu Bang was back in camp again at Guangwu, even though he was not fully recovered and life in the campaign tent was by no means comfortable. But he needed to stay close to his generals at a time when the fight against Xiang Yu had reached a true turning point. A string of victories scored by Hann Xin in Qi (<u>Shandong</u>) had not only brought this ancient domain into the fold, but also vanquished Xiang Yu's main force under his most redoubtable general Long Ju. In fact, the territory under Xiang Yu's effective control was now reduced to the Pengcheng area and the easternmost part of the Central Plain. Liu Bang was again setting his sights on Pengcheng.

At a routine meeting with his top advisers and generals, Liu Bang sat in the seat of honor with Zhang Liang and Chen Ping on either side. An attendant gentleman came over to deliver a roll of bamboo slips—an urgent letter from Hann Xin. At Liu Bang's request, Chen Ping started reading it aloud.

Liu Bang listened with obvious interest and delight as Chen Ping continued,

Qi is a cunning state notorious for its flip-flops. Furthermore, it is bordered by Chu on the south, and is prone to external invasion. Please appoint me as its acting king so as to better defend the area.

"Shit!" Liu Bang exploded. "The bastard wants to be acting king?!"

Zhang Liang tugged at his sleeve and whispered something into his ear. Apparently ignoring Zhang, Liu Bang continued with his obscenities. "If that fucking bastard is man enough, why doesn't he ask to be a *real* king?"

"Considering his merit, I think, he should be raised to king of Qi," opined Zhang Liang.

"All right," said Liu Bang, "pay him a visit with the king's seal and his patent of appointment, will you?"

"With pleasure, Great King," replied Zhang Liang.

After they got out of the tent, Chen Ping asked Zhang Liang, "How did you make him change his mind?"

"I just warned him, 'If you don't approve Hann Xin's request, he may stop paying homage to you.' Hann Xin is the only one in the world who can defeat Xiang Yu. Besides, the court is not strong enough to prevent Hann Xin from naming himself king, anyway."

"I agree," said Chen Ping.

Kuai Che's Advice (203 BCE)

ON HIS VISIT TO Linzi, Zhang Liang, on behalf of the King of Han, conferred the king's title upon Hann Xin, while commanding him to march his troops south to take part in the final campaign against Chu.

No doubt Hann Xin was thrilled with his new royal title, but was hesitant to move his army. After the conquest of Qi, Hann Xin had emerged as the most formidable military figure in the realm. Of course, he did not want to challenge the authority of the King of Han; still, he expected a tangible reward from his master before committing his troops to another campaign.

Then a mysterious visitor called Wu She arrived. Only when host and guest were behind closed doors did Wu reveal his identity as Xiang Yu's secret envoy. The visit aroused in Hann Xin a mixture of feelings. On the one hand, he felt gratified, almost flattered, that the legendary Hegemonic King had reached out to himself; on the other, he felt vindicated by the fact that Chu was on the verge of collapse in part because its imperious king had refused to listen to his advice.

"The world suffered a great deal under the tyrannical Qin," the envoy said, "and all the heroes under Heaven joined forces to fight it. Consequently, the Qin fell, the realm was divided up among the newly enfeoffed kings, and peace prevailed. The King of Han, however, raised an army and moved east, seizing territories allotted to others. After taking Guanzhong, he invaded the Central Plain, and went on to attack Chu. He will never rest until he achieves his ultimate goal: the domination of all under Heaven.

"But this overambitious man is not necessarily invincible. He has fallen into King Xiang Yu's hands several times. Each time King Xiang Yu let him live out of generosity and pity. And each time he reneged on his promises and started attacking King Xiang Yu again. So he is a man of little credibility. You may think that the King of Han has treated you well. But mark my words: even if you put your life on the line for him, sooner or later you will fall into his trap. The reason that he has not brought you down is because King Xiang Yu is still there. On the other hand, as the two kings are engaged in a fierce rivalry, only you, General, can tip the balance of power. If you join forces with King Xiang Yu against Han, the world will be divided into three kingdoms, and one of them will be your own. If you don't, you will only fight Chu for others. I guarantee it will spell ruin for you."

After a moment of silence, Hann Xin said, "Thank you so much for the advice. I was grateful to King Xiang Yu for giving me a job. But my duty then was to stand guard with a halberd. In spite of General Zhongli Mo's recommendations, I never got a promotion. My words carried no weight with him, and my suggestions went unheeded. That was why I left Chu and joined Han. The King of Han appointed me general-in-chief to command an army of tens of thousands. He not only listens to my advice, but acts upon it. To betray his trust is immoral *and* unlucky. So this is something I will never do, even if threatened by death. Give King Xiang my best regards and tell him I am sorry."

After Wu She was secretly escorted out of the Linzi Palace, Hann Xin summoned his counselor and confidant Kuai Che.

"I have to thank you for advising me to attack Qi," said Hann Xin. "And your prediction turned out to be right: the King of Han did not take me to task for Li Yiji's death."

"Well, Great King, my advice was not entirely my own. It was actually based upon a divination."

"You do divinations as well?" asked Hann in astonishment.

"Yes, I am a physiognomist by trade."

"Can you divine my future based on physiognomy?"

"Yes, Great King, I am at your service," said Kuai Che as he moved closer to Hann. He studied his facial features closely for a while, then stepped away to look him up and down from a distance. In the end, he said, "Great King, I see in your physiognomy an appointment with uncertain destiny. You will be demoted to marquis, and your life will be fraught with danger. But examining your back I can still see that you possess signs that suggest the highest possible nobility."

"Let me guess: do you mean that I may have a choice between two different futures?"

"Yes, that's precisely my point. What you choose to do in the next couple of years will be crucial."

"Enlighten me on that."

"Well, after the conquest of Qi, the overall situation has changed. The fate of the two sovereigns—Liu Bang and Xiang Yu—now rests in your hands. In my opinion, your best strategy is to take advantage of the situation and stake out your territory to create the third power. With your wise and sage rulership and massive army, this new state of yours, based in Qi, Zhao, and Yan, will eventually dominate the realm. As the proverb says, 'If you don't take what is afforded to you by Heaven, you will reap the consequences.'"

"But the King of Han has treated me very well. How can I abandon righteousness for my own benefit?"

"You know the celebrated friendship between Zhang Er and Chen Yu, don't you? When both were commoners, they were bosom friends, who were like father and son at the same time. After they took up arms against the Qin, they came to hate each other. After Chen Yu made an attempt to eliminate Zhang Er, Zhang trounced him in battle and lopped off his head. Why? Because they are human, and human hearts are unknowable. Thus your claim that the King of Han will never harm you is wrong.

"Take another example. Wen Zhong, a senior official of Yue, who rescued that wretched state from the verge of destruction and helped his sovereign King Goujian to gain hegemony. What happened next? After achieving success and fame, Wen Zhong had to fall on his own sword on the king's orders. As the saying goes: 'After all the animals are hunted down, the good hounds are cooked.'

"Zhang Er and Chen Yu were the best of friends; and Wen Zhong was the most loyal of officials. Both Chen and Wen were betrayed and ended up losing their lives tragically. Furthermore, 'Those who threaten their sovereign because of their bravery and strategic wisdom are in danger.' And you are one of them. If you submit to Chu, Chu will not trust you; if you submit to Han, Han will be terrified. You don't have to choose between them, do you?"

"Stop right there! Mr. Kuai. I've heard enough!" exclaimed Hann Xin as he stood up to leave.

"Great King, please hear me out. If you still are not convinced I will leave for good."

"All right," Hann Xin said apprehensively, sitting down again.

"What is a good listener? Someone who can watch for eventualities. What is a good planner? Someone who can seize opportunities. But no matter how much one tries to avoid mistakes through careful listening and how much one attempts to keep failures at bay through meticulous planning, in most cases, one just cannot achieve one's goals as expected and enjoy one's peace of mind for long. Thus we know he who makes decisive moves is intelligent and he who hesitates is an enemy to himself. Success is hard to attain, but harder to maintain. A good opportunity is hard to catch, but easy to miss. When it's gone, it's gone, and may never come back."

"I see your point. However, with due respect, I don't think I am convinced. Because of my merit, the King of Han will never attack Qi."

"Alas!" Kuai Che sighed, stood up, and left the room.

Peng Yue and Hann Xin (203 BCE)

IT WAS NOW OCTOBER. Xiang Yu was almost at the end of his resources: his army's grain supply was running low; his officers and men's efforts to extort grain from the villages were increasingly ineffectual because of recent harvest failures; virtually all military-age males had been drafted, leaving the women and the old and young to attend the crops; it had become nigh impossible to replenish units of reduced troop strength with new recruits.

Xiang Yu began to toy with the idea of moving south. A Han envoy paid him a surprise visit. He brought with him Liu Bang's new offer for a peace deal. According to it, the Hong Conduit, an artificial waterway that ran from Xunyi (Kaifeng) to Chen (Huaiyang, Henan), would mark the new boundary with Chu; Han would cease hostilities; and in exchange Liu Bang's father and wife and the butler Shen Yiji would be returned to Han (see Map 4).

To Xiang Yu, this offer was a life-saver. He affixed his seal to the Treaty of the Hong Conduit without a moment of hesitation. He knew that the promises Liu Bang made in the treaty would inevitably be broken. But Xiang Yu needed a break from the desperate situation he found himself in. On his orders, the three hostages were released. And Liu Bang withdrew his troops to the west of the new border.

The uneasy truce held for almost a month. The Han leadership started planning for its next move. But Liu Bang did not show much interest. Years of military life, on or off the saddle, had taken its toll. Admittedly, as king, he often resided in palatial houses inside walled cities and was relatively well provisioned. But when he was out campaigning, which was not that infrequent, he had to content himself with living in a tent and eating poor food. To say nothing of the battle wounds that he sustained. Lately, he felt so drained of strength that he was disinclined to lead another military operation. When the proposal on the final offensive against Chu was presented to him, he put it on hold indefinitely. Instead, he planned to move back to Yueyang (northeast of Lintong, Shaanxi) in Guanzhong for another spell of recuperation.

"However," said Zhang Liang, the strongest voice in the pro-war camp, "as of now, Han has conquered most of the realm; all the local lords have submitted; the Chu army has run out of grain, and is thoroughly exhausted. But, like a wounded tiger, if it is not killed right now, once healed, it will come back to bite you."

"Do you agree?" asked Liu Bang, addressing Chen Ping.

"Yes, Great King," answered Chen. "This is a godsend. If you let it slip away, it may never come again."

"But my chest wound has not healed yet. I need more time."

"If you crush Xiang Yu, you can recuperate as long as you like."

"Damn!" cried Liu Bang. "Both of you want me to do it. But it is going to kill me."

"I assure you, it won't," said Zhang Liang.

"No, it won't," echoed Chen Ping.

"All right," said Liu Bang petulantly, "I'll do it."

***

IN A WEEK'S TIME, Liu Bang's final campaign against Xiang Yu was underway. At Guling (south of <u>Taikang</u>, in central <u>Henan</u>), his troops caught up with Xiang Yu and encamped. Before the night was out, the enemy launched a sneak attack and routed Liu's forward units. Liu Bang then issued an urgent order that the troops must stay inside their camps and fortifications and refuse battle. He was waiting for reinforcements from Peng Yue and Hann Xin. Weeks later, when they were not forthcoming, Liu Bang exploded, "These two bastards will screw things up again!" He could not help recalling the eerily similar situation at the time of the siege of Xingyang.

"Well, I am afraid it is not as easy as it seems," commented Zhang Liang. "It is true that the Chu army is on the verge of total collapse, but the two local lords, Peng Yue and Hann Xin, are probably not too enthused about joining the fight. The reason is obvious: neither has received his share of land. You raised Hann Xin to king of Qi, but have yet to grant him a fief. Of course, Hann has not asked for one either. But at heart, he absolutely lusts for it. As for Peng Yue, after he captured the Liang (Wei) area, he was made chancellor of Wei under King Wei Bao. Now the king is dead, Peng wants to be king himself with his own feudatory. At any rate, if you let it be known that you intend to share your lands with them, they will join the campaign in no time."

"I don't mind granting them fiefs at all," said Liu Bang. "Do you have any idea where I should enfeoff them?"

"How about this: the area north of Suiyang is enfeoffed to Peng Yue; and the area east of Chen to the sea is enfeoffed to Hann Xin?"

"Fine. I really don't mind," said Liu Bang.

So two vast feudatories were created in the Central Plain and Qi (<u>Shandong</u>) for Peng Yue and Hann Xin. In a matter of weeks, their troops began arriving in large numbers. As for the third member of the triad, Ying Bu, having been recently raised to king of Huainan, he had already joined the campaign with a large army. Not only that. Thanks to Ying Bu's work, Zhou Yin, commander-in-chief of Xiang Yu's army, had defected to Han.

Gaixia (202 BCE)

Scipio Africanus had brought a sizeable army to Carthage. Hannibal was forced to move back from Italy to fight the Roman invasion. A decisive battle was fought in Zama (130 km SW of Carthage) in which Scipio trounced Hannibal.

EARLY IN THE YEAR, Xiang Yu's mighty army, which had once numbered more than 400,000 men, was reduced to a rabble of a few thousands. They huddled inside a fortified camp in Gaixia (southeast of <u>Lingbi</u>, <u>Anhui</u>), encircled by multiple layers of Han troops.

At dusk, a cacophony of singing wafted in from all sides. Xiang Yu pricked up his ears and listened attentively. These were not jingoistic Han battle songs, but some familiar melancholy strains. Suddenly, Xiang Yu shouted in astonishment, "They are singing Chu songs! Have they conquered Chu already? Where do so many Chu soldiers come from?"

After dark, inside his campaign tent, Xiang Yu and a dozen men—bodyguards and senior officers—were sitting around a fire, drinking and singing. Wrapped in Xiang Yu's arms was a petite woman in her mid-20s, whom everybody called Concubine Yú. Ever since she had been gifted to him by one of his generals four years before, she had been by his side, sharing every grief and joy with the Great King. With a forlorn expression on her face, Concubine Yú looked particularly charming that night. Caressing her black hair, Xiang Yu began to sing a song composed for the occasion:

> *My strength can pull up hills,*
>
> *My might can shadow the world;*
>
> *But, in this unlucky time*
>
> *My horse Dapple can no longer run.*
>
> *Alas, Dapple can no longer run,*
>
> *What can be done?*

Alas, Yú my concubine!

Alas, Yú! What's to be done?

The concubine responded:

Our land has been taken by the soldiers of Han,

We are drowned out by Chu songs from every direction.

The end has come for the Great King of Chu,

Why should his wretched concubine be spared?

After they went back and forth for several rounds, Xiang Yu was drowned in a flood of tears. All present bent their heads in sorrow.

Suddenly, Concubine Yú freed herself from Xiang Yu's embrace and stood up. "I know what should be done, Great King," she said, with tears streaming down her cheeks.

"Don't, Yú. I forbid you!" shouted Xiang Yu.

It was already too late. Yú had plunged a dagger deep into her neck and collapsed.

Holding her in his arms, Xiang Yu shouted, "Why?"

Yú murmured indistinctly, "Now you can...leave."

Some of Xiang's men carried the lifeless body outside. Xiang Yu watched as they buried his beloved concubine beneath a tree. Grief-stricken, he reentered the tent. After a brief silence that felt like an eternity, Xiang Yu shouted, "We will break out tonight!" It was well past midnight.

Leading 800 riders, Xiang Yu fought his way out of the encirclement and charged south. General Guan Ying with a cavalry of 5,000 chased after him. By the time Xiang Yu crossed the Huai River at dawn, barely 100 of his mounted followers remained.

In Yinling (east of <u>Bengbu</u>), they lost their way. Xiang Yu saw an old farmer working in the field and asked him for direction. The farmer simply said, "Left."

Following the direction (toward the east), they were soon bogged down in a massive swampland. As the pursuing Han army was bearing down upon them, Xiang Yu and his men galloped further east to Dongcheng (northwest of <u>Chuzhou</u>).

Xiang Yu stopped at the foot of a hill and found 28 riders were still with him. With a long sigh, Xiang Yu said, "It has been seven years now since I raised my first army. In the more than 70 battles I fought, I defeated all those who resisted me, and vanquished all those whom I attacked. I never lost a battle, and became the hegemon of all under Heaven.

"Look at me now: stranded in this god-forsaken place, chased around like a thief. Not that I can't fight, but that it is Heaven's will that I should perish. But before I go, let's fight one more battle. Follow me!"

With an ear-piercing roar, Xiang Yu galloped towards one group of Han pursuers, all of whom dodged for cover. By then he had already struck and unhorsed a Han general. Another Han general came rushing and Xiang Yu gave a thunderous roar that sent him and his horse fleeing. Xiang Yu then spurred his Dapple to charge against another group who had gathered, killing one senior officer and a large number of his followers. Xiang Yu had lost two more riders.

With the Han army in hot pursuit, Xiang Xu rode all the way to Wujiang (northeast of <u>Hexian</u> and southwest of <u>Nanjing</u>) on the Jiangshui (<u>Yangzi</u>), losing all his men along the way. Moored to the bank was a ferryboat. An elderly ferryman came out to greet him. Surprised at the wretched sight of the legendary king, he said, "Come aboard, Great King. The boat can take you to Jiangdong ["East of the River"]. It is a small area all right, but it has a population of hundreds of thousands, enough for a small kingdom." (See Map 3)

Xiang Yu answered resignedly, "No use trying to escape across the river. Heaven wants me to die." He raised his head to look at the vault of the sky, and continued, "I remember vividly the first time I crossed the river from the east. I led 8,000 men, all from Jiangdong. Now I am the only one who survives. The good folks of Jiangdong may crown me as king out of pity, but I will be too ashamed to face them."

Xiang Yu paused for a moment to gaze at his horse, and said, "Listen. Here is my warhorse Dapple. I have ridden him for the last five years. He can run 1,000 *li* in a day. There is no match for him. Since I can't bear to kill him, I want you to have him, if you don't mind."

The ferryman, thanking Xiang Yu, led the horse away.

The Han pursuers were closing in on their quarry. Sword in hand, Xiang Yu plunged himself into battle, killing many more Han troops and sustaining more than a dozen wounds. Then one middle-aged Han rider rode close to him. Just Xiang Yu was about to engage this new adversary, he stopped and asked, "Aren't you Lü Matong, my old acquaintance?"

Lü Matong shouted to his fellow officer Wang Yi, "This is Xiang Yu!"

Xiang Yu responded, "I heard that Liu Bang puts a price on my head: 1,000 catties of gold and marquisate of 10,000 households. Take it." As he said so, he slashed his sword across his neck, and dropped to the ground as blood spurted from his wound.

Wang Yi, who had dismounted, rushed forward to cut off the head while other Han officers and men struggled to seize a piece of the body. In the scuffle that followed, dozens lost their lives. In the end, five men, including Wang Yi and Lü Matong, acquired one key part of the body each, and all five were later enfeoffed as marquises.

***

WITH THE FALL OF Xiang Yu, the entire realm save Lu came under the rule of Liu Bang. Lu had been the home state of Confucius during the Spring and Autumn period and was annexed by the state of Qi in the Warring States period. In the civil war, it had pledged its allegiance to Chu. After the death of Xiang Yu, a Han army laid siege to the Lu capital (Qufu, Shandong), demanding surrender. The inhabitants rejected the demand. The Han commanding general escorted by two dozen cavalry and attendant gentlemen rode to the front to assess the situation. They were surprised to hear the sound of people reciting poems, playing the zither, and reading the classics emanating from inside the city through the gate. They realized that these inhabitants were adherents to the Confucian teaching of ritual, righteousness, loyalty, and integrity. If the city were sacked, many of them would rather die than submit. So the commanding general did not attempt a storm, but ordered his troops to stay put instead.

Acting on the advice of a counselor, the general ordered to have Xiang Yu's severed head impaled on a pole, to be raised up high for the defenders on the city wall to see. Only then did the Lu residents stop their resistance.

Xiang Yu's head was then transported on Liu Bang's orders to Luoyang, where it was joined to the other parts of the body in a coffin. The remains of this fallen hero were then buried with proper ritual befitting his noble title, the Lord of Lu. At his funeral service, Liu Bang knelt down and sobbed emotionally. Xiang Yu, though a most vicious foe, had proven himself to be a worthy opponent. With him gone, the world had become a much poorer place.

***

LIU BANG HAD MADE good on his promises to the heroes of Gaixia. Hann Xin, the King of Qi, was renamed the King of Chu; and Peng Yue was named the King of Liang. They divided up the vast lower Huai valley between them, with Hann in the south and Peng in the north.

Hann Xin was especially pleased with the fact that his feudatory included the hometowns of Liu Bang and most of the top leaders. At the suggestion of some senior officials, Hann took it upon himself to write a joint memorial, which urged Liu Bang to take the imperial throne.

Upon reading it, Liu Bang said, "An emperor must be a worthy. His title is not an empty name without substance. Now you local lords all want to elevate me to such a high post, how can you justify it?"

"You, Great King," Hann Xin replied, "rose from a humble background to vanquish the Qin and awe all within the four seas with authority. From the remote place of Hanzhong, you were able to exercise authority and dispense justice, execute the unrighteous, and support the meritorious. You have brought stability to the entire realm and extended your virtue to the four corners of the earth. In contrast, what the local lords have achieved is hardly worth mentioning. It is thus highly appropriate that you should serve as emperor so as to benefit all under Heaven."

Liu Bang remained quiet as he took another look at the dozens of names affixed to the memorial: Peng Yue king of Liang, Ying Bu king of Huaibei, Hannwang Xin king of Hann (who had escaped from Xiang Yu's camp and rejoined Liu Bang), Zhang Liang, Chen Ping, Xiao He, Cao Shen.... Standing up, he said, "What the heck! I'll do it!"

Part III.

The Emperor

Accession (202 BCE)

ON THE MORNING OF February 28th, an auspicious date chosen by the leading ritualist Shusun Tong lord of Jisi, Liu Bang ascended the throne as the founding emperor of the Han dynasty on the northern bank of the Si River, southwest of Dingtao (in <u>Shandong</u>). Simultaneously, his wife Lü was raised from "queen" to "empress," and his son, Liu Ying, was renamed from "crown prince" to "imperial crown prince." Wu Rui, formerly king of Hengshan, was made king of Changsha, now based in Linxiang (<u>Changsha</u>, <u>Hunan</u>). A general amnesty was announced, whereby all inmates including those on death rows were pardoned.

An open-air altar was set up, where sacrificial ceremonies were conducted to honor the martyrs—Li Yiji, Ji Xin, Zhou Ke, General Cong, and numerous others— who had laid down their lives for the cause.

No one took issue with the title "emperor," first adopted by the First Emperor. It referred to an august sovereign on earth who was the doppelgänger of the Lord on High. Although the tyrannical rule of the First Emperor was universally execrated, this title of his is a perfect fit for the founding sovereign of our Han dynasty.

There had been a widespread story about the Emperor's "celestial" origin. It was like this: once while his mother was sleeping on the bank of a great marsh she had an incubus in which she encountered a divine being accompanied by thunder and lightning. Her husband went looking for her and saw a red kraken on top of her. She then became pregnant and later gave birth to Liu Bang, who, as the son of the Red Dragon, was destined to slay the son of the White Dragon, and found a great dynasty. Some skeptics like Wang Chong (the leading philosopher of the Eastern Han) doubt the credibility of this story, but it is adopted as the official version of Liu Bang's birth by the court.

A debate soon arose among the top leaders on the choice of the capital. There were essentially three candidates: Pengcheng, Xianyang, and Luoyang.

Pengcheng in the lower Huai valley was in Liu Bang's home region, and was a vital hub of transportation. Until recently it had served as the capital of Xiang Yu. But it was soon ruled out, because it had no natural barriers for its defense. Xianyang, formerly the Qin capital, had been thoroughly ravaged by Xiang Yu. Besides, it was too far away from Liu's home base. So it was passed over. Luoyang then emerged as the top choice. The Qin city at Luoyang (known previously as Chengzhou), which was east of the Eastern Zhou capital in the same area, had survived the devastation of war relatively unscathed. The two palaces, Northern and Southern, were still functional. The location was convenient for receiving grain and produce from the provinces, and one boat ride away from the lower Huai valley, where the hometowns of the top Han leaders were located.

In June, the Emperor Liu Bang took measures to demobilize many of his troops. They would retire to their hometowns or home villages they had left years before. This was followed by his first important imperial edict on policy, dealing with such issues as the exemption of taxes and corvée, and the granting of titles, with a clear message on leniency. [13]

Clearly, this was an effort to please everybody, from the local lords to the commoners, and to bring a war-torn people together, who had suffered tremendously during the years of Qin rule and the civil war.

***

ONE MORNING, THE EMPEROR Liu Bang hosted his first imperial wine party to entertain his meritorious officials and officers in the Southern Palace of Luoyang. He asked the marquises and generals present a deceptively simple question, "Why was it that I gained all under Heaven whereas Xiang Yu didn't?"

One of them answered, "As soon as Your Majesty captured cities and towns and territories, Your Majesty gave them away, sharing the gains with others. As a result, people flocked to Your Majesty. Xiang Yu was different. He was stingy with lands and titles, persecuted the meritorious, and distrusted the worthy. That's why he lost all under Heaven."

"Well, that's true. But there are other reasons. In terms of making strategic decisions in a campaign tent that would guarantee victories 1,000 *li* away, I am not as good as Zhang Liang; in terms of supporting the state, pacifying the people, and providing an unending supply of grain to the army, I am not as good as Xiao He; in terms of leading a combined force of one million in carrying out attacks and

---

[13] Liu Bang's 202 BCE Edict on Policy:

Local lords' sons who have remained in Guanzhong shall be exempt from taxes and corvée labor for a duration of 12 years; those who already returned home shall be exempt from both for a duration of six years.

Commoners who took shelter in the mountains and swamplands for self-protection were not recorded in the household registry. Now that the world has been pacified, they are ordered to return to their counties; and their titles, lands, and houses shall be restored to them. Officials should follow the letter of the law and admonish and edify them, and are prohibited from insulting them by flogging.

Commoners who sold themselves into bondage to avoid hunger shall be restored to their previous status.

Officials with criminal records are pardoned at the time of the amnesty. Officials who have neither a criminal record nor titles, or who have titles lower than that of counselor (*dafu*), shall be granted the title of counselor. Those who already received the title of counselor shall be elevated to a higher rank. Those with the title of rank-7 counselor and above shall all be given fiefs.

winning battles, I am not as good as Hann Xin. These three people are all geniuses. By comparison, I am a man of mediocre ability. But I know how to use *them*, the geniuses, and that was why I gained all under Heaven. Xiang Yu had one such genius, Fan Zeng. But he could not use him, and that was why he failed."

Cheers and applause erupted among the marquises and generals, who raised their goblets to toast His Majesty's sagacity.

Tian Heng (202 BCE)

IN THE WAKE OF the Wéi River debacle of 203 BCE, the kingdom of Qi had collapsed, and many members of the Tian clan had perished while others had been captured. One major exception was Tian Heng. He had fled to the east where he had declared himself king of Qi and dropped out of sight shortly thereafter.

Now that the war was over, Tian Heng made his way back to Qi (east Shandong). He had gathered around him more than 500 loyalists. Together, they went as far as the eastern shore and put out to sea. Eventually they settled in a small, uninhabited island (northeast of Qingdao, Shandong) nearby.

Soon an imperial envoy arrived with an edict, which granted a pardon to Tian and his followers despite their past anti-Han activities, but enjoined them to resettle inside the Qi area on land. The Emperor was concerned that these ex-Qi subjects staying together on a remote island might make trouble.

Tian Heng replied, "I am sorry I can't comply with the request and return. Let me explain. I had a hand in the death of the Han envoy Li Yiji. Right now, his brother Li Shang is a top Han general. How can I return? Please let me live a commoner's life, guarding the island for His Majesty."

When the Emperor was briefed on the situation, he issued an edict to Li Shang, warning him not to take any vengeful action against Tian Heng and his followers, on pain of being executed with members of his clan. The Emperor then sent the envoy back with a copy of the edit. After showing it to Tian Heng, the envoy said, "If you are willing to come back, the Emperor will grant you an audience in Luoyang and enfeoff you as king or at least marquis. If you don't, the Emperor will have to launch an expedition."

"Is it possible that I will make the trip first and my people will leave the island a couple of months later?" Tian Heng asked.

"Yes, of course," answered the envoy.

"All right, I will go," said Tian Heng with decision. After bidding farewell to his followers, Tian Heng, escorted by two attendant gentlemen, embarked on the envoy's boat and headed for the shore. Once on land, they started to travel by stagecoach toward Luoyang. At the last posthouse before the destination, they made a stop.

Tian Heng said to the envoy, "Look at me. I am covered with dust. I would like, if I may, to wash myself before being received by the Emperor."

"Not a problem," said the envoy.

Tian and the attendant gentlemen entered their room in the posthouse.

As soon as they were by themselves, Tian said to his attendant gentlemen, "Not long ago, both the King of Han and myself were sovereigns. Today, he is the Emperor, and I am his captive. As if that is not shameful enough, I was involved in the killing of Li Shang's brother, and I am now expected to serve the Emperor at the same court with Li Shang! Even if he does not touch me because of the imperial edict, how can I not feel ashamed for what I've done? The Emperor has granted me an audience only because he wants to see my face. Luoyang is just 30 *li* from here. If you take my head there in haste, by the time you arrive, my face will look fresh enough for him to see." Thereupon, he fell on his own sword. The two gentlemen dutifully cut off their master's head, and went with the envoy posthaste to the entrance of the palace. They were immediately let in. When the Emperor saw the severed head and was told what had happened, he cried, saying between sobs, "Alas, wasn't he a great worthy?"

On the Emperor's orders, the two gentlemen were appointed commandants. Tian Heng was given a ritual burial befitting a king with 2,000 people in attendance. After the burial ceremony, the two gentlemen stayed behind. They dug a large hole into the tomb, struck their necks with their swords, and tumbled down to follow their master to the netherworld.

When the tragic tidings of these deaths were brought by the imperial envoy to the small island in the Eastern Sea (<u>Yellow</u> <u>Sea</u>), Tian Heng's followers, numbering more than 500, were thrown into grief and despair. The envoy made an attempt to console them. But it was no use. They had made up their minds. In an ultimate act of loyalty, the followers ended their lives, by sword or by rope, with their own hands. The Emperor, grief-stricken by the news of their deaths, granted the island a new name, "Tianheng," in honor of the brave king and his loyal followers. And to this day the island still goes by that name.[14]

Lou Jing (202 BCE)

WHEN LOU JING WAS called up for garrison duty on the western frontier, he was already in his 40s. On his way there, this poor peasant from Qi (Shandong) stopped at Luoyang. There he paid a visit to an old friend, General Yu, and told him that he had a remonstrance to make to the Emperor. Having debriefed him, General Yu, a high-ranking officer at court, realized the importance of the matter and arranged an audience.

On the day of the audience, the Emperor saw this middle-aged, gray-haired man in a scruffy sheepskin vest enter the audience hall and was very displeased.

"Didn't General Yu tell you to wear proper attire for the audience, Lou Jing?" he asked.

"Yes, Your Majesty," said Lou Jing, making a deep obeisance. "He did tell me that, and even offered to loan me his silk garments. But I turned him down. Because I wanted Your Majesty to see the real me. I have been wearing this vest for many years. If I doffed it to wear something else I would feel ill at ease."

"All right, Lou Jing. I am not one to stand on ceremony either," said the Emperor, in a more pleasant tone. "I heard you've got some interesting ideas about my capital."

"Yes. May I be so bold as to begin with a question?"

The Emperor nodded his head.

"It is this: 'By making Luoyang the capital, does Your Majesty expect to see the Han surpass the Zhou royal house in prosperity?'"

---

[14] Tianheng Island can still be found on modern maps.

"I suppose so," the Emperor answered without too much conviction.

"But Zhou and Han captured the throne under entirely different circumstances. The Zhou house, from Houji to King Wen and King Wu, had amassed virtue for more than a dozen generations. After the local lords had willingly submitted to it, the Zhou went on to vanquish the Shang. During the reign of the second king Cheng, the Duke of Zhou, then chancellor, built Luoyi (Luoyang) at the center of the universe in a location convenient for receiving tribute from the local lords. From there one can rule as king with ease so long as one possesses virtue; but one can also lose power as soon as one loses virtue. At the height of the Zhou's power, all under Heaven was in harmony; the local lords and barbarians all submitted and paid tribute to the central court. Then the Zhou went into decline, and all under Heaven stopped paying homage and tribute. This was brought about by the loss of virtue, but was made worse by the momentous force of circumstances.

"Your Majesty, on the other hand, arose from Feng and Pei, took Shu and Hanzhong, and conquered the Three Qins. Your Majesty fought Xiang Yu at Chenggao and Xingyang and elsewhere, in a total of 70 major battles and 40 small conflicts. Countless men died in horrible conditions with their brains dashed out and their corpses exposed to the open sky. People have not yet recovered from the loss of their loved ones; and most of the maimed and wounded have not been able to stand on their own feet. This is the sorry situation the Han finds itself in. That being the case, can the Han of today compare with the Zhou of the past when it built its capital at Luoyang? I do not think so."

"If not Luoyang, where do you think the capital should be?"

"The Qin area in Guanzhong. It has rivers and mountain barriers. In times of emergency, it can easily gather a force of one million. It has vast riches. And that is why it is called the 'Heavenly Kingdom.' If Your Majesty sets up the capital there, the court will be sheltered from chaos in the east. In hand-on-hand fighting, one does not achieve total victory without having the opponent in a chokehold. By setting up the capital in Guanzhong, Your Majesty will have the entire country in a chokehold."

The Emperor was very impressed. But moving the capital was a serious business. So he put Lou's proposal to his ranking court officials. Their strong opposition to it surprised him. One of them, Fan Kuai, argued, "The Zhou based in Luoyang lasted 500 years while the Qin based in Guanzhong survived only for two generations. Luoyang has the Chenggao Pass to its east and the Yao and Hangu Passes to its west, the Heshui (<u>Yellow</u> <u>River</u>) to its north, and the Yi and Luo Rivers to its south. It has enough natural barriers to depend upon."

The Emperor was not pleased. He then asked Zhang Liang, "Why is it that my senior court officials all oppose the idea of moving the capital?"

"Location," answered Zhang Liang. "The current capital Luoyang is in the east; and all of the top officials are from the east. Basing the capital in Guanzhong is inconvenient for them, to say the least."

"You are from the east as well. What do *you* think?"

"Personally, it would be nice to have Luoyang as the capital forever. But for the country, it is a different story. First off, the Luoyang area is too narrow—just about a couple of hundred *li* across. Besides, its land is of poor quality. It has a few natural barriers all right; but they are not really defensible in times of war. It could become vulnerable when surrounded by enemies on all sides. In contrast, Guanzhong has the Yao and Hangu Passes to its east, Long (<u>Guansu</u>) and Shu with their fertile land to its west, grazing land to the north, and the South Mountains to the south. Thus it is a place from which to dominate the local lords in the east. When the local lords are at peace, goods from the entire realm can be transported to the capital in Guanzhong; when the local lords are rebellious, water transportation can still supply the city's needs. So a capital in Guanzhong could be described as one with metal walls in a Heavenly Kingdom. Here I am with Mr. Lou Jing."

Thereupon, the Emperor issued an edict to move the capital. The new capital called Chang'an would be built near the city of Xianyang. Later that day, the Emperor set off with his entourage for the erstwhile capital of Qin, Yueyang, in Guanzhong, which was to serve as the *ad hoc* capital of Han.

As for the peasant Lou Jing, he was appointed court gentleman (*langzhong*) and granted the honor of assuming the imperial surname "Liu." Of course, as a court official, he was no longer obligated to perform his garrison duty.

Hann Xin's Homecoming (202 BCE)

HAVING TAKEN UP HIS post as king of Chu in Xiapi, Hann Xin paid a visit to his hometown, Huaiyin.

Upon arrival, the first thing he did was to summon the laundry woman who had fed him when he was starving. After treating her to a sumptuous luncheon, Hann gifted her with 1,000 catties of gold to make good on his promise and express his gratitude for having saved his life.

He then went to the home of that community head whose wife had refused to let him eat and said to him, "Sir, you are a caitiff, don't you know? You simply couldn't finish a good deed you started." The man was too scared to utter a word. Hann Xin threw a string of 100 bronze coins on the table and left.

In the government guesthouse where he was staying, he had the young butcher who had humiliated him in public brought into his presence. Pointing a finger at the butcher, Hann commented to his generals, "This was the man who forced me to crawl between his legs. At that time, could I have killed him? No, I couldn't have. If I had, it would have been without sufficient cause and surely I would have been executed. Am I mad with him because of the insult? Not really. Actually, I should thank him instead for testing my stamina to the limits." Addressing the butcher, he said, "Hey, young man. What should I do with you?"

His usual bravado gone, the butcher stood there speechless, shaking as if from a bitter cold.

"You had the guts to confront the future general-in-chief. For that alone, you deserve something.... How about serving as an officer in my army?"

The young butcher nodded his head in silent agreement. He then bowed in obeisance three times and took leave of the king.

***

BACK IN XIAPI, Hann Xin felt excited by the powers he now enjoyed as the peace-time ruler of a major kingdom. Although he had to pay annual tribute to the central court in Chang'an, and pledge his allegiance to the Emperor, he was allowed to keep a massive army and a significant amount of independence in governing his kingdom. But that sense of excitement soon began to wear off, as a growing sense of unease crept upon him. Universally acknowledged as the greatest military genius of his time, he felt somehow that his talent was unfulfilled now that the country was at peace and there were no longer any wars to fight.

An adjutant came in and informed him that a suspicious-looking "old friend" of his wanted to see him. But the problem was: this old friend refused to give his name. Hann Xin was intrigued and granted the request. A man in his mid-50s wearing a commoner's kirtle was brought in. As soon as he recognized the visitor, he exclaimed in astonishment, "General Zhongli Mo! It has been a long time!"

"Great King!" said Zhongli as he bowed to make obeisance.

"Don't, General," said Hann Xin, putting out his hand to stop him. "How have you been?"

"I have been on the run in these parts since Gaixia. The Emperor Liu Bang is looking for me. I wonder if you can help me for now."

"Of course," said Hann. "Does anyone know you are here?"

"No."

"You can stay with me. I'll treat you as a house guest."

"Thank you so much!" said Zhongli Mo as he bowed with deep gratitude.

Zang Tu King of Yan (202 BCE)

IN JULY, WU RUI, the king of Changsha and Ying Bu's father-in-law, died in the south. He was barely 50 years old. About the same time, Zhang Er, the king of Zhao, died in the north. The Emperor Liu Bang could have ended their kingdoms by an edict, but he chose not to. Instead he allowed the heirs of both kingdoms, Wu Chen and Zhang Ao, to succeed. Both the Wus and Zhangs, it would seem, were loyal to the court.

On coming to power, the Emperor Liu Bang had enfeoffed all his nonroyal kings, except for Zang Tu king of Yan. A general in the state of Yan during the

Warring States period, Zang had been raised to king of Yan by Xiang Yu as early as 206 BCE, and annexed the neighboring Liaodong under King Hann Guang (who had previously been king of Yan). In the wake of Hann Xin's victory against Zhao, Zang Tu had submitted to Han. Of all the nonroyal kings, the Emperor was most suspicious of Zang Tu. He did not contribute anything to the defeat of Xiang Yu. Nor did he owe anything to the Emperor Liu Bang. Although Yan was a peripheral kingdom in the northeast corner of the realm, it was the buffer area between the Xiongnu and the Central Plain, and thus too important to be left in the hands of someone of dubious loyalty.

About two years before, a solar eclipse had taken place in the stellar lodge Dipper (Dou). Solar eclipses are always considered ominous for the sovereign. In this case, the location of the event was telling. The so-called Dipper was actually the allotted field of Yan. And that suggested trouble would likely break out in Yan. From that point on, the Emperor Liu Bang had been monitoring the area very closely.

In August, it was put about in official circles that Zang Tu had declared independence in Yan (north Hebei and Liaoning). The Emperor Liu Bang reacted swiftly by leading an anti-Yan expedition north, taking with him his best friend Lu Wan. Because of the massive defection of its inhabitants and garrison troops, the Yan capital Ji soon fell to Han attacks. Zang Tu king of Yan was captured and brought to the Han camp, where he was subsequently beheaded. Lu Wan was then appointed as his replacement.

Among the captured Yan officers the most famous was Luan Bu. Originally from Liang (Shangqiu, Henan), he had become friends with Peng Yue (now king of Liang) when both were poor. In the last years of the Qin, they, like most people, fell on hard times. Peng Yue joined a group of outlaws in the Juye Moors to the north of Changyi (south of Juye, Shandong). Luan Bu was abducted to Yan (north Hebei) to work as a bondman. While there, he gained some notoriety by taking revenge for his master. Admiring his courage, then-General Zang Tu recruited him into his army after freeing him. Under Zang, Luan Bu had risen through the ranks to become general. Now as Zang Tu's accomplice, Luan Bu was slated for execution. However, his friend Peng Yue intervened, paying a hefty sum that not only saved him from the gallows but also got him out of prison. Luan Bu then went back to Liang to serve as his benefactor's counselor.

The Secret Meeting in Luoyang (202 BCE)

EMPRESS LÜ HAD MIXED feelings about her rescue from the clutches of Xiang Yu the year before. She was thankful that she had come out alive, but bitter that no serious effort had been made until then to save her. Even worse, the Emperor Liu Bang had shacked up with that slut as she herself had struggled to take care of the kids and the grumpy father-in-law. After the Pengcheng disaster, she was forced to go through hell, trying to survive war and capture and captivity at the hands of His Majesty's murderous enemy. When a rescue mission was finally under consideration, the main purpose was not even to save her but her father-in-law. Ever since her release, Empress Lü had never had an intimate moment with the Emperor. His Majesty shared his bed with younger consorts, especially the slut. The Empress had to swallow her pride and jealousy and treat them with courtesy. However, perhaps out of a guilty conscience, the Emperor granted the Empress ready access to the throne. At their meetings, the Emperor would try to address her concerns, whenever possible, and would listen attentively to her views on palace and government affairs. Although he would never permit a female consort to meddle in policy, he would sometimes find her ideas on politics refreshing and insightful. He even occasionally acted upon them. In this regard, he subscribed to the Confucian saying: "A gentleman does not accept a person because of what he says; nor reject sayings, because the speaker is what he is."

***

BY CAMPAIGNING AGAINST ZANG TU, the Emperor had attempted to give a warning to the local lords that he would not tolerate any challenge to his hold on power. With the fall of Zang Tu, the immediate threat to the throne was removed. The empire was at peace again. Then the Empress made a startling revelation: based on a secret report filed by her informants in Chu, Hann Xin was providing shelter to Zhongli Mo, the top general of Xiang Yu. After a series of serious discussions with his closest advisers, the Emperor was convinced that Hann Xin harbored evil intentions toward the throne.

The next day, the Emperor held a secret meeting in the Southern Palace of Luoyang, where he broke the news to his top generals.

"Send an army to crush the son of a bitch," one general shouted and several murmured their approval.

The Emperor fell silent for a while before he said, "I will make a decision soon. Meanwhile, keep it a secret, will you?"

"Yes, Your Majesty," the generals answered in unison.

***

AS SOON AS CHEN PING arrrived in Luoyang, he came rushing on an imperial sommons to the palace.

"Should I follow the advice of the gencrals, and send an army against him?" asked Liu Bang on seeing his confidant.

"This secret report—does Hann Xin know anything about it?"

"No."

"And the others?"

"Only the top generals at the meeting and a few close advisers know."

"All right," said Chen Ping, with a sigh of relief. "Let me ask Your Majesty a few questions. First, who has the better army, Your Majesty or Hann Xin?"

"Hann Xin."

"Second, among the generals under Your Majesty, who can defeat Hann Xin?"

"None."

"Fighting a war with an inferior army and a bunch of inferior generals—that worries me. I am afraid it will place Your Majesty in jeopardy."

"Then what should be done?"

"In ancient times, the Son of Heaven often went on tours of inspection in the provinces. Your Majesty can go on one such tour in Yunmeng (near Jingzhoushi, south Hubei). It was famous for its hunting grounds for the Chu kings. You can then stop in Chen and summon a meeting of the local lords including Hann Xin."

"Sounds like a great idea," said the Emperor. "I hope he will come."

"I am sure he will," answered Chen Ping.

General Zhongli Mo (201 BCE)

Carthage, now a Roman client state, was forced to greatly reduce the size of its navy, and pay a large amount of annual tribute to Rome for 50 years.

THE NEWS OF THE Emperor Liu Bang's tour of inspection in Yunmeng made Hann Xin suspicious and nervous. To him, the timing of the tour—so soon after his coronation—and its destination—virtually in Hann's backyard—were perhaps no coincidence. *What would Kuai Che say now?* he wondered. He sent his men to look for the eccentric counselor. They then located him in the marketplace. Apparently, he had gone mad; clothed in rags and begging for alms, he spoke nothing but gibberish.

Now Hann Xin himself had to make a decision whether to attend the gathering in Chen or not. If he went, he might risk being captured by Liu Bang. If he did not, it would mean war against the Emperor. When he was still agonizing over what to do, an attendant gentleman gave him an important piece of advice. He decided to give it a try.

***

"ARE YOU SATISFIED WITH everything here, General?" asked Hann when he met with Zhongli Mo in his house a few days later.

"I am eternally grateful to you for having taken me in. In fact, you are the only one who has the courage to provide me with a safe haven."

Hann paused briefly as his face darkened, and said, "But I have to tell you the unpleasant truth: soon I won't be able to provide that safe haven any more."

"What?" asked Zhongli Mo in disbelief. "What has happened?"

"The Emperor is getting suspicious. Someone tipped him off about your presence here. And it deepens his suspicion that I am disloyal to him."

"Are you going to give me up?"

"No, I will never do that. If I did, you would be dragged down to the marketplace and quartered in public. I will never, never allow you to suffer that kind of humiliation."

"What are you going to do?"

There was a long silence in the room as Hann Xin fixed his eyes on the floor. Then he raised his head and said as if with a heavy heart, "Well, for the sake of our friendship, I have decided to allow you to end your life honorably."

"Don't you understand?" asked Zhongli, losing his composure. "The only reason that the Han has not attacked you is my presence. If I die today, you will die tomorrow!"

"The Emperor trusts me. And I've never wavered in my loyalty to him."

"Loyalty my ass! You are such a hypocrite!"

His face flushed with embarrassment, Hann Xin departed. After crying for a long time, Zhongli Mo picked up the sword that Hann had left behind and fell on it.

The Gathering in Chen (201 BCE)

IN CHEN (HUAIYANG, HENAN), the Emperor Liu Bang, accompanied by his close advisers Chen Ping and Zhang Liang, was holding a morning banquet to entertain high-ranking local officials and nobles from the Huai area. Among the distinguished guests was Hann Xin who had arrived two days before, under the escort of a small troop of cavalry. As soon as he was settled in a guesthouse, Hann Xin paid a visit to the Emperor with a special gift, and the Emperor was delighted. At the banquet, Hann was seated in a place of honor on the south side facing the Emperor.

Hann Xin felt a twinge of unease as the seating reminded him of the infamous Hongmen banquet, from which the Emperor Liu Bang barely escaped alive.

With the beating of a gong, the murmur of conversation quieted down. The Emperor stood up and began to address the guests: "The day before yesterday, I received a special gift from Hann Xin king of Chu: the head of General Zhongli Mo! I want to propose a toast to King Hann." He raised his goblet, and all present did the same.

"To King Hann," shouted the Emperor as he downed his goblet, and all present followed suit.

"However," the Emperor resumed in a sharp tone, turning to Hann, "I issued the edict for Zhongli's arrest two months before. Why did you wait until the day before yesterday to deliver the head?"

"Zhongli Mo was an old friend of mine. I extended a helping hand when he was in dire need."

"What about my edict?"

"After I received it, I never stopped trying to persuade him to give himself up until he finally took his life."

"I just don't find that convincing."

"Your Majesty," said Chen Ping, "in my humble opinion, we cannot rule out that Hann Xin has been sitting on the fence."

"No! No!" shouted Hann Xin, as his face turned crimson, "I am always loyal to the throne!"

The Emperor waved his hand, and four musclemen sprang on Hann Xin and trussed him up. As two armed guards dragged him away, Hann murmured audibly, "Once the cunning hare is killed, the good hound ends up in the boiling-pot."

Nonroyal Kings (201 BCE)

ONE AFTERNOON, THE EMPEROR issued a general amnesty in the audience hall, which set free those meritorious officers who had been imprisoned because of ignorance of law. Court and local officials all offered felicitations to the Emperor on such a wise decision.

When his turn came, the counselor Tian Ken, a nobleman of Qi, offered something more—his personal advice on the kingdoms. He said, "It is wonderful that Your Majesty is in firm control of Guanzhong and Qi, whose king Hann Xin was recently subdued. Guanzhong and Qi are two most important areas for the Great Han. Guanzhong—the land of Qin—with its excellent terrain is a state onto itself. Bordered by the Heshui (<u>Yellow</u> <u>River</u>) and protected by the mountains, it can keep at bay an army of one million men armed with halberds with a force of 20,000. Because of its unique location, when troops are sent down from Guanzhong to fall on the local lords in the east, they will be like water from the roof of a tall house pouring down a downspout.

"In Hann Xin's Qi, on the other hand, there are the riches of Langye and Jimo in the east, Mount Tai in the south, the Heshui in the west, and the Bo Sea to the north. With its area of 2,000 *li* across, it can keep an army of one million men armed with halberds at bay with a force of 200,000. Not nearly as good as Guanzhong, but good enough under usual circumstances. Because of this, no one of *nonroyal* descent should be allowed to rule in either Guanzhong or Qi as king."

"Great idea indeed," said the Emperor as he turned to one of his attendant gentlemen. "Reward Mr. Tian Ken with 500 catties of gold from the state storehouse."

After Tian Ken took leave, the Emperor turned to Chen Ping and Zhang Liang, asking, "What do you think of Tian Ken's advice?"

"Your Majesty, it is sound and doable," answered Chen Ping.

"I agree," said Zhang Liang. "Mr. Tian touches on a very important principle. The key term here is *nonroyal*. Kingdoms should only be granted to the princes of the blood. That applies not only to Qi and Qin. I used to favor the revival of the state of Hann simply because my family had been indebted to the Hann royal house. On my proposal, Hann Cheng, a Hann royal, was named king by Xiang Liang. Now with the unification of the realm and the founding of the Han Empire, the situation has changed forever. A kingdom with its independent political and military powers poses too much of a threat to the court. During the civil war, it was necessary to share power with the mightiest of the *nonroyal* local lords by granting them kingdoms. But now, under a united empire, their *raison d'être* no longer exists."

"The current king of Hann, Hannwang Xin," said the Emperor, "is a Hann royal as well, and one of your favorite generals. Do you think, he too has to give up his kingdom?"

"Absolutely, Your Majesty," answered Zhang Liang.

"And you?" asked the Emperor, turning to Chen Ping.

"In principle, I agree with Zhang Liang," said Chen Ping. "Upon the founding of the Han Empire, Zang Tu king of Yan raised the standard of rebellion and Hann Xin king of Chu was bold enough to defy court orders."

"Then why 'in principle?'" asked the Emperor.

"There are still a few nonroyal kingdoms in the realm. We may have to deal with them with different policies. Take Hannwang Xin for example. A descendant of the Hann kings of the Warring States period, he is now also defender-in-chief at court. We have to watch him carefully. Another one is Peng Yue king of Liang, one of the triad of powerful players. His domain has been significantly expanded after Gaixia. And his allegiance to the throne is by no means certain. Ying Bu king of Jiujiang, also one of the triad, is in a similar situation. Too much independence and not enough loyalty. However, Zhang Ao king of Zhao, Zhang Er's son, is quite different." (See Map 4)

"He does not worry me at all," said the Emperor. "Firstly, he is my son-in-law. Secondly, he is loyal and obedient."

"That is precisely my point. The same is true of Wu Chen king of Changsha," said Chen Ping. "Besides, his chancellor, Li Cang, has been great as the court's eyes and ears. As for Lu Wan king of Yan, Your Majesty is the best judge of his character."

"Let me see," said the Emperor. "Both of you agree that we should follow a long-term plan to eliminate the nonroyal kings?"

"Essentially, that is the case," said Chen Ping.

"I concur," said Zhang Liang.

***

WITH THE TOUR OF inspection over, the Emperor departed. In the rear of the long imperial procession, a heavily guarded prison cart rumbled along in which sat Hann Xin in cangue.

Liu Bang's Marquises (201 BCE)

WITH HANN XIN IN captivity, the Emperor had time to reconsider the intention behind the recent action of his greatest general. It was true that he had provided sanctuary to Zhongli Mo, the most wanted man by the court, which may have been a sign of disloyalty to the throne. But it may also have been actuated by friendship. After all, Zhongli had been the first one to spot Hann Xin's talent. The two had been on friendly terms even after Hann Xin had joined the Han. Furthermore, deprived of military powers, Hann Xin would not be able to cause much trouble, even if he wanted to. About two weeks after Hann Xin's capture, the Emperor issued an order to set him free.

At an investiture ceremony held in the Southern Palace of Luoyang, the Emperor enfeoffed Hann Xin as marquis of Huaiyin. The title was a few notches below that of king of Chu. Still, it indicated his partial rehabilitation. On the same occasion, the Emperor conferred titles and ranks on his most meritorious officials and officers. Xiao He ranked first among the marquises, followed by Zhang Liang, Chen Ping, Fan Kuai, Xiahou Ying, and Guan Ying; and each was given a fief of 10,000 households. Fan Kuai was granted the hand of Empress Lü's younger sister as a special favor. This was probably the Emperor's way to express his gratitude for, among other things, saving his life at the Hongmen banquet.

General Lü Ze, Empress Lü's elder brother, was also created marquis. One should point out that it was not necessarily due to nepotism, because Lü Ze had been one of the first followers of the Emperor and played a crucial part in checking the advance of the Chu forces that chased after the Emperor following the Pengcheng debacle (205 BCE).

After the ceremony, the Emperor had a chat with Hann Xin over wine. In the middle of the conversation, the Emperor asked abruptly, "How many troops can I command?"

"To tell the truth, one hundred thousand at most," answered Hann Xin.

"How about yourself?"

"As for me, the more the better."

"Oh? Why, then, were you captured by me?" the Emperor asked with a grin.

"Your Majesty is not the best commander of troops, but the best commander of generals. This is so-called 'power by divine sanction,' beyond the power of mortal humans."

"Do you really think so?" asked the Emperor.

"Of course, Your Majesty," Hann answered without hesitation.

The Emperor responded with a smile.

The following morning, another top general who had been raised to marquis came to see the Emperor in his sanctum in the Southern Palace. He wanted to voice a grievance on behalf of many other generals.

"Your Majesty," he began, "there are people like me who took part in numerous battles, anywhere from several dozens to more than one hundred. Still, we rank below Xiao He and people of his ilk—those civil officials who did nothing but wield a writing brush and engage in the exercise of rhetoric. I wonder why."

Struggling to control his anger, the Emperor asked, "You like hunting, don't you?"

"Yes, Your Majesty," the general replied, wondering if that had anything to do with the ranking of officers.

"In hunting, who goes after deer, boars, and hares? The hounds. Who sends the hounds after game animals? The hunters. You and people like you, who go after the enemy in the battlefield, have an important role to play, but that is the role of a dog. Xiao He and other key civil officials, on the other hand, send you into battle, so they play the role of hunters. That's why they outrank you. And deservedly so. Understand?"

"I see," said the general, his face flushed with embarrassment.

***

IN THE AFTERNOON the Emperor set off for the Northern Palace. As his palanquin proceeded leisurely on the short covered passageway that connected the two palaces, he caught sight of a group of uniformed officers sitting under a tree outside.

On his orders, the bearers stopped the palanquin. He got down, walked to the east side of the corridor, looked through the lattice of a window, and recognized the faces.

"What are those generals doing over there?" the Emperor asked Zhang Liang who accompanied him.

"I am not sure. But it is possible they are plotting something."

"Against whom?"

"Probably against the throne. As Your Majesty is aware, the recent granting of titles and ranks has left quite a few of them disgruntled."

"But the whole world is unified and peaceful. Why do they want to rebel?"

"It is hard to say why. If Your Majesty asks me to take a guess, I would say, it is probably because of this. Your Majesty started out as a commoner. It was with the help of generals like these that Your Majesty conquered all under Heaven. As Son of Heaven, however, Your Majesty has enfeoffed more than 20 meritorious nonroyal officials—all are Your Majesty's close followers. Your Majesty has also executed a number of officials—all are Your Majesty's personal enemies. Your Majesty cannot possibly enfeoff everybody—they got it. But they resent what they consider unfair enfeoffments and fear that they themselves may get executed for their past wrong-doings. That is why they are probably plotting against the throne."

"Too bad! What am I supposed to do?" asked the Emperor, looking worried.

"Well, among the top officials, who does Your Majesty hate the most?" asked Zhang Liang.

"Yong Chi, without a doubt. He bears an old grudge against me and has insulted me on many occasions. I want to kill him, but cannot bring myself to do it, because I can't find a legitimate reason. Besides, he has been rewarded many times for merit."

"Then enfeoff him."

"What? You want me to enfeoff my worst foe?"

"Yes. If Your Majesty does that, everybody will feel secure."

"Is that so?" asked the Emperor with suspicion.

"I know it is hard. But for the sake of the empire, Your Majesty may have to swallow your pride and grant titles and fiefs to those powerful men even though they are Your Majesty's personal enemies."

There were also generals who were prevented from receiving noble titles because of their close association with Yong Chi. One of them was Wang Ling. Initially, Wang had been a small-time warlord with several thousand men based in Pei. For a long time, he could not decide whether he should join Liu Bang or not, because Xiang Yu had taken his mother hostage. He then sent an envoy to see her. The mother cried for joy, and babbled on about not wanting to burden her son, which did not seem to make a lot of sense. When the envoy stood up to leave, she suddenly seized him by the arm and said with clarity, "Please tell my son: don't sit on the fence because of me. Join Liu Bang. He is a kind-hearted man." Abruptly, she pulled out the sword the envoy wore and struck her neck with it and died.

Xiang Yu was so incensed that he ordered to have the old woman's corpse flung into a boiling cauldron. Grief-stricken, Wang Ling not only went over to Liu Bang's camp with his army, but also made fighting Xiang Yu to revenge his mother's death his lifetime mission.

Several days after his talk with Zhang Liang, the Emperor granted a few more marquis' titles. Among the recipients were Yong Chi and his intimates including Wang Ling. It is believed that because of these perspicacious measures, the generals were appeased and a possible crisis was avoided.

Hannwang Xin's Fateful Decision (201 BCE)

IN FEBRUARY, THE EMPEROR made several moves to royalize the kingdoms in accord with the proposals of Tian Ken and Zhang Liang. The Kingdom of Chu was divided in two, with the area south of the Huai, now called Jing, headed by Liu Jia

(Liu Bang's cousin); and the area north of the Huai, now called Chu, headed by Liu Jiao (Liu Bang's brother). Dai (northeast <u>Shanxi</u>) was now headed by Liu Xi (Liu Bang's brother), and Qi (<u>Shandong</u>) by Liu Fei (Liu Bang's non-heir son).

Hannwang Xin king of Hann was ordered to relocate from the east Central Plain to a new domain in the Taiyuan and Yanmen area (in central and north <u>Shanxi</u>), where he would have Jinyang as his capital. Additionally, he was given the charge of defending the northern frontier against the Xiongnu.

In his letter to the Emperor, Hannwang Xin obeyed the orders without complaint. But in private, he was irate beyond measure. Two weeks after settling in Jinyang, Hannwang Xin summoned his confidant into his study, and said with a sigh, "To force me out of the state of Hann is to uproot me from my people and land. Hann has been the homeland of my ancestors for centuries."

"Indeed, Great King," answered the middle-aged confidant.

"Why do you think he did this to me? Lack of trust?"

"Yes. But there is more to it. Didn't you notice that the Emperor has been conducting a campaign to eliminate the nonroyal kings? It started with Zang Tu (king of Yan) and Hann Xin. Now it is your turn."

"Do you really think so? But the Emperor raised me to king twice. His closest adviser Zhang Liang is a Hann loyalist and a strong supporter."

"*Was*, Great King. Don't you remember that it was Zhang Liang who opposed Li Yiji's plan to revive the royal houses of the Six States? From that point on, his loyalty to Hann has been dead."

"Do you suspect that he was behind the plan to relocate me to the north?"

"Perhaps. But I don't know for sure. However, what's really important is that he has stopped supporting you. That's enough to make you lose sleep at night."

"What's going to happen next?"

"They will find an excuse to lure you out of your domain to capture you."

"What kind of excuse?"

"A *fengshan* ceremony on Mount Tai, a tour of inspection in Changshan, Julu, or Handan (all in <u>Hebei</u>), or something like that. An occasion when you are obligated to pay a visit to the Emperor."

"Am I done for?"

"No. But a solution has to be sought elsewhere."

"Where?"

The confidant pointed his right hand to the north.

"The Xiongnu?" Hannwang asked in astonishment.

"Yes, Great King. We can first move the capital further north. That will allow us to sit on the fence. If our worst fear comes to pass, that is, if the Emperor goes after you, we can seek support from the north."

***

AFTER ITS ANNEXATION OF Donghu in 208 BCE, Xiongnu under Modu had grown into a sprawling empire north of the Great Wall (extending from Manchuria to Mongolia). The Xiongnu forces recaptured Henandi (in the Ordos Loop) in the bend of the Heshui (Yellow River) (previously seized by General Meng Tian); expulsed the Yuezhi from the Hexi Corridor after killing their king and making a drinking vessel out of his skull; and even encroached upon Dai (northeast Shanxi) and Yan (north Hebei). With a force of more than 300,000 cavalrymen, Xiongnu was a most formidable military power (see Map 5).

As the Emperor Liu Bang shifted his focus to the northern frontier, a clash with the Xiongnu became inevitable. When Hannwang Xin made a request to move his capital further north, the Emperor gladly gave his approval, because it complemented his own border defense strategy.

Three weeks later, Hannwang Xin and his entourage moved into Mayi (Shuozhoushi, north Shanxi), a frontier town surrounded by flatlands and hills (see Map 4).[15]

To the Xiongnu *chanyu* Modu, Hannwang Xin's move was a serious provocation. Thereupon, he launched a southern invasion that overwhelmed the Han frontier defenses, and laid siege to Mayi. Hannwang Xin sent a secret emissary to Modu, suing for peace. But the unexpected arrival of Han reinforcements from Jinyang and elsewhere prevented Hannwang from striking a peace deal, and

---

[15] Its northern suburb merged into the Mongolian steppes.

eventually the Xiongnu invaders were repulsed.

The Emperor was infuriated with Hannwang Xin's apparent lack of a strategic plan and the poor showing of his troops on the northern frontier, particularly at Mayi. He sent Hannwang a scathing letter, which said:

> *Whereas to die recklessly is no valor, to try to survive at any cost often results in neglect of duty. In view of what took place at Mayi, which was exposed to grave danger by the Xiongnu invasion, I must censure you in the strongest possible terms.*

Seized with anger and fear, Hannwang Xin hastily sent his emissary back north.

The *chanyu*, seated on a thick felt futon, received the emissary in his vaulted yurt.

"I expected you to return soon after your last visit. Why did you come so late?"

"My apologies, Your Highness. But with the sudden arrival of the Han rescue forces, we were under constant surveillance."

"Suppose that was true, what do you want from me now?"

"My master Hannwang Xin wants to make a deal."

"Does he? How can I be sure this is not one of Liu Bang's tricks?" asked Modu as he stared at his guest intensely.

"As Your Highness knows, Liu Bang had been suspicious of my master ever since he returned from Xiang Yu's camp. Recently, what little trust there was between them is completely gone." The emissary produced from the folds of his garment Liu Bang's recent letter on silk. An attendant showed it to the *chanyu*, while explaining its contents in the Xiongnu language. Modu then said, addressing the emissary, "I'll take your words for it. But what exactly does your master want?"

"He wants to submit to the authority of Your Highness."

Modu, taken aback, entered into a lively discussion with his close advisers for about half an hour. In the end, he said to the emissary, "Tell your sovereign, Mayi is now under our protection."

The emissary rose to make a deep obeisance, thanked the *chanyu* profusely on behalf of Hannwang Xin, and was led out of the yurt.

In October, Modu launched another southern invasion. This time, Hannwang Xin joined him. The combined forces of Xiongnu and Hann advanced as far south as Jinyang.

The Ritual Scholar Shusun Tong (201 BCE)

SINCE HIS ENTHRONEMENT IN 202 BCE, the Emperor Liu Bang had divided his time between Luoyang, Yueyang (northeast of <u>Lintong</u>, <u>Shaanxi</u>), and Chang'an. When he was in Chang'an, which was constantly under construction, he would stay in the Changle (Long-lasting Joy) Palace. Originally known as Xingle (Rising Joy), it was the only Qin palace complex in the city that had survived the war relatively intact. Under the direction of Chancellor Xiao He, it was being converted into a splendid palace complex. The Emperor loved the idea of holding court in the principal basilica of the Changle with its vast floor space, cavernous ceiling, and thick pillars. However, many of his senior officials and top generals, especially those who had been on intimate terms with him, did not know how to conduct themselves appropriately on an official occasion in the basilica or elsewhere.

The Emperor summoned Shusun Tong, the leading ritual official at court, for advice. He said, "When I came to power, I disliked the cumbersome Qin rites. So I did away with many of them. Come to think of it, I have probably gone too far. Nowadays there isn't much ritual on the books to govern the conduct of court officials. Sometimes they get drunk at my banquet and make an awful din as they try to outbrag one another. The other day, a general pulled out his sword and hit a pillar in the basilica. I am totally pissed off."

"Your Majesty, many of these high-ranking officers were originally peasants under the previous regime..."

"Like myself," the Emperor butted in with a grin.

"I am awfully sorry, Your Majesty. I did not mean to..."

"That's all right. Go on."

"And these officers know practically nothing about ritual. It is no surprise sometimes they behave boisterously under the influence of wine. And that is absolutely unacceptable especially in Your Majesty's presence. I could formulate a ritual code for behavior at court. This is what is needed to reign in the unruly officers."

"Can you do that?" asked the Emperor.

"I think so. Perhaps Your Majesty knows about those ritual scholars. It is hard to persuade them to take part in the founding of a new dynasty, but it is relatively easy to ask them to help manage it. In the ancient state of Lu, quite a few ritual scholars of the Confucian school have survived the First Emperor's campaign to eliminate them. I could enlist their help."

"But it'll be difficult, isn't it? I heard that all the ritual books have been put to the torch."

"It is not going to be easy. The First Emperor's burning of books is absolutely disastrous for ritual books. But there is no lack of scholars who committed some of the ritual classics to memory. Since ritual varies from age to age, what I can do is to create a Han code essentially based on ancient rites with certain Qin elements."

"You can give it a try. But you have to make it easy enough for peasants like me to use," said the Emperor with a grin.

Shusun Tong headed for Lu (in <u>Shandong</u>), the birthplace of Confucianism. Many ritual scholars resided there. But Shusun Tong was surprised and disappointed that some of them turned down his offer.

One of them explained, "It is true that order has been established in the realm. But many of the dead have yet to be buried and many of the wounded have yet to heal. This is not the time to revive ritual and music. One can perhaps do it after amassing virtue for a hundred years."

When Shusun Tong insisted, the scholar was annoyed, and shouted, "I don't care whom you work for! I don't approve of what you are doing. Get out of here!"

Shusun Tong retorted, "Don't be such a pedant! Times have changed. You have to get used to it."

But the scholar refused to be swayed.

At length, after much hard work, Shusun Tong managed to recruit 30 Lu scholars and brought them to Chang'an. Working with Shusun, they created dozens of ritual rules for various occasions, including court audiences and sacrificial ceremonies. Shusun Tong then set up a ritual camp in the wilderness. Under his direction, the Lu ritual scholars and about 100 court scholars and their Chang'an students began to train themselves in ritual ceremonies on a daily basis. About a month later, a ceremony rehearsal was staged for the Emperor. Liking what he saw, the Emperor commented, "With a bit of coaching, I can probably do it. I am so glad!" Therewith, he ordered court officials to start taking ritual lessons with Shusun Tong and his associates.

***

IN NOVEMBER, THE CHANGLE Palace was completed. At dawn on the inauguration day, a grand ceremony was taking place in the immense courtyard of the Anterior Basilica, one of the 14 spacious palatial structures of the palace. The court officials lined up at the main entrance. As the court receptionists guided them orderly to their designated places, hundreds of guards holding banners and weapons were standing in formation inside the quadrangle and halberd-holding guard officers were ranged along the East and West Corridors that led to the basilica proper. A silence fell on the crowd. Suddenly, the sonorous voice of the lead ritual officer sounded, "His Majesty, the Emperor." Liu Bang emerged from inside of the basilica on a canopied palanquin borne by eight men and flanked by members of the Guard of Honor carrying embroidered banners and canopies. As the palanquin stopped on the front terrace, he descended with the help of two eunuchs to take up his seat in front of the main gate.

The kings, marquises, and other high officials down to those at the rank of 600 bushels (*shi*) one by one ascended the marble steps to the terrace to offer felicitations to the Emperor. When the ceremony was over, they were invited to a banquet inside the basilica. The Emperor was now seated on the dais at the northern end, with a dominating view of the hall. Everyone lowered his head to show respect as required by ritual. They then rose one after another, according to rank, to offer toasts of longevity to the Emperor. All of this was done as half a dozen presiding censors watched on. As soon as someone made an inappropriate move, he would be escorted out of the hall. The banquet went on orderly without a major hitch. Not a single person got drunk.

After the ceremony was over, the Emperor called Shusun Tong into his sanctum, and commented, "Only today do I realize what it really means to be an emperor!" Thereupon, he awarded Shusun with promotion to chamberlain for ceremonials (*taichang*), the highest ritual post, and 500 catties of gold.

Siege of Baideng (201 BCE)

FOLLOWING CHEN PING'S ADVICE, the Emperor Liu Bang had ordered Hannwang Xin to move to Taiyuan. He had expected a pushback and was not surprised when he learned that Hannwang had gone over to the Xiongnu. What he did not expect was the fact that Hannwang Xin would join the Xiongnu in launching an invasion so soon after his defection. The invading forces pushed south beyond Taiyuan into southern Hedong (south Shanxi). Ignoring the opinion of his close advisers, the Emperor led a counteroffensive in person, which brought him as far as Tongdi (south of Qinxian).

In the first major engagement, the Emperor defeated Hannwang Xin's army, killing one of his top generals. Hannwang himself fled north. The Han army pushed beyond Jinyang, routing the Xiongnu forces. It continued to give chase until it was forced to come to a halt when a cold spell hit and one quarter to one third of the soldiers had lost one or more fingers to frostbite.

But the Emperor was in no mood to call off the operation, especially after he had been informed by army scouts that Modu and his troops were in the Dai Vale (in Fanshi, Shanxi) close by.

Leading an army of 320,000 men, the Emperor stopped at Jinyang to assess the situation. All the Han emissaries returning from recent missions to Xiongnu reported that the enemy army was staffed with the frail and old, and their horses were small and weak. To be on the safe side, the Emperor dispatched one more mission, led by one of his savviest advisers, Liu Jing (Lou Jing).

During Liu Jing's absence, the Emperor received further confirmation of the previous reports, and ordered his army to march forward before Liu Jing returned. In the Gouzhu Mountains (north and west of <u>Daixian</u>, <u>Shanxi</u>), the Han army camped for the night. Early the next morning, Liu Jing came back and headed straight for the Emperor's campaign tent.

"Do you have something new to report?" asked the Emperor sulkily.

"Yes, Your Majesty. During my trip there I saw a strange lunar appearance one night. In an otherwise brightly lit night sky, the moon had this large halo that shrouded a number of stellar lodges: Triaster (Shen), Net (Bi), and Mane (Mao). Between Mane and other lodges is Celestial Avenue that separates the Han from the barbarians. The stellar lodge Mane, of course, is also the allotted field of the Xiongnu. All this together suggests that the lunar *yin* force of the barbarians is posing a threat to the Han court. It is ominous for Your Majesty's current campaign."

"Astrological predictions like this don't always work, especially when you don't believe in them. What else?"

"Just like the other emissaries, I saw frail and old soldiers, and weak warhorses and sumpter animals. That is exactly what makes me suspicious. When a country is at war, it should flaunt its strength and hide its weakness. The fact that the Xiongnu parade their weakness shows that they have set up a trap for the Han army."

"Really? But while you were away, I received reliable intelligence about the weak points of the enemy that contradicts your report. Furthermore, my army is already on its way."

"Pull it back, Your Majesty!" urged Liu Jing.

"No! I can't. The horse has left the barn. My vanguard troops are approaching the Dai Vale at this moment!"

"But it only takes an oral rescript to stop the troops from advancing any further."

"No! I won't do it!" replied the Emperor sharply.

"I entreat Your Majesty," said Liu Jing as he fell on his knees. "I am almost certain there is a trap somewhere."

Flying into a rage, the Emperor responded, "You lowly slave from Qi with a slick tongue! How dare you halt the advance of my mighty army?" With a motion of his hand, four soldiers stepped forward to seize Liu Jing and took him into custody.

The Emperor stepped out of the tent. It was already broad daylight. He gave the order to set off immediately. An attendant gentleman approached him and asked, "What are we going to do with Liu Jing?"

"That son of a bitch? Keep him locked up. Wait until I come back. I'll then have his head ripped off, son of a bitch!"

***

A FEW DAYS LATER, the Emperor arrived in Pingcheng, a small frontier town (northeast of Datong, Shanxi). Excited that the Han vanguard forces were closing in on the Dai Vale, the Emperor ventured out of the protective walls of Pingcheng to go on a secret mission, under the escort of hundreds of armored cavalry and imperial guard troops.

When the Emperor's party approached the Baideng Hill in the northeast suburb, it came to a stop as an adjutant rode up to the Emperor hastily to report on an unexpected development. A massive Xiongnu force had now environed the hill and the town. The person of the Emperor was not in imminent danger, since the Xiongnu were not sure of His Majesty's whereabouts. But an effort to break out of the encirclement could be suicidal.

On the hill, a few dilapidated palatial structures were left standing. These were what remained of the Baideng Terrace set up by the First Emperor. Liu Bang and his attendant gentlemen took shelter in the main building. But soon a more direct threat loomed: the dwindling supply of food and water. Something had to be done soon if the Emperor was to come out of this ordeal alive and free.

The siege of Baideng was part of a larger campaign launched by Modu and Hannwang Xin, leading a combined force of 400,000, against Yanmen and Taiyuan (Shanxi). Modu, who was the overall commanding officer of the campaign, had positioned himself outside Pingcheng.

***

ON THE THIRD DAY of the siege, a secret Han emissary sent by Chen Ping arrived at the rear command camp of the Xiongnu for a meeting with the *yanzhi*, Modu's consort.

"The Emperor sends his best regards," the emissary said. "Here are some gifts from His Majesty." He put down on the rug at her feet a pair of white jade bracelets, a translucent jadeite necklace, and a silk painting.

Fingering the verdant necklace in her hands, the charming *yanzhi* in her late 20s could not help noticing the purity of the material and the exquisiteness of the workmanship. "The necklace alone must be worth a bundle," she commented.

"Yes, Your Highness," answered the emissary meekly.

"Why don't you contact the *chanyu* himself?" asked she.

"The *chanyu* now is like an arrow on a bowstring."

"What do you mean?"

"I mean, only Your Highness can stop him."

"Oh yeah?" The *yanzhi* stared down at the silk painting. It was the portrait of a beautiful maiden with dark bright eyes framed by long lashes and a faint smile that exuded confidence.

"What's this?"

"The picture of a maid. We want to give her to the *chanyu* and you as a gift."

"How old?"

"Sixteen years old, Your Highness."

"She is still very young," said the *yanzhi*, her eyebrows furrowing. "All right, I probably can help. But don't send the girl. The *chanyu* has enough maids already."

"Yes, Your Highness," the Han emissary answered.

***

ON THE MORNING OF the seventh day of the siege, the Emperor and his men broke out under the cover of a thick fog. They had received intelligence that the Xiongnu had withdrawn their troops from the eastern front. On Chen Ping's orders, the riders had arrows set to bowstring while moving forward at a slow trot. As soon as the imperial carriage was on the road to Pingcheng, the Emperor shouted urgently to his coachman Xiahou Ying, "Hurry!" But Xiahou refused to rush. He was afraid that a sudden increase of speed would alert the enemy. So the procession maintained a steady pace until it entered the town. By then, the main force of the Han army had arrived. The Xiongnu had moved north.

An intelligence report later revealed what had happened. Before tightening the noose on Pingcheng and Baideng, Modu expected the friendly forces under Hannwang Xin's generals to join him. But for days they were nowhere to be found. This gave rise to the suspicion that these former Han officers might be colluding with the Han army. Then an urgent report arrived from his *yanzhi* that the Han troops were threatening his rear command camp. Thereupon, the *chanyu* withdrew his invading army. It would seem that the real reason why the *yanzhi* wanted to help Liu Bang at all was perhaps the fear that Modu, if victorious against Liu Bang, would import beautiful young girls from the Han court. These girls would surely compete with her for the *chanyu*'s favors.

***

MOVING SOUTH PAST the Gouzhu Mountains the Emperor soon reached Guangwu. There he stopped and issued two orders: first, to execute those emissaries who had recommended the northern campaign; second, to raise Chen Ping to marquis of Quni (Shunping, Hebei). He then went directly to the county prison.

"I regret I didn't follow your advice," the Emperor said to Liu Jing. "If I did, the Siege of Baideng would not have happened." The Emperor then helped an attendant gentleman unlock the cangue on Liu Jing's neck and take it down.

"From this day forward, you are free. Not only that. I am raising you to marquis of Jianxin with a fief of 2,000 households."

Liu Jing made an obeisance in acknowledgement of the Emperor's munificence.

A Visit to Handan (200 BCE)

The Second Macedonian War broke out between the Macedonians and the Romans over dominance in the western Balkan Peninsula. The Greek historian Polybius was born circa this year.

A LARGE CROWD GATHERED in the square outside the main entrance to the Handan Palace. Standing out from the crowd was Zhang Ao king of Zhao in his late 20s, dressed in his best ritual attire. He was accompanied by his consort Princess Luyuan, close advisers, key officials, and top commanders. Behind them were nearly one thousand mounted and foot troops holding banners, halberds, and swords. Inside the palace courtyard, 12 bronze tripods and quadripods (*ding*), containing heads of oxen, lambs, and swine, were on display in a row. Behind these ritual vessels, a group of musicians stood ready to perform ritual music on a set of bronze chime bells and other musical instruments.

After Zhang Ao and his men had waited in the biting January wind of Handan for four hours, the imperial procession finally arrived. A weary-looking Emperor descended from his carriage. Without casting a glance at the troops, the Emperor, helped by two eunuchs, climbed into a waiting sedan-chair. Zhang Ao made a deep obeisance to His Majesty as he was being carried into the palace in a sedan-chair borne by eight bearers. Since it moved swiftly across the courtyard, the Emperor sitting inside hardly caught a glimpse of the host and the ritual paraphernalia and musical instruments set up for the occasion.

At the evening banquet, the Emperor gulped down one goblet after another of the celebrated Handan wine until he became somewhat inebriated. He then made a string of vulgar jokes, punctuated by obscenities hurled at Zhang Ao and his wife. Zhang Ao did not make a single attempt at riposte. Instead, every now and then he rose from his seat to serve food and wine to the Emperor in person. In the end the Emperor collapsed onto the floor. Several eunuchs rushed to carry him away.

***

"WHY DID THE EMPEROR keep Your Highness waiting for hours?" asked Guan Gao, chancellor of Zhao, the next morning.

"I was informed by the imperial herald," answered Zhang Ao, "that His Majesty was due to arrive around eight in the morning. But Chen Ping later told me that the Emperor was delayed after he stopped by a tavern to taste local wine."

"Why did he refuse to review the troops?"

"I don't know."

"Why didn't he attend the ritual ceremony in his honor?"

"I don't know! I don't know! Probably His Majesty was too tired."

"Why then did he treat Your Highness like a piece of dirt last night?" Guan Gao, a bearded stout man in his 40s, struggled very hard to contain his anger.

"I really don't know," answered Zhang Ao defensively. "But the Emperor is not one who stands on ceremony. By doing what he did, he did not intend to harm anybody."

"Whatever he did, Your Highness behaved like a weakling."

"No, I merely carried out my duty as a loyal subject and a filial son-in-law."

"Duty my ass, Your Highness. We can't take it anymore."

"What do you want?"

"By Your Highness' leave," said Guan Gao, kneeling down on one knee, "we will get rid of this apology for an emperor."

"Absolutely not," shouted Zhang Ao as he bit his right index finger until it started bleeding. He then used the blood-dripping finger to write on a piece of silk the character *zhong* (忠 /jong/ [loyal]). "I am a loyal subject of the Emperor and will remain so so long as there is breath in me. Why don't you shut up?"

This assassination plot was stopped in its tracks.

Like Wu Chen king of Changsha, Zhang Ao was a second-generation king. His kingdom of Zhao was small and hardly mattered to the throne. Although a nonroyal king, Zhang was unlikely to be targeted for elimination. Moreover, his marriage with Princess Luyuan, the only imperial daughter by Empress Lü, added another layer of security to his position. Still, King Zhang Ao felt insecure and was constantly worried that he would run afoul of the Emperor and suffer the fate of Hann Xin.

Marriage Alliance (199 BCE)

THE SIEGE OF BAIDENG had left the Emperor exhausted. Thereafter, he had led one campaign against the remnants of Hannwang Xin's forces with limited success, but avoided confrontation with the Xiongnu. Meanwhile, the Xiongnu under Modu had continued to conduct raids into the farming communities and towns in the northern border area with almost immunity.

"I want to hold the Xiongnu at bay. Is it possible?" the Emperor asked Liu Jing, whose advice on the barbarians he had come to value.

"Civilians and soldiers have been war-weary for a long time, and are thankful that peace has been established throughout the realm. Xiongnu is our only problem. Recent experience shows that a total military victory is out of the question. However, a barbarian chieftain like Modu, who kills his own father and marries his mother, is unlikely to be moved by the ideas of benevolence and righteousness."

"What should we do?"

"I have got a plan that may assure their long-term submission. But I am afraid that it may offend Your Majesty."

"Come on, Liu Jing! Tell me whatever is on your mind! I grant you full immunity."

"Well, the only way, it seems, to satisfy Modu is to marry off a young lady of the blood, a princess."

"No! I won't let Yuanyuan go. She is my only daughter."

"That is precisely my point, Your Majesty. Let me explain. If Princess Luyuan marries Modu, she will then become the *yanzhi*. Once she gives birth to a son, he will become the crown prince. The *chanyu* Modu will be your son-in-law. After he dies, the next *chanyu* will be Your Majesty's grandson. And he will never challenge his grandfather. That way, they can be subdued for generations without a fight."

"But Yuanyuan is a married woman. Her husband is Zhang Ao king of Zhao."

"Yes, Your Majesty. However, virginity is of little consequence to the Xiongnu, and her marriage can be annulled with an edict."

"Is that so?" asked the Emperor with a cold smile.

***

THAT NIGHT, AS THE Emperor was about to retire—Lady Qi was already lying in bed—he received a request for an audience by Empress Lü.

The Emperor put on his robe and went into the reception room and saw the Empress kneeling on both knees, her eyes filled with tears.

"What's the matter, Empress?" the Emperor asked.

"Spare Yuanyuan, Your Majesty. I beg you."

"I haven't made up my mind yet."

"She is our only daughter. If you send her to the Xiongnu, you may never see her again."

"But to conclude this marriage alliance, someone has to go."

"Why Yuanyuan?"

"She is the only imperial princess."

"Someone else can receive a princess' title and go in her place."

"What if they find out?"

"They will never find out. If they do, it will be too late."

"All right, I probably can use your plan," said the Emperor as he helped the Empress to her feet.

***

WITHIN A MONTH, a 20 year-old young lady of good family background was chosen as the Han bride to the Xiongnu chieftain. Before she left, she had been granted the title of "princess." Liu Jing, the originator of the idea of "marriage alliance," headed the mission.

While on the trip, Liu Jing was surprised at the relatively short distance between Chang'an and Henandi (in the <u>Ordos</u> <u>Loop</u>)—700 *li*, which could be covered by light cavalry in a day and a night. This realization prompted him to offer the Emperor another piece of advice later, "In today's Guanzhong, the population is too small. On the Central Plain to the east live the great clans of the Six States. If trouble breaks out there, people in Guanzhong may become restless. I would like to suggest that descendants of those former royal houses and members of the great clans be transferred to Guanzhong so that we can keep an eye on them. They can also help defend the capital in the event of a Xiongnu attack. Furthermore, if a rebellion breaks out in the east, they can join the expedition against it."

Concerned about the recently subjugated elites, the Emperor readily accepted Liu Jing's advice. A massive migration was soon underway. By the end of the year, more than 100,000 individuals from the east had been settled in Guanzhong.

Guan Gao's Wish (198 BCE)

CONFINED TO A SMALL prison cell in the Office of the Chamberlain for Law Enforcement (*tingwei*) in Chang'an, Guan Gao lived now for the sole purpose of clearing the name of his master Zhang Ao. The ex-king of Zhao had been toppled and imprisoned after Guan Gao's plot to assassinate the Emperor had been exposed by one of his personal enemies. More than a dozen people were implicated as confederates. All had fallen on their own swords. At his trial, Guan Gao insisted that the ex-king was innocent.

"It was my idea. And I alone should be held accountable," Guan Gao shouted to the judge.

Taking his cue from the Emperor, the judge attempted to force him to implicate Zhang Ao by flogging. But Guan Gao refused to change his statement, even after he had received more than 1,000 lashes and his back had been completely mangled. Moved by Guan Gao's pain and suffering, Empress Lü, by no means a tender-hearted woman, attempted to convince the Emperor to accept Guan's confession. "King Zhang Ao is Yuanyuan's husband, and should not have a motive," she argued.

"That's crap!" the Emperor fumed. "If Zhang Ao seizes the throne, he won't give a damn about your daughter."

Yet, upon hearing the briefing by the chamberlain for law enforcement on Guan Gao, even the Emperor could not help commenting, "Brave man!"

"What should I do, Your Majesty?" asked the chamberlain.

"Send a different interrogator. Someone who knows him very well," said the Emperor.

The next day, Ordinary Counselor (*zhong dafu*) Xie, Guan's childhood buddy, went to see him in prison. They started the conversation by reminiscing about their childhood, shared anecdotes about themselves, and even had a few hearty laughs together.

At length, when Xie rose to bid goodbye to his friend, he said casually, "By the way, they all say that Zhang Ao was behind the plot. You don't think so?"

"No, I don't," Guan Gao responded impulsively. "As I have said all along, the king had nothing to do with it. Hey, listen! Isn't it human nature that we all love our parents, wives, and children? Today, because of my crime, my Three Clans (that is, his father's, mother's and wife's clans) will suffer extirpation. Do you really think I love the king better than my family?"

Two days later, Mr. Xie came again. "My friend, I've got great news for you," he said excitedly. "The Emperor finally accepted your account, and set Zhang Ao free."

"Heaven be thanked!" Guan Gao exclaimed, falling on his knees. Wiping tears off his face, he continued, "That's really great! Is he now king of Zhao again?"

"No. Prince Liu Ruyi son of Lady Qi was made the new king."

"But Ruyi is king of Dai."

"No longer. And because of his young age, he now spends most of his time in Chang'an."

"What has become of Zhang Ao?"

"He was made marquis of Xuanping."

"That's fine. What's going to happen to me?"

"You are free, too," answered Mr. Xie.

"Really?!"

"Of course!"

Guan Gao collected his belongings, and with the help of Xie started walking toward the exit. When they were outside the prison gate, Gan Gao stopped and said, "The reason I clung to life was to clear the name of Zhang Ao. Now his name is cleared, I can die without regrets."

"Don't be silly!" replied Xie. "The Emperor pardons you, because he holds you in high esteem and wants you to serve him. Don't disappoint His Majesty."

"I have tainted my name with a failed attempt on the Emperor's life. How can I show my face at the court of His Majesty? Even the Emperor doesn't want to kill me, I am too ashamed to go on living." When Mr. Xie was not paying attention, Guan Gao pulled out his sword and struck his neck.

The Succession Debate (197 BCE)

The Second Macedonian War ended with the defeat of Philip V of Macedon, who had to give up all the cities he had conquered, pay a large indemnity, and surrender most of his fleet.

NOW IN HER MID-20s, Lady Qi had blossomed into a beautiful woman. Apparently, all these years, she had been the Emperor's most intimate partner. The Emperor insisted that she address him as "Fourth Brother," instead of "Your Majesty," and spent most of his nights with her. He took her on all his travels whether for business or for pleasure. The birth of their son Liu Ruyi did much to enhance her status at court.

At the age of nine, Liu Ruyi bore a strong physical resemblance to his father, and showed himself to be a smart boy with a strong personality. The Emperor often said, "Ruiyi is really like me." In contrast, regarding his elder son, the Emperor often commented, "Yingying is too nice to be a sovereign." Still, Liu Ying was secure as crown prince, because he was the only son by the Emperor and Empress Lü, and the Emperor had no plans to replace him.

Many a night Lady Qi had besought His Majesty, on her knees or in bed, often with tears in her eyes, to change his mind. The Emperor had put off giving her a definite answer. As he was approaching 50, the Emperor became increasingly aware of his own mortality, and began to seriously worry about what would happen to his favorite woman and their child Ruyi after his passing. No doubt, Liu Ying as emperor would treat them as kindly as before and would probably go out of his way to protect his half-brother and his mother. The problem was that Liu Ying was not strong enough to offer the kind of reliable protection they needed. More likely, he would remain a weakling dominated and outwitted by his mother, Empress Lü. A strong-willed woman, Lü was politically astute and ambitious, and would have every reason to remove the challenger to her own son.

After pondering over the issue for weeks, Liu Bang finally agreed to Lady Qi's request in the belief that only by placing Ruyi on the throne could his favorite son and woman be saved, without endangering the safety of Crown Prince Liu Ying and his mother.

He then took the issue to his close advisers. The response astonished him: to a man they opposed the idea of replacing the current crown prince.

One of the strongest opponents was Zhou Chang, Zhou Ke's paternal cousin and a man of great probity and integrity. As censor-in-chief (*yushi dafu*), he was the top surveillance and disciplinary officer at court. He was known for one problem: he stammered when he was angry or nervous. On hearing the Emperor's intention, Zhou shouted angrily, "As your subject, I don't know what to say. But I know it can...can...can't be done! If Your Majesty issues an edict to depose the crown prince, I will not o...o...o...bey it."

The Emperor burst into a smile and dismissed him.

Although the Emperor did not want to give up the idea of making Ruyi crown prince, he put it aside for the moment. But the issue of how to protect his favorite woman and son from harm after his passing still had to be dealt with. It could only be possible, according to one adviser, if someone held in high esteem by the Empress, the current crown prince, and the bureaucracy was made chancellor of Zhao, where Ruyi was king. Eventually, on the recommendation of the same adviser, the Emperor appointed Zhou Chang, the stammering censor-in-chief who opposed the deposition of Liu Ying, to the post.

***

THE EMPEROR'S ATTEMPT TO depose Liu Ying, though not successful, left Empress Lü deeply worried. She instructed her brother Lü Ze to go to Zhang Liang for help. Old and frail, Zhang was living in seclusion.

"Previously," said Zhang, "when the whole world was in turmoil, I offered a few pieces of advice and they were adopted by the Emperor. Today, however, the world is at peace. If His Majesty wants to replace the crown prince with his favorite son, it is his family business. One hundred advisers like me won't be able to make a difference."

"Can't you think of anything?" Lü Ze asked insistently.

Zhang Liang was deep in thought for a few moments. Then he said, "There is one trick the Empress can probably use. But under no circumstances should you mention my name."

"No, we won't," said Lü Ze hastily.

"Well, there are four elderly men, all in their 80s, known as the Four White-hair Recluses of Mount Shang. You've heard of them before, haven't you?"

"Yes. I know them by reputation."

"They were the most learned scholars in the Qin dynasty. All are men of great probity. They went into reclusion in Mount Shang rather than serve the Han Emperor, because they can't stand his abusive tongue. Still, the Emperor respects them tremendously. If you can send an envoy to Mount Shang, with valuable gifts and a letter from the crown prince, begging them in humblest terms to serve as his mentors, they may come out of reclusion. When the Emperor realizes that the crown prince is being edified by these great gentlemen, he may stop thinking of replacing him. There is no guarantee it will work. But this is the best I can think of."

Following Zhang Liang's instructions, the Empress sent one of her advisers to Mount Shang, bearing with him the crown prince's letter and several large boxes of gifts (including gold, jades, and silk). To the chagrin of the envoy, the Four Recluses adamantly refused to take the gifts. On reading the letter, however, they decided to come out of reclusion.

The Chen Xi War (197 BCE)

IN LATE SPRING, a mysterious person visited the city of Handan, the capital of the kingdom of Zhao. Reportedly, he traveled with a caravan of more than 1,000 carriages and wagons. People in his entourage had filled up all the official guesthouses and upscale inns. Eventually, the secret visitor was identified by Zhou Chang's men as none other than Chen Xi, an erstwhile subordinate to General Hann Xin. Apart from his staff officers and attendant gentlemen, most of the people accompanying him were advisers.

As de facto ruler of the kingdom, Zhou Chang suspected that something underhanded was afoot. Chen Xi, as superior chancellor (*xiangguo*) of Zhao, was in charge of the frontier forces of both Dai and Zhao. He had no reason to conceal his presence in Handan, where he also had his own office.

As soon as Chen Xi left for Dai, Zhou Chang rushed to Chang'an to report the situation to the Emperor. The Emperor responded by sending a secret team of law-enforcement officers to investigate. The result, which came back two weeks later, was inconclusive. For the moment, the Emperor decided to take no action, apart from asking his men to keep an eye on Chen Xi.

By June, Chen Xi had learned about his investigation. He was afraid that although what he had done—passing through Handan with a large entourage after his vacation—was entirely innocent, the harm was done. Once he came under suspicion, it would be almost impossible to clear his name.

Then the Emperor's father died. The court summoned key officials in the provinces to Yueyang in Guanzhong to attend the funeral. Chen immediately thought of Hann Xin, under whom he had served. He was caught after attending a gathering in Chen in response to an imperial summons.

As Chen Xi was pondering how to respond to the court's request, he received a secret letter from Hannwang Xin, offering to enter into an alliance with him with the backing of the Xiongnu. To prove his good faith, Hannwang Xin would provide Chen with two of his best generals Wang Huang and Manqiu Chen. Chen Xi thereupon accepted Hannwang Xin's offer. Meanwhile he sent a letter to the Emperor, asking permission not to attend the funeral for health reason.

The Emperor was furious and suspected foul play. But he did not censure Chen Xi's behavior for fear that it might drive him into the arms of the enemy. With the best frontier army under his command, Chen Xi could cause much trouble.

In October, Chen Xi surprised everybody by declaring himself king of Dai. Supported by Hannwang Xin and leading a sizeable army, he struck south and advanced as far as Handan (in south Hebei). Suddenly the entire northeast became vulnerable.

As the highest-ranking leader of Handan, Zhou Chang was in charge of its defense. He withdrew the garrison troops into the city, and closed the city gates. Faced with a much more numerous invading army, Zhou Chang could only hope that the city would hold out long enough to be rescued by Han reinforcements. But to his surprise, for days, the enemies had not made an attempt to sack the city. Soon the first Han rescue army arrived, bringing with it a large stock of provisions that could help the city sustain a siege for at least a month.

Of the three walled cities that made up Handan, the Western City, which had been the Zhao royal city in Warring States times, was home to the palace. In the audience hall of the principal basilica of the palace, Zhou Chang was holding court one morning when a court envoy arrived with a large retinue without announcement. The envoy was wearing a helmet and mask, which was not unusual for a courtier on a secret mission. After his attendant gentlemen had been dismissed, the envoy unmasked himself. An astonished Zhou dropped on his knees to make obeisance. The "envoy" came over and helped him to his feet.

"I came here incognito because of a matter of utmost urgency," said the Emperor Liu Bang.

"I am so grateful that Your Majesty braved the danger of war to grace us with this visit."

"Don't mention it. Tell me about the current situation."

"Yes, Your Majesty. Chen Xi's men reached the outskirts of Handan," Zhou reported. "But instead of trying to take the city, they have moved to the south of the Zhang River."

"Good! I am glad he did that. I suppose that it is safe now to announce my visit?"

"I think so, Your Majesty."

"All right, do it after this meeting. Now about Changshan. What happened there?"

"I am sorry to inform Your Majesty that the situation there is terrible. Of its 25 cities and towns, 20 have fallen. The local officials—governors, magistrates and defenders—all failed to defend them. All deserve to be executed."

"Why? Did they rebel?"

"No."

"Then they should not be punished for the loss of the cities and towns. The fact of the matter is that the troops they had there were not strong enough to resist Chen Xi. Although I brought with me a large army, we still can't take the battle to the enemy."

"What do we do next then, Your Majesty?" asked Zhou Chang.

"We just stay within the city walls. More reinforcements are on the way. I have ordered the Defender-in-chief Zhou Bo, Peng Yue king of Liang, and Hann Xin marquis of Huaiyin to join me."

After pausing for a while to think, the Emperor continued, "There is one thing I want to ask you to do before I forget. Before the arrival of the reinforcements, we need talented local officers who can serve as my generals. Can you recommend a few?"

"Certainly, Your Majesty," answered Zhou Chang.

***

WHEN ZHOU CHANG ENTERED the audience hall again early the next morning, the Emperor was waiting. Zhou brought with him four men, all in their 30s. Each introduced himself and gave a short presentation as the Emperor watched. Suddenly the Emperor stood up and yelled loudly, "What the fuck makes you think you can be my generals?"

All four dropped on their knees in awe. The Emperor abused them with more obscenities and sent them packing. Zhou Chang knelt down and asked the Emperor to punish himself for failure to accomplish his task.

"No," the Emperor answered. "You've done an excellent job. It seems all of them can be my generals. I want you to do this: enfeoff each of them with 1,000 households before officially appointing them as generals."

"Yes, Your Majesty," answered Zhou Chang. "But why did Your Majesty reproach them in the first place? Why then enfeoff them with large fiefs before they even score a single victory?"

"Well, Chen Xi has taken most of Dai and Zhao. My top generals are still miles away. I have no choice but to depend on these local officers. To secure their allegiance, I awed them before pacifying them with fiefs and appointments."

"Inspiring fear and gratitude in equal measure?"

"Exactly," said the Emperor. "If I can achieve my goal, 4,000 households and four general's appointments are a very small price to pay."

"Excellent, Your Majesty. I will carry out the orders today."

"One more thing. About Chen Xi's top generals, Wang Huang and Manqiu Chen—who are they?"

"Both were merchants before. So were many of Chen Xi's other officers."

"Oh? I didn't know about that. Well, we can certainly set aside some gold and put it to work."

Hann Xin's Summons to Luoyang (196 BCE)

BY LATE 197 BCE the tide of the Chen Xi War had turned in the Han's favor. Zhou Bo had arrived with a massive army, and Peng Yue had sent a few thousands of his troops, although he himself had not come to join the Emperor because of poor health. Hann Xin, however, had not provided any troops, nor had he come in person. He too cited poor health as the reason for his absence. The Emperor, of course, was not pleased. But he did not send him a letter of censure, because he wanted to focus on the task at hand: fighting and destroying Chen Xi.

With the reinforcements from Zhou Bo, Peng Yue, and others, the Emperor felt confident enough to launch a full-scale counteroffensive on the Yanmen and Dai (both in north <u>Shanxi</u>) areas. General Zhou Bo led his contingent from Taiyuan to advance on Mayi (in north <u>Shanxi</u>), where Hannwang Xin, Chen Xi's main ally, had been based. Although Zhou Bo did not sack the town, he had done much damage to its defenses.

Early the next year (196 BCE), the Emperor led a force north from Handan to lay siege to Dongyuan (northeast of <u>Shijiazhuang</u>, <u>Hebei</u>), a stronghold held by Chen Xi's men. The tenacity of the defenders surprised him. Repeated efforts to win them over were ignored. And some of the defenders even shouted obscenities from atop the wall. The Emperor had no choice but to launch an attack, and the town fell in two days. Among the captives, those who had cursed the Emperor were identified and executed, while the rest were branded on the face and brought into bondage.

By then, Wang Huang had been captured and beheaded; Manqiu Chen had vanished. Other key officers were mostly turned in by their minions, lured by the massive bribes placed by the Han. The backbone of the Chen Xi Rebellion was broken.

***

WHEN DID THE IDEA of rebellion first enter Chen Xi's mind? It could be traced to a secret meeting he had had with Hann Xin in Huaiyin (southwest of <u>Huai'anshi</u>,

Jiangsu) a few years before. Chen was then on his way to Zhao where he would take up position as superior chancellor. After dismissing his attendant gentlemen and guards, Hann Xin took him for a walk in the tree-covered courtyard. Suddenly, Hann Xin stopped, looked him in the eyes, and said with a sigh, "Can I have a heart-to-heart chat with you?"

"Please, General," answered Chen Xi, full of deference to his erstwhile commander.

"The Zhao and Dai troops are among the best in the country. At court, people will surely bad-mouth you out of jealousy. Since you are a most trusted subject of His Majesty, should someone malign you, the Emperor would not believe it. But if it happens the second time, the Emperor will become suspicious. If it happens the third time, the Emperor will be so enraged that he will personally lead an army against you."

"I know the Emperor mistrusts everybody," said Chen Xi. "But I don't see why he would go after me. First of all, he has personally appointed me to this key position. That is a sign of trust, is it not?"

"Yes, it is. But the Emperor can change his mind easily. True, he has vested much power in you, but that's precisely what makes you vulnerable. Events over the last few years show that the Emperor is trying to take power away from nonroyal kings. You, of course, are not one of them. However, the new king of Zhao, Prince Ruyi, seldom resides in his kingdom, if at all. Besides, Ruyi is too young to rule. In reality, you are the boss. Of course, there is Zhou Chang, chancellor of Zhao. You, however, as superior chancellor, outrank him and, what's more important, have direct control of the frontier armies. If truth be told, you are as powerful as a king, even though you don't have the title."

"So?"

"The Emperor will remove you from power once the northern border is pacified."

"What should I do, in your opinion, General?" asked Chen Xi, his face turning pallid with anxiety.

"Watch out for policy changes at court. If things begin to move against you, take action. I can then respond by staging an uprising at the center."

Hann Xin's loyalty to the throne had died the moment he was arrested in Chen in 201 BCE. Whenever he thought of it, his face turned scarlet with shame and anger. To be sure, he was later released and even named marquis of Huaiyin. But most of his territorial and military power had been taken away. In Huaiyin, he was closely watched by Liu Bang's agents, to whom he had to report every trip he made outside the city. Whenever he was served with an imperial summons, he had to travel posthaste to the national capital, or a touring palace, in order to attend on that country bumpkin and to be insulted by his coarse remarks. Every day, Hann Xin was consumed with a desire to dethrone Liu Bang. But Liu's iron grip on power deterred him from taking action.

When the news of the Chen Xi Rebellion reached him, Hann Xin was elated. He regarded it as the once-in-a-lifetime opportunity he had been looking for and was determined not to let it slip through his fingers. When the edict commanding him to join the Emperor's war effort came, he ignored it.

"Luoyang is now in the hands of Crown Prince Liu Ying and his mother Empress Lü," said Hann Xin at an emergency meeting he summoned with his close advisers in a secret place outside his residence. "It does not have a strong garrison force at all. If we seize Luoyang, it will be a terrible blow to Liu Bang, who is now campaigning in the northeast."

"There are a large number of bondservants working inside the palace," one adviser said. "We can set them free through our agents, arm them, and use them to stage an uprising from within."

"Good idea!" exclaimed Hann Xin.

"How soon are we going to take action?" asked another adviser.

"I will send an envoy to Chen Xi. As soon as we hear good news from him, we will launch our uprising. Be prepared. It may happen any day."

Before the meeting broke up, at Hann Xin's instance, his followers took an oath that bound them in loyalty to the marquis.

***

TWO MONTHS LATER, as Hann Xin was waiting for a message from Chen Xi, he received a eunuch envoy from the court with an imperial edict that informed him of Chen Xi's capture and death and requested Hann's presence at a grand ceremony in Luoyang to celebrate the defeat of the rebels. All the key officials and marquises in the Central Plain would attend the gathering. The envoy then produced a private letter by Chancellor Xiao He, whom Hann Xin held in the highest esteem.

"In spite of your illness," wrote Xiao in the letter, "you should make an appearance in Luoyang. Your failure to do so will only deepen the Emperor's distrust of you."

After the envoy left, Hann Xin summoned another emergency meeting with his followers, where he put the plan of rebellion on hold indefinitely. On their advice, he set off on horseback with a small escort.

***

UPON ARRIVAL IN LUOYANG, Hann Xin checked into the government guesthouse, and went alone to the Southern Palace. He was led into the audience hall of the main basilica, where he waited for about half an hour before Empress Lü entered with Chancellor Xiao He.

The moment Hann Xin was about to make obeisance, half a dozen musclemen sprang on him from behind and knocked him down. As Hann Xin was being bound with rope, he shouted, "I demand to see His Majesty!"

"His Majesty," answered the Empress sharply, "is still in Zhao."

"But I swear I received this edict to attend the gathering to celebrate the defeat of Chen Xi."

"To tell the truth, Chen Xi is still alive, and there is no gathering. I ordered your arrest for conspiracy to usurp the throne."

"On what evidence, Empress?"

"I am sure you know Yue Yue?"

"Yes, he was one of my retainers. But what's wrong with that?"

"Recently, you incarcerated him for disloyalty and decided to put him away. But by then, he had already divulged to his brother your sinister plan to seize the throne in collusion with Chen Xi. Only lack of good news from Chen Xi prevented you from carrying out your plan. If you don't believe what I've said, we can bring in more eyewitnesses in a couple of days. We have arrested all your confederates in Huaiyin. They are already on their way here."

His face ashen, Hann Xin lifted his icy gaze to Xiao He, and asked, "Chancellor, aren't we great friends? Why did you trick me with that letter?"

"Hann Xin, we *were* great friends. I was the one who recommended you to His Majesty. And I was proud of that. Without your help, His Majesty would not have gained the entire world the way he did. But you have crossed the line. Admittedly, I treasure friendship greatly, but I treasure loyalty to the throne even more."

Hann Xin fell silent. Momentarily he was frogmarched out of the audience hall. After he was led by armed guards through several long corridors and courtyards, Hann Xin ended his journey in the Chamber of the Bronze Chime Bells in the Changle Palace. He suddenly found himself faced with his executioner, a stout man armed with a broadsword. Hann Xin said with a sigh, "How I wish I used Kuai Che's plan. Now I am outwitted by a woman. If that's not fate, what is?" The greatest military genius of the age placed his neck on the chopping block, and received the fatal stroke.

The Last Days of Hannwang Xin (196 BCE)

The Rosetta Stone was created in Egypt.

WHILE THE EMPEROR was laying siege to Dongyuan, Hannwang Xin and the Xiongnu launched a coordinated attack on Dai, capturing its northern outpost Canhe (in the northernmost part of Shanxi). Ever since he joined the Xiongnu, Hannwang Xin had been living the life of a nomad chieftain, sleeping in a yurt at night, roaming the steppes during the day, and periodically moving with the Xiongnu tribes from place to place. The barren landscape and biting wind often made him sad. Although he did not mind eating beef, mutton, and camel meat, he found cheese intolerable and could not get used to the overwhelming smell of milky tea. The greatest hardship for him, however, was emotional. Although the Xiongnu treated him as their distinguished guest, he could not understand a word of their language. Despite the vast expanse of the steppe, he could not find a single intimate to chat with. When he moved into Canhe, he hoped to be able to stay in this Han frontier town for a while. But the Han expedition army was approaching. The Xiongnu general who accompanied him wanted to retreat back north and urged him to go with him. Hannwang Xin turned him down. The general left with his cavalry.

The Han army soon arrived. On General Chai Wu's orders, the troops fanned out to environ the town. One of the earliest rebel leaders against the Qin, Chai had later joined Liu Bang and taken part in the battle of Gaixia in 202 BCE. For his merit he was raised to marquis. His task was to take back the town of Canhe and capture Hannwang Xin alive, if possible.

After Han troops were arrayed in battle formation, some of his field commanders urged Chai to launch an attack. But Chai found the situation perplexing: Hannwang Xin had had plenty of time to evacuate, but he had chosen not to despite the numerical advantage of the Han army. Furthermore, it was obvious that the town was not particularly well fortified. Why had he acted this way? Chai Wu put off the attack and sent Hannwang Xin a letter, which said:

His Majesty is benevolent even to a local lord who rebels or escapes, so long as he returns later. Not only will he not be executed, but he will have his title restored. You, Great King, know this very well. Today, you have taken shelter among the Xiongnu. That is no major crime. I sincerely hope that you will rejoin the Han soon.

***

IN HIS REPLY LETTER, which arrived promptly, Hannwang Xin said:

> *His Majesty promoted me when I was a nobody from a city neighborhood.*
> *When he declared himself emperor, I felt both proud and happy. But at*
> *the siege of Xingyang, instead of laying down my life like Ji Xin and Zhou*
> *Ke, I betrayed His Majesty's trust. This was my first crime. At the battle of*
> *Mayi, instead of defending the town, I surrendered it. This is my second*
> *crime. Today, commanding an army to fight against you, this is my third*
> *crime. In the past, Wen Zhong and Fan Li did not commit a single crime.*
> *Still, one of them had to kill himself and the other had to flee. With those*
> *three crimes of mine, I would stand as much chance of surviving in the*
> *Han as Wu Zixu in the state of Wu.*
>
> *Taking shelter in mountains and dales and on the steppes and living off*
> *of the largesse of the barbarians, I pine for my return. But that is wishful*
> *thinking, like a cripple who hopes to stand up, or a blind man who longs*
> *to see with his eyes. The situation I have found myself in is irreversible. So*
> *I have no choice but to turn down your request.*

***

UPON READING THE LETTER, General Chai ordered a general assault and sacked the town in two days. Hannwang Xin had fought bravely until he fell. In choosing to die this way, he probably hoped to erase the shameful memory of defeat and surrender at Xingyang.

***

IT WAS WITH A MIXTURE of grief and relief that the Emperor Liu Bang received the news of Hann Xin's capture and execution. He grieved over the tragic end of his greatest general. Had it not been for him, Liu Bang would not have conquered all under Heaven. But he was also relieved that Hann was finally eliminated. There was no doubt that, should he have lived, Hann Xin would have threatened the throne.

"What did Hann Xin say before his death?" the Emperor asked as he wiped tears off his face.

"He just said that he wished he had acted on Kuai Che's plans," said Empress Lü.

"That counselor from Qi (Shandong)?"

"Yes, Your Majesty."

"Where is he now?"

"Still in Linzi."

"All right," said the Emperor. Turning to one of his attendant gentlemen, he ordered, "Have Kuai Che brought there."

***

TO THE EMPEROR the elimination of both Hann Xin and Hannwang Xin, plus the retreat of the Xiongnu, showed that the Han Empire was clearly in favor with Heaven. A general amnesty was announced and a major rite was performed to appease and worship Heaven so that peace on earth would endure. After the ritual ceremony, the Emperor retired into his sanctum to read memorials submitted by his senior officials. A few moments later, Kuai Che was brought in.

"Where have you been after you left Hann Xin?" asked the Emperor.

"Your Majesty, I begged for a living in Linzi's marketplace."

"I heard you have gone mad."

"To tell the truth, I feigned madness for self-preservation after my advice had been turned down by my master."

"Didn't you advise him to rebel?"

"Yes, I did, Your Majesty. If he followed my advice, he would not have ended his life in such an ignominious way."

"You son of a bitch have owned up to your crime before I got started. That makes things easier for me." Turning to his attendant gentlemen, the Emperor shouted, "Cook him alive!"

"Injustice! The punishment does not fit the crime!" Kuai Che screamed desperately.

"Why not? You enticed Hann Xin to rebel."

"When the Qin lost power, all under Heaven chased after it. The most talented and the fastest-footed seized it. Robber Zhi's dog barked at Yao, not because Yao was not benevolent, but because Yao was not the dog's master. When I was advising Hann Xin, he, not Your Majesty, was my only master. Furthermore, there were a large number of people who wanted to do what Your Majesty was doing. Should all of them be cooked?"

"Get him out of here!" the Emperor fumed. "I don't want to hear him."

After the guards marched Kuai Che out of the room, the Emperor issued an edict to pardon him.

The Fall of Peng Yue (196 BCE)

DURING THE CHEN XI WAR, Peng Yue king of Liang had turned down an imperial summons to join the fight. The Emperor responded with an angry letter, accusing him of disobedience. Peng sent a reply to take the blame for his absence. That seemed to be the end of it, but Peng was still worried, spending many sleepless nights pondering how to assuage His Majesty's wrath.

One day as he was riding in a carriage in Dingtao, the Liang capital, Peng Yue said to his companion and favorite general Hu Zhe, "I've decided to travel to Luoyang to apologize to His Majesty in person. What do you think?"

"I do not think it is going to work, Your Highness."

"And why is that?" asked Peng Yue, feeling nervous.

"You want to ask for forgiveness after receiving the imperial censure—don't you think it is too late? If you make the trip, I am afraid, you will fall into a trap and never be able to come back. However, if you don't go, suspicion will grow even stronger."

"So I am damned either way?" asked Peng, his anxiety giving way to anger.

"Well, there is a third way. But I don't know if you, Great King, are ready for it or not."

"Yes?"

"Go it alone."

"No! Forget about it! I will never do that."

And that was that. Except that the coachman had overheard part of the conversation, not very distinctly, but enough to be convinced of Peng Yue's involvement in a conspiracy. Two weeks later, the coachman slipped away to Luoyang, where he exposed the "plot" of his master.

Before the week was out, a court envoy with an imperial edict arrived under heavy armed escort in Dingtao. Completely taken aback, Peng Yue rushed to the entrance to the palace just as the eunuch officer with a nonchalant expression on his face was descending from his carriage. Peng went up to greet him, but was stopped and arrested by six guards. Momentarily, General Hu Ze was taken into custody.

That evening, General Hu Zhe took his own life, probably out of fear that he would implicate his master under torture. Peng Yue was transported to Luoyang, where he was held in the prison of the Censor-in-chief's Office.

What was to be done with Peng Yue? It became the topic of a heated debate at court. Some recommended that he be subject to interrogation in the Office of the Censor-in-chief (*yushi dafu*), which routinely used torture. Others wanted to convict him of treason on existing evidence. In the end, the Emperor weighed in, saying, "When I was stranded in Xingyang, Peng Yue gave us the much needed help, distracting attention from Xiang Yu and capturing cities and towns in the Central Plain. At the battle of Gaixia, his contribution was inestimable. I owe him greatly. Besides, all the evidence we have comes from an allegation of his coachman. For these reasons, I am willing to give him a light punishment. I will set him free, after reducing him to the status of a commoner, and banish him to Qingyi in Shu (<u>Leshan</u>, <u>Sichuan</u>) for life."

***

FROM LUOYANG PENG YUE set off on a long journey to his place of banishment in a semi-barbarian area in the southwest. Being a convicted criminal, he was not permitted to bid farewell to his relatives in Dingtao, let alone bring with him his personal belongings. In fact, his family assets, including his mansion and country estates, had been confiscated. But he was alive and unharmed, for which he should be thankful. Neither was he required to ride in an open prison-cart, wearing cangue and shackles. Instead, he travelled in relative comfort in his own horse-drawn carriage, complete with a coachman and two attendants. He was also allowed to stay in government guesthouses, enjoying all the dining and accommodation privileges for senior officials, which he had taken for granted. The Emperor had given instructions to officials along the way to give Peng Yue this special treatment.

After he and his party had traveled slowly in the direction of Chang'an for several days, they stopped at a guesthouse in Zheng County (Huaxian, Shaanxi), not far from the capital.

As Peng Yue got off the carriage near the gate, the arrival of a group of armed riders attracted his attention. They cordoned off the open space in front of the gate. Momentarily, a large carriage with phoenix patterns on its exterior emerged, escorted by more armed riders. The carriage door was slowly flung open, out came Empress Lü. With the help of two palace ladies, she stepped down from the carriage.

Peng Yue hurried forward and shouted, "Your Majesty." A guard brought his halberd down to block him, shouting, "Keep off, you mad dog!"

"Let him pass," the Empress said to the guard.

Peng Yue went up to her and made obeisance.

"Where are you going, King of Liang?" asked the Empress.

"Your Majesty, I am no longer a king, but a commoner. In fact, I am now on my way to Qingyi, my place of banishment."

"Oh? What happened?" asked the Empress in great astonishment.

"They accused me of treason," said Peng Yue, as tears rolled down his cheeks.

"Really?"

"But, I swear by my ancestors I am completely innocent."

"I am sure you are. I have been in Chang'an recently and haven't heard a thing about this. Is there anything I can do to help?"

"I would be eternally grateful if Your Majesty would try to persuade the Emperor to let me spend my old age in Changyi in the company of my childhood friends."

"Indeed. Why don't you travel back to Luoyang with me? I am sure I'll change His Majesty's mind."

"Your Majesty," said a grateful Peng Yue, bowing his head in deep obeisance, "I do not think I can ever, ever repay you for your kindness."

***

BACK IN LUOYANG, Empress Lü had Peng Yue settled in a guesthouse, and went straight to the palace to see the Emperor.

"Why did you bring him back?" asked the Emperor, who was infuriated by his wife's decision.

"When I met him in Zheng County, he complained bitterly about his banishment."

"What did he want?"

"He hoped to move to his hometown Changyi instead."

"This is why you had pity on him and brought him back?"

"No, Your Majesty. As Your Majesty knows, to the north of Changyi is the Juye Moors, an area infested with outlaws. It was there that Peng Yue launched his career as a bandit leader. I am afraid that he may harbor sinister designs."

"Well," responded the Emperor, his eyebrows smoothing out. "What should I do, Wife?"

"Let me handle it on behalf of Your Majesty, if I may."

The Emperor, whose ire had vanished, nodded his assent.

In less than two weeks, the Empress uncovered crucial evidence that Peng Yue had been involved in a seditious plot. It took the form of an exposé letter by one of Peng Yue's retainers, who had received a small amount of gold from the Empress' men.

This criminal act in addition to Peng's previous connivance with General Hu Zhe pushed the Emperor over the edge. "I have been trying to shield him from harm," said the Emperor. "But I can't do it any more."

With the Emperor's permission, the chamberlain for law enforcement put the accused through the routine prosecution process. Although subjected to a whole range of torture aimed at extracting confession, Peng Yue always protested his innocence, clinging to the hope that His Majesty would save him in the last minute. In the end the chamberlain proposed a severe punishment: the execution of the accused and the extirpation of his Three Clans. And the Emperor gave his approval.

In the fourth month, having exhausted all avenues of appeal, Peng Yue, in cangue and shackles, was brought to Luoyang's marketplace, where he was beheaded.

On the Empress' orders, Peng Yue's severed head was impaled on a pole and put on public display outside the gatetower of the city's main southern entrance for the duration of a month. Because of the potential threat Peng posed to the throne and because of the particularly egregious nature of his crime (high treason), an ancient type of cruel punishment, known as *hai*, was revived and inflicted posthumously on him. His flesh was ground up and cooked into a paste, which, at the Empress' insistence, was distributed to the kings and marquises.

***

SEVERAL DAYS LATER one morning, a middle-aged man with a gray mustachio stopped beneath the severed head on display outside the gatetower. Looking up, he spoke to the head for a few minutes, and proceeded to make an offering of fruit. Two guards rushed forward to arrest him, and disposed of the offering.

On the following afternoon, the man, trussed up, was brought into the presence of the Emperor in the commodious audience hall. At the center there was a gigantic cauldron full of oil perched on a burning stove.

"Name and post?" asked the Emperor sharply.

"Your Majesty, my name is Luan Bu, and I am a counselor in Liang."

"What did you say to the dead criminal?"

"I had been sent by my master, Peng Yue king of Liang, on a mission to Qi. Even if he was dead, I thought I had a duty to report to him on my mission."

"Why did you make that offering?"

"I was his servant and he was my master. Isn't that true that a servant should honor his master even in death?"

"You fucking asshole! Don't you know that my edict prohibits it on pain of death?" shouted the Emperor furiously. Turning to his attendant gentlemen, he ordered, "Cook him alive!"

Four men lifted up Luan Bu and carried him towards the cauldron. The oil inside was fuming.

Suddenly, Luan Bu screamed at the Emperor, "Your Majesty, could I have my last word before I die?"

"Stop," the Emperor shouted to the gentlemen. "I'll hear him out." And they dropped Luan Bu onto the floor.

"After Your Majesty was defeated at Pengcheng and Xingyang," started Luan Bu, who had risen to his feet, "suddenly Xiang Yu became unstoppable. But eventually he did not succeed. A main reason was the presence of Peng Yue king of Liang, who allied himself with Han. Later, at Gaixia, had it not been for Peng Yue's support, Xiang Yu would not have perished.

"After peace was achieved in the entire realm, the King of Liang was given his patent of enfeoffment, allowing him to pass down his title to later generations. Recently, when Your Majesty summoned him to the campaign against Hannwang Xin, he did not go because of an illness. This caused Your Majesty to suspect him of plotting rebellion and to kill him. But he did send a large contingent of Liang troops. And there was not enough evidence against him. I think he remained loyal, and until the last moment he clung to the hope that Your Majesty would pardon him...." With tears choking his voice, Luan Bu continued, "Well, why am I talking about this? The king is dead and life has lost its meaning anyway. Your Majesty, I think I am ready. Let them throw me into the cauldron right now!"

His eyes watery with tears, the Emperor muttered, "Brave man." Addressing his attendant gentlemen, he said, "Free him!"

"Appoint him to commandery defender (*duwei*)," the Emperor added.

Zhao Tuo King of Nanyue (196 BCE)

LU JIA WAS SITTING in the waiting area of the Palace of Panyu (Guangzhou). It was at the center of the Yue area, where, separated by the Five Mountain Ranges (the Wuling) from the Jiangshui valley, the Han imperial writ did not run. A famous philosopher in his own right, Lu Jia was here on his first foreign mission as a Han emissary. With his oilcloth cape and bamboo hat by his side, he was holding the imperial scepter in his right hand. Outside, the rain was lashing down on the roof. Lu Jia lifted his eyes to look at the cavernous ceiling of thick reed thatch and the surrounding bamboo panel walls (see Map 4).

Momentarily, an attendant gentleman appeared and ushered him into an expansive audience hall. Zhao Tuo, a man in his mid-40s, was sitting hatless and cross-legged on a cushion at the far end of the hall, his hair arranged into a large bun at the back of his head.

"Isn't Your Highness from in the Central Plain with his ancestral tombs in Zhending (Zhengding, Hebei)?" asked Lu Jia, his eyebrows knitting into a frown.

"Yes, I grew up in Zhending in Qin times."

"Why do you wear that hairstyle?"

"I have lived among the barbarians for long and have adopted their customs."

"Why did Your Highness refuse to greet me—the imperial emissary from the heavenly court—in the suburb, as is required by ritual?"

"I have been away from the Central Kingdom for so long that I have forgotten about ritual and propriety. Since it is not doing any harm, I suppose you can put up with it," said Zhao Tuo, who sounded almost light-hearted.

"I know Your Highness has reigned over Nanyue as king for quite a while. But your kingship has yet to be confirmed by the court. For that to happen, the court wants to know, for instance, under what conditions Your Highness gained the throne. "

"Well, I have to go back to the very beginning, if you don't mind. Not long after the First Emperor came to power, I followed General Tu Sui to this area with a mandate to pacify the local populace. The locals, intolerant of Tu's high-handed ways, rose in arms and killed him. General Ren Xiao took over command and went on to subdue the whole region. By the time of Huhai's reign, Ren Xiao was dying. And I was called upon by the Qin court to exercise his power. Soon, Ren Xiao died and the Qin dynasty itself crumbled, which was followed by a period of turmoil and civil war. After annexing some neighboring areas, I declared myself King Wu of Nanyue."

"That was fair enough. But the problem is, when the Son of Heaven was fighting Xiang Yu to unite all under Heaven, Your Highness refused to render help in spite of repeated requests from him. In fact, it enraged him so much that he even considered launching a campaign against Nanyue. Only the fear of burdening the masses gave him pause. It seems that Your Highness is of the view that, with the freshly founded state of Nanyue, you can defy the authority of the Han. But Your Highness is gravely mistaken. Today, the entire realm has been pacified. The Han court could easily exterminate your kinsmen, destroy your ancestral tombs, and send an army of 100,000 under a second-rate general to conquer Nanyue and bring it into the fold."

A silence descended upon the spacious hall, as Zhao Tuo looked pensively at the floor, his flippant air vanishing. He then stood up and said, with a seriousness in his voice, "Mr. Lu, please accept my sincere apologies. During the civil war, it was hard for me, living in this remote corner of the world, to take sides. I simply did not know better. You can put it down to my ignorance. But I never intended to defy the authority of the Son of Heaven." He then ordered some wine. The conversation continued in a more relaxed manner.

"Tell me, Emissary, who is the most worthy: Xiao He, Cao Shen, Hann Xin, or me?" Zhao Tuo asked.

Lu Jia paused briefly before saying, "You are, it seems."

"How do I compare with the Emperor?"

"His Majesty," Lu Jia replied, "has inherited the great cause of the Five Emperors and Three Sovereigns and is now reigning over the entire Central

Kingdom with a land thousands of miles across and a population in the tens of millions. Its bounty is vast and its wealth unparalleled. How can Your Highness, as king of Nanyue, a country the size of a Han commandery, with its rugged terrain and sparse barbarian population, compare with the Emperor?"

Zhao Tuo broke into a hearty laugh, saying, "I was just teasing you. I know I can't compare. If I were in the Central Kingdom, however, I might have been second to none!"

"Well, one can never know what might have happened."

"I agree, Mr. Lu." Zhao Tuo raised his goblet towards his guest, saying, "Have some more," and drank.

After this meeting, Zhao Tuo requested Lu Jia to visit his palace often to talk with him over wine. Lu Jia obliged him.

"I don't really have someone to talk with in Nanyue," Zhao Tuo said to Lu Jia in one of their subsequent conversations. "That's why I sincerely welcome your company." And Lu's sojourn in Nanyue continued.

At the end of the third month, Lu Jia was ready to leave. Then he surprised his host by holding an investiture ceremony at his palace in which he officially granted the latter the title of king of Nanyue, and bestowed upon him a gold seal. A delighted Zhao Tuo pledged his allegiance to the Han court and loaded Lu Jia with treasures and gifts worth 2,000 catties of gold.

Upon his return to Chang'an, Lu Jia was called into the palace to give a briefing on Nanyue. Delighted with the success of his mission, the Emperor gifted him with 1,000 catties of gold and promoted him to senior counselor of the palace (*tai zhong dafu*), a post of great prestige that allowed him to offer advice to the Emperor on key policy issues.

Before long, however, the Emperor became disillusioned. Not one to take political theory seriously, the Emperor based his policy decisions on pragmatism. Nevertheless, he was more or less in tune with the prevailing trend among scholars in the early Western Han that favored Daoism with its stress on non-action, spontaneity, and non-interventionism. While Lu Jia paid due respect to Daoism, he was at heart a Confucian. He routinely interspersed his discourses with quotes from such Confucian classics as the *Classic of Documents* (Shujing) and the *Classic of*

Songs (Shijing). Both works had been edited by Confucius himself, and targeted for destruction during the Burning of Books campaign in 213 BCE under the Qin. As a result, both the *Documents* and the *Songs* vanished. Incomplete copies resurfaced under the Han dynasty.

Lu Jia was among those Qin scholars who had managed to commit much of the Confucian works, including the two in question, to memory. And he could not help citing pithy sayings from these works to make his point. On one occasion, in a short piece on rulership, he cited the *Documents* and the *Songs* more than a dozen times. The Emperor flared up: "You fucking son of a bitch! I—your daddy— conquered the world on horseback. What did that have to do with the *Documents* and the *Songs*?"

"Your Majesty," answered Lu Jia, his face flushed crimson. "It is true that Your Majesty conquered the world on horseback. But is it possible to *rule* the world on horseback?"

"How should I know?" countered the Emperor in a less combative tone. "You tell me!"

"Well, in the past, King Tang of Shang and King Wu of Zhou both took power by military force, but both governed successfully with a civil approach. These cases prove that only a combination of civil and military power and of the literary and martial spirits can guarantee a sustainable long-term rule. There are examples in which sovereigns relied excessively on military force, for instance, Fuchai king of Wu and the First Emperor of the Qin. Both states collapsed, either during the reign of the sovereign or not long after his death. If the First Emperor, after conquering all under Heaven, practiced benevolence and righteousness and followed the great kings of the past as his models, his empire would not have fallen. Of course, that would not have created the opportunity for Your Majesty."

The Emperor sipped his wine meditatively for a few moments and said, "It seems that I have abused you for no good reason. Well, I apologize. Hey, why don't you write a book for me? A book on why the Qin lost the world and why I gained it, as well as on lessons from the successes and failures of the ancient states."

Lu Jia accepted the challenge with alacrity. In two months, he had completed a short philosophical book of 12 chapters that discusses a whole array of issues regarding government from the perspective of Confucianism and Daoism. Each time Lu finished a chapter, he presented a copy to the throne, which never failed to impress the Emperor. After the last chapter was submitted, the whole book was given the title of *New Discourses* (Xinyu). It would serve as the guiding light for government for the Emperors and top leaders for generations to come.

The Ying Bu War (196 BCE)

ONE SUMMER MORNING, on the outskirts of Lù (<u>Lu'an</u>, <u>Anhui</u>), Ying Bu, the King of Huainan, was hunting when an attendant gentleman reported the visit of a court envoy. Ying Bu turned his horse around and rode to a hunting lodge, where the envoy had been waiting.

After greeting the king, the eunuch presented a small jar, and made a matter-of-fact announcement, which ended with, "Contained in this jar is a meat paste—a gift from the court."

Ying Bu broke the wax seal, and opened the lid. A pungent, fishy odor rose to assault the nostrils. To show his appreciation, he stuck his index and middle fingers into the jar to scoop out some dark-brown paste, and put it in his mouth.

"How does it taste?"

"Strange, a bit like fish paste," answered Ying Bu.

"It is made from the flesh of the rebel Peng Yue."

Suddenly, hit with a bout of queasiness, Ying Bu felt a strong urge to vomit, which he suppressed with great difficulty as his face turned ashen. After a long pause, he murmured a few words of condemnation against Peng Yue's treachery. The envoy, his mission completed, left the lodge.

Ying Bu cut short his hunting trip and returned to his palace inside the town of Lù. There he became bed-ridden, sick with revulsion and horror. For several days, he refused to give audience even to his closest associates, and only allowed his favorite concubine Madam Zhang, a local beauty in her late 20s, to keep him company.

When he at length emerged from his bedchamber, looking gaunt and wan, the king summoned a secret meeting with his confidants and most trusted senior generals. There it was decided that troops would be placed on high alert kingdom-wide, especially in the northern border area. Ying Bu had made up his mind to go rogue at the first sign that the Emperor would go after him.

***

WORN DOWN BY THE long hours she had spent taking care of the king, Madam Zhang was finally taken sick. Ailed by a persistent cough she could not shake, she was sent by the king to a certain Doctor Li for treatment.

Doctor Li's home consisted of three houses in a small courtyard. The principal house was used as his office. Thanks to his reputation as the greatest physician of Lù, he had attracted patients from far and near. Some came from north of the Huai River, and others lived in the neighborhood. One of them was Ben He, a rising star in Ying Bu's inner circle, who lived across the street. At the relative young age of slightly over 30, he was an ordinary counselor (*zhong dafu*).

When Counselor Ben He met face-to-face with Madam Zhang in Doctor Li's courtyard, he felt hopelessly smitten. Not deterred by the fact that the beauty was the king's woman, he bribed the physician heavily to arrange for a meeting.

So, one day, after Madam Zhang finished her consultation with the physician, she stepped into the eastern wing at his request to have a drink with the counselor. The two hit it off. From then on, they were able to rendezvous on a regular basis until a disgruntled maid tipped off the king.

One night, when Ying Bu and Madam Zhang were lying in bed in the palace, Ying Bu asked casually, "Did you happen to see someone called Ben He at Doctor Li's?"

"No. Who is he?" she asked back, with an innocent look on her face.

"Just someone who works for me," he said calmly and went on to talk about other things.

The concubine soon fell asleep. But the king was wide awake. Although he hoped to give her the benefit of the doubt, he suspected something fishy. *Why did the maid report on her? Did she make it up? If yes, what did she stand to gain?*

He summoned the maid for further questioning the next afternoon. The maid not only stuck to her original story, but provided more damning details about the rendezvous. The king sent half a dozen of his palace guard troops to bring Counselor Ben in for interrogation. By then the counselor had fled. Apparently, somebody had tipped him off.

***

EVER SINCE HE WAS wounded in Guangwu in 203 BCE, the Emperor had been in declining health. Recently, for health and other reasons, the Emperor had turned increasingly inward, so much so that he gave out orders to his doorkeepers at the entrance to his residential basilica to refuse admittance to even his closest advisers. He spent much of his time in the company of the eunuch officers. For more than two weeks, his top military leaders, Zhou Bo, Guan Ying, and others, had tried times and again but failed to see him.

When General Fan Kuai came for a visit, he too was refused entry by a doorkeeper. Fan Kuai got into a heated exchange with him, and lost patience. He shoved the doorkeeper aside, and dashed into the inner quarters of the basilica, followed by the other top leaders.

What they saw shocked them: the Emperor was lying in his canopy bed with his head resting on the lap of a young eunuch officer with handsome features. Startled, the Emperor sat up; the eunuch got off the bed and disappeared behind a dark curtain that draped from ceiling to floor.

Fan Kuai could not help but drop on his knees, and the others did the same. With tears streaming down his unkempt mustache, Fan Kuai said, "We followed Your Majesty since the days of Feng and Pei to conquer the world. At that time Your Majesty was so brilliant and powerful. Today the world is at peace, but Your Majesty has become spent and exhausted. When we wanted to discuss matters of national importance, Your Majesty refused to see us, but had time to keep a eunuch company. We are seriously concerned. Has Your Majesty forgotten the lesson of Zhao Gao?"

Overcoming his initial astonishment, the Emperor said smilingly, "I am fine. Why don't you wait in the adjoining audience hall? I'll be there in a moment."

The meeting with the top leaders that followed was the first in two months. Thereafter, the Emperor resumed his normal responsibilities, giving audiences and reading memorials. One of them submitted by a certain Ben He caught his attention. It accused Ying Bu of plotting rebellion. The Emperor passed it on to Chancellor Xiao He, asking, "What do you think?"

"Ying Bu? Rebellion? I find it hard to believe," said Xiao, full of suspicion. "It is highly likely that one of his enemies has tried to malign him." After a long discussion between the two, it was decided, with the Emperor's approval, to take two simultaneous steps: to take the accuser into custody, and to dispatch a special team headed by an envoy to Huainan to investigate.

The court envoy with his team arrived in Lù about a week later and was immediately thrown into jail. By then, Ying Bu king of Huainan had declared an open rebellion. What had triggered his decision was that fateful night when his guards had failed to capture Counselor Ben He. The arrival of the court envoy convinced Ying Bu that Ben He must have informed against him. On his orders, Ben He's home was ransacked, and all members of his family were arrested and subsequently executed.

***

WHEN THE EMPEROR READ Ying Bu's Declaration of War, he was livid with anger. Nobody had seen it coming, not even the sagacious Xiao He. He regretted to have gone along with his wife's idea of sending that jar of human paste as a way to awe him into obedience. Unfortunately, it had pushed him in the opposite direction.

The Emperor released Ben He and appointed him general. He then called an emergency meeting with his advisers and top generals. With furrowed eyebrows, he brought up the issue of the Ying Bu rebellion.

"The rebellion was unavoidable," said an old man called Xue, who, formerly chancellor of the state of Chu before the rise of Qin, was now attending the meeting as a special guest of Xiahou Ying.

"Why do you say that, Mr. Xue?"

"The three great heroes of the age, Hann Xin, Peng Yue, and Ying Bu, were all enfeoffed as kings under Your Majesty. Recently, Your Majesty eliminated Hann and Peng in rapid succession. It was bound to arouse suspicion in Ying Bu that he would be next. Thus his rebellion was all but unavoidable."

The Emperor then asked, "Now that he has already rebelled, how are we going to fight him?"

Before Mr. Xue could answer, several generals stood up to offer their views. They had nothing but contempt for Ying Bu, and were confident of a quick victory. The Emperor, however, was still worried. He knew from experience that Ying Bu was a great field general.

Mr. Xue then said, "As I see it, Ying Bu should not be treated lightly, but undoubtedly he will be defeated."

"Tell me why," said the Emperor.

"Essentially, there can be three options for him. His first option is to invade Chu in the west and Wu in the east before moving north to capture Qi (in Shandong), Zhao, and Yan (in Hebei). If he can hold on to those areas, much of the north and east will be under his control. His second option is to capture Chu and Wu first before moving northwest into Hann and Wei in the Central Plain while seizing control of the Ao Granary. His third option is to go south to capture Yue (Zhejiang) and move his base to Changsha (in Hunan). The first plan is the best. His chances for success diminish greatly with the second and third. I can say with assurance that whatever option Ying Bu pursues it will not get him very far."

"Why?"

"Because since his days as a corvée laborer at Mount Li he has always acted in self-interest without consideration for others. Thus it is hard for him to attract dedicated followers to his cause, and the strategy he adopts will likely be ineffectual."

Several officers stood up to attest to Xue's claim.

After the meeting, the Emperor felt much assured about his chance of victory against Ying Bu and awarded Mr. Xue with a fief of 1,000 households.

Liu Ying's Assignment (196 BCE)

CROWN PRINCE LIU YING was excited when he received his appointment as commander-in-chief of the expeditionary army. In his short life of 14 years, he had never had a chance to see a real battle, but had heard many stories about the heroic exploits of his father and his followers. He was eager to embark on this new adventure.

Empress Lü, however, was not sure what to make of it. Was it a great opportunity where her son could gain some valuable military experience? Or was it a trap set up by that foxy "slut" to compromise his position? As recently as two days before the Emperor had insisted on leading the campaign against Ying Bu in person, in spite of widespread opposition on account of his declining health. In fact, to lead an anti-rebellion campaign in person had become an unspoken convention for the Emperor. She was told that, now, however, the Emperor had come down with a throbbing headache, which made it impossible for him to undertake a strenuous journey, let alone direct military operations in the field. But she remained suspicious.

The Four Recluses, now the crown prince's mentors, gave their analysis of the situation when Lü Ze came for a visit. In their opinion, this appointment would place the crown prince in great peril. If the crown prince led the campaign and succeeded, he would not reap any benefit. It was more likely, however, he would lose and suffer the consequences. The generals the crown prince was supposed to command were all great soldiers who had helped the Emperor conquer the world. Letting the crown prince command them was no different from letting a sheep lead a pack of wolves.

"No doubt," one recluse said, "the generals will not accept his leadership, and he is doomed to fail. What's worse: something may happen to his status as crown prince. We all know the proverb, 'When a mother is favored, so is her son.' The most favored woman obviously is Lady Qi. She is with the Emperor day and night. Their son Ruyi king of Zhao often keeps them company. During Liu Ying's absence from Chang'an, the Emperor may indeed appoint Ruyi as the new crown prince to replace him."

The Empress panicked when Lü Ze told her what he had heard from the Four Recluses. In desperation, she sent him to seek advice from Zhang Liang. However, even the resourceful strategist could not find a way out. While he promised he would think of something, he insisted that it was vital that the Empress should try to reason with the Emperor herself.

That night, the Empress entered the Emperor's residential basilica with an urgent request for an audience. The Emperor was already in bed. He freed himself from the embrace of Lady Qi and went into the adjoining audience hall, feeling annoyed.

"Does Yingying have to go?" asked the Empress without ceremony.

"Yes."

"Why?"

"First, it's time that the crown prince acquired some experience in directing a military operation; second, this is my own political decision and I resent the fact that you, a woman, interfere with it; third, I am too weak to go myself."

"Your Majesty, I am not opposed to Yingying gaining military experience. But too much is at stake in this campaign. It is likely that his orders won't be followed nor will he be able to stop infighting should it occur. Furthermore, he is just 14 years old, has never seen battle before, and is unlikely to make sound decisions. However, his adversary, Ying Bu, is a great general and strategist. If the campaign does not go as planned, the crown prince will be discredited, and the throne will be in danger. For the sake of our son, the country, and the Great Han, I, your humble subject, beseech you to reconsider."

The Emperor paused a long time before saying, "It is getting late now. Why don't you turn in?" He rose and walked back into the bedroom.

The next day, the Emperor attended a ritual ceremony. There he was greeted by a white-haired man with a cane, who looked familiar.

After a brief moment of hesitation, the Emperor exclaimed excitedly, "Good heavens! Aren't you Zhang Liang?!"

"Yes, Your Majesty," said Zhang Liang as he made obeisance with difficulty.

"You've changed. Almost unrecognizable!" said the Emperor as he looked at Zhang from head to toe.

"I have to admit, Your Majesty, I have been in poor health, and it is getting worse. Had it not been for my trouble, I would have gone on the campaign myself."

"Of course not. I hope you continue to enjoy peace and quiet in your old age. Yingying will lead the campaign. Hopefully, he will gain some military experience."

"Good idea, Your Majesty. Sooner or later he has to bond with the military," said Zhang Liang, who then paused to think for a while before continuing, "It would be even better if he could start with commanding a force based in Chang'an, instead of going into combat on his first assignment."

"You think so?"

"Yes, Your Majesty," said Zhang Liang, nodding his head.

Two days later, the Empress raised the issue of Yingying's assignment again. With his headache gone, the Emperor relented, saying, "That son of yours is no good, anyway."

The Emperor therewith ordered the setup of the Crown Prince Guard to be staffed with 30,000 officers and men from inside and outside the capital. The prince would serve as its commander.

The Emperor then embarked on the last campaign of his life. Escorted by a large entourage, he first stopped at a guesthouse in Quyou, a place in the northeast suburb of Chang'an, where he met with Zhang Liang again.

"I heard that Your Majesty is going to war," started Zhang Liang. "So I am here to bid Your Majesty goodbye."

"Do you have any suggestions?" asked the Emperor.

"Well, it always pays to be extra careful. The Chu people are brave and quick. Your Majesty should avoid the thrust of their attack."

"Good advice! I'll be very careful."

The Last Campaign (196 BCE)

YING BU WAS UNDETERRED when he heard that the Emperor Liu Bang had personally taken up command of the expeditionary army.

"So what?" said Ying to his generals, "Zhang Liang once talked about the three military geniuses of the time: Hann Xin, Peng Yue, and myself. Both Hann and Peng are dead and I am the only one left. Who should I fear? Certainly not the old creep himself, who, by the way, is in poor health. There is a good chance we can win this war."

After striking out at neighboring Chu and Wu to the west and east, Ying Bu scored a major victory against the kingdom of Jing, defeating its army and killing its king, Prince Liu Jia. He then marched north across the Huai. In so doing, he was actually following the first of the three strategies laid out by Mr. Xue. Before his army could move further north to capture Qi and Zhao (Shandong and Hebei), its advance was checked by the arrival of the Han expeditionary army. The Emperor moved most of his 30,000 troops into the fortified town of Yongcheng (south of Suzhou, in north Anhui), which was then besieged by Ying Bu's army of greater size and strength.

Early one morning, the Emperor was carried in a palanquin to the east gatetower. Helped by two attendant gentlemen, he climbed with labored breath several flights of steep steps to the top story. From an embrasure, he looked toward the open field that lay beyond and saw lines of enemy troops that extended into the distance. The sea of soldiers in yellow-brownish tunics and their officers in black armor reminded him of the siege of Xingyang a few years back, where he had only narrowly avoided capture by Xiang Yu. Suddenly, he felt overcome by revulsion and started retching. "Damn, I don't like it a bit," the Emperor murmured, and stepped away from the embrasure.

With a roll of drums, the gate was thrown open and the drawbridge let down. A Han envoy waving a white flag rode to the enemy camp with the Emperor's request for a meeting. A few moments later Ying Bu, armored and helmeted and under the escort of about 200 cavalry, emerged on horseback in the distance and came to a halt at the far end of the drawbridge.

"Can we make peace and spare the people the ravages of war?" asked the Emperor, as he stood behind an embrasure in the gatetower.

"On what conditions, Your Majesty?" replied Ying Bu.

"So long as you cease hostilities with the Han, I will pardon you, and you can be king of Huainan as before."

"As a vassal king under Your Majesty? No way, I won't do it. I'm sure you haven't forgotten our first meeting in Xingyang. You kept me waiting and waiting while you washed your stinking feet with two young whores by your sides. Whenever I think of it I feel like throwing up. After that I had to put up with your bossy manners and foul tongue all the time. It is demeaning to live under you, even as a king. Besides, how can I trust you? Just look at the two other great heroes: Hann Xin and Peng Yue. Both were captured and beheaded. Peng's flesh was even made into a paste. Yes, Hann Xin may have been privy to a plot. But you forced him to do it. You had stripped him of his titles and power and 'pardoned' him after humiliating him in public. As for Peng Yue, he was completely innocent. You know it!"

"What exactly do you want?" The Emperor tried very hard to keep his anger under control.

"Well, since I already started it, there is no going back. I want the throne."

"You fucking bastard!" yelled the Emperor in a fit of fury.

"There you go again, you filthy-mouthed old jerk!" Ying Bu turned his horse around and rode away.

***

CONVINCED OF HIS SUPERIOR military leadership, Ying Bu overcame opposition from his generals and made a ferocious attack on the town the next day, throwing wave after wave of soldiers into the fray. The Han defenders on the walls fought bravely, using bows and arrows, spears and broadswords, stones and boiling water. By the end of the day, they had prevented the enemies from breaching the walls or storming the gates. The attack continued for three more days. Both sides were exhausted. The attackers in particular suffered significant casualties. Eventually, it was the arrival of a large contingent of Han troops from the north that broke the stalemate. They routed the rebel forces and went on to envelope Ying Bu's camp.

The east town gate was thrown open, and the Han troops that had huddled inside sallied forth to engage the enemies. The Emperor Liu Bang, escorted by a troop of light cavalry, was seen armorless among them, riding in his imperial carriage, shouting words of encouragement, and brandishing a sword in the air. He wanted to be in the thick of action, directing the campaign in person.

As the banners at Ying Bu's camp were being pulled out and replaced with the red banners of Han, the Emperor could no longer contain his excitement. He ordered his coachman to drive him closer and closer to the front until, abruptly, he tumbled backward into the carriage, having been hit in the chest by a stray arrow.

By then, it became obvious that the Han army was winning. Ying Bu had fled the battlefield with a few hundred riders. They went south, crossed the Huai, but were immediately intercepted by Han troops. After a desperate fight, Ying Bu and a small number of his men managed to break through. By the time Ying Bu crossed the Jiangshui (<u>Yangzi</u>), he was left with just about 100 followers. After two more battles, on the northern and southern banks of the Tao River, Ying Bu lost all his men.

As Ying Bu was walking across a wilderness with trees, shrubs, and wildflowers, the landscape reminded him of the old days when he was the leader of a gang of outlaws in the Lake Peng area. *Those were the days*, he thought with nostalgia. *I wonder what would have become of me if I had not come out of the wilderness. But the diviner was certain I was destined to be king. I'll start over. I'll rise again.*

"Hail to the king," a man in his 30s greeted him.

"Who are you?" asked Ying Bu, his right hand clutching the hilt of his sword.

"I am an envoy sent by Wu Chen king of Changsha," said the man.

"Of course. How is my brother-in-law doing?" asked Ying Bu, more relaxed.

"He is fine. In fact, he plans to run away with you to Yue (<u>Zhejiang</u>)."

"Does he?" asked Ying Bu, his eyes showing a glimmer of hope.

"Yes, he does. If you don't mind, follow me to Zixiang Village. The king is waiting for you there."

"Yes, I am coming with you."

About an hour later, hot and thirsty, Ying Bu saw this nondescript cottage in the distance.

"We are almost there," said the stranger, sitting down under a pagoda tree. Pointing to the cottage, he continued, "You can go there, and get some water to drink."

Ying Bu made directly for the cottage, pushed the door open, and went in. Before he said a word, a heavy sword struck his head from behind, and he sank down like a sack of rice.

The self-styled envoy entered, cut off the head, and wrapped it in a hemp cloth.

"I'll have to send it to the King of Changsha," he said to the assassin, a tall muscular man in his mid-20s. "He'll keep his promise and pay you."

***

AFTER VANQUISHING the Ying Bu Rebellion, the Emperor decided to appoint a member of the royal Liu family to head the newly created kingdom of Wu, which now replaced the kingdom of Jing. Since the locals had the reputation for being unruly, the Emperor picked his nephew Liu Pi, a fierce-looking man of 20, as their king.

At a pompous ceremony held at the Anterior Basilica, the Emperor, struggling to hide the pain from his fresh arrow wound, conferred the king's seal upon the nephew. When Emperor had a close look at his physiognomy, he almost regretted his decision.

"You do have that rebel look, Pi," the Emperor said, half in jest. "About 50 years from now there is going to be a major rebellion in the southeast. Is it going to be started by you?"

"No, Your Majesty. Of course not."

"Don't you ever take up arms against other Lius! You belong to the same family."

"I will never dare to do that, Your Majesty."

The Emperor patted him on the back with a smile and let him go.

The Drinking Party (196 BCE)

IN EARLY WINTER, the Emperor felt recovered enough from his fresh chest wound, so he made a trip to his adopted hometown, Pei. He had longed to pay this visit for quite some time. *After you made it big, you must return to your hometown to thank your relatives and friends*, as an old saying goes.

In the Pei Palace, a modest structure by Chang'an standards, the Emperor held a drinking party. The invited guests included all the old acquaintances he could find, as well as the local elders and their sons. The official taboo for the name of the Emperor was lifted. The guests exchanged anecdotes about the young Fourth Brother and themselves, and made jokes, which were often met with uproarious laughter. They drank without restraint until many of them became dead drunk. Abruptly, the Emperor struck the first note of a song he had composed for the occasion on the *zhu*, a large-sized zither, and started singing:

A strong wind rises as clouds fly in the sky;

Ruling over the lands within the seas, I return home;

But where can I find brave men to guard the Four Quarters?

As 120 local boys joined in the singing, tears poured down the Emperor's cheeks. When it was finally over, he rose and said to the guests, "I am a wanderer all over the world. But my heart aches to return to my hometown. My capital is in Guanzhong, but I miss Pei all the same. Long after I am gone, my soul will continue to miss it." Pausing briefly, the Emperor continued, "Thirteen years ago, as the Lord of Pei, I started out from here on a mission to fight the despotic and the rebellious, and in the process I conquered the world. I owe my good fortune to Pei; and I hereby declare that, from this day forward, this town, Pei, will be designated as an imperial bath-town. The residents will be exempt from taxes forever." All present cheered as the Emperor raised his goblet and drank up.

The drinking party continued into the wee hours of the night and kicked off a period of festivities that went on for more than ten days. In the end, the Emperor bid farewell to the local people, and departed, much to the reluctance of the latter.

Lady Qi and Prince Ruyi (195 BCE)

AFTER HIS RETURN TO Chang'an, the Emperor's health declined precipitously. The chest wound which had never been healed now began to fester. He was constantly running a low fever, and often sweated profusely during the night.

One morning, he woke up and saw a teary-eyed Lady Qi bending over him. Holding her hand, the Emperor said affectionately, "Treasure, I've made up my mind. I am going to replace Yingying with Ruyi as crown prince."

"Are you, Fourth Brother?" asked Lady Qi, unconvinced.

"Yes, I have to do it."

"But when?"

The Emperor paused a while to collect his thoughts. Then he said, "Tomorrow. I will hold a special meeting with the leading officials at court and make the announcement."

The meeting took place as planned, but the announcement elicited strong opposition. Zhang Liang, frail but still sharp, argued against it on two grounds. In succession, he said, heir-sons (born by the Empress) always took precedence over non-heir sons, and the older always trumped the younger.

Shusun Tong attempted to dissuade the Emperor with historical evidence, and said, "Duke Xian of Jin disposed his crown prince at the request of Consort Li. The state of Jin was plunged into chaos. The First Emperor's failure to set up Fusu as crown prince allowed Zhao Gao to enthrone Huhai, which led to the ruin of the dynasty. All under Heaven know that Crown Prince Liu Ying is benevolent and filial thanks to efforts by Your Majesty and the Empress to edify him. If Your

Majesty wants to replace him with his younger brother, I will be the first one to oppose it even if it means death!"

"Get out of here!" shouted the Emperor.

Then, to His Majesty's great displeasure, four more senior officials stepped forward to voice their misgivings. Eventually, there was not even one supporting voice. The Emperor had no choice but to back off from his position, saying, "I was just kidding!"

Shusun Tong responded in an agitated voice, "The crown prince is the anchor of the country. If the anchor is unmoored, the whole country will come adrift. How can Your Majesty joke about it?"

"You are right, I should not have done it," said the Emperor, looking sullen.

The meeting broke up without reaching a decision.

At the banquet that evening, the crown prince was in attendance. The Emperor was surprised to see four elderly men keep him company. He was struck by their distinguished features, particularly the snowy whiteness of their hair, eyebrows, and beards.

"Who are those old men?" he asked an attendant gentleman.

"The Four White-hair Recluses."

"I'll be darned!" the Emperor exclaimed. Approaching the old men, he said, "A few years ago, I tried to get you to work for me. But you turned me down. How come you are willing to serve my son?"

They looked at each other for a moment, before one of them spoke, "Your Majesty loves to insult scholars in public, which we found hard to bear. So we went into hiding. Then we heard about the crown prince. He was benevolent and filial, and treated the scholars with great deference. In fact, there was no lack of people willing to die for him. So we decided to serve him."

"Is that right? It's incredible. Well, I thank you for taking the trouble to educate and protect my crown prince."

"No trouble at all, Your Majesty," they answered almost in one voice.

After the crown prince took leave of the Emperor, with the Four Recluses in tow, the Emperor fell into a brown study for a while before saying contemplatively to Lady Qi, "Didn't you see, Treasure? I want to replace the crown prince, but the Four Recluses back him. I think under their guidance he has come into his own and it is hard to remove him."

Lady Qi fell silent as tears streamed down her cheeks.

"Don't cry, Treasure. If Yingying becomes emperor, he will be kind to you. He is an awfully nice boy. I know you and the Empress don't get along. But so long as Yingying is there, both you and Ruiyi are safe. Besides, Zhou Chang, as chancellor of Zhao, will keep Ruyi from harm."

Lady Qi wiped off her tears in silence. The Emperor then said with a forced smile, "Cheer up. I just wrote this song in my head. Do you want to hear it?"

Lady Qi nodded her head. He began to sing as she danced:

The swan flies on high,

One thousand li in a single leap;

Having become full-fledged,

It flies across the Four Seas.

It flies across the Four Seas,

What can be done?

Even if you have bows and arrows,

What can you do about it?

By the time the song was over, Lady Qi was drowned in a pool of tears.

Lu Wan King of Yan (195 BCE)

Hannibal of Carthage was denounced to the Romans and chose to go into exile.

AS KING OF YAN in the northeast part of the realm, Lu Wan willingly lent support to the Emperor's campaign against Chen Xi. Once, on his orders, a sizeable army went south to intercept the rebel forces, only to be bested by the Xiongnu cavalry. This was followed by a major Han victory over Chen Xi elsewhere. The fluidity of the situation prompted the king to send his most trusted adviser, Zhang Sheng, north: to deliver the news of Chen Xi's defeat to the Xiongnu in the hope of deterring further attacks.

Upon arriving at the headquarters of Xiongnu, which was surrounded by endless steppeland, Zhang Sheng was surprised to meet an old acquaintance.

"What are you doing here, Zang Yan, living among the barbarians?" asked Zhang Sheng.

"I am thankful the Xiongnu took me in, after my father was killed," answered the son of Zang Tu, the former king of Yan.

"As a fugitive, your best hope is to return to the Han Empire and the Emperor will pardon you in an amnesty."

"Don't worry about me. I am doing fine here. You should worry about yourself."

"Seriously?" asked Zhang Sheng doubtfully.

"Of course. For now, all King Lu Wan wants is to crush Chen Xi in the shortest possible time. But have you ever thought of what is going to happen next? It is going to be Yan's turn soon. The reason the Emperor has spared Yan so far is that he has been busy fighting the other local lords. Once he is done with them, the Emperor will take your master captive."

"Why?"

"Isn't it clear enough that the Emperor cannot tolerate nonroyal kings? He is now going after them one by one."

"Suppose what you just said is true, what should we do?"

"Have you seen the *chanyu* Modu yet?"

"No, I am planning to see him tomorrow and deliver the news on Chen Xi."

"Instead of that, you should make peace with the Xiongnu leader and stop fighting Chen Xi. That will allow Lu Wan king of Yan to stay in power for a long, long time. Backed by the Xiongnu, even if the Han attack, you can keep them at bay."

Zhang Sheng spent the rest of the day and night mulling over his options. The next morning, at Modu's court, at his instance, he concluded a preliminary alliance with the Xiongnu. Following his advice, the Xiongnu sent out a cavalry force to prop up what remained of Chen Xi's army. They jointly defeated the Han expeditionary army and intruded into Yan territory.

King Lu Wan was frustrated not only by the aggressive move of the Xiongnu but also by the prolonged stay of Zhang Sheng in Xiongnu territory. After Zhang Sheng missed the expected return date by two weeks, Lu Wan concluded with great reluctance that Zhang must have defected, which could account for the recent Xiongnu invasion. He ordered to have Zhang Sheng's family members taken into custody, and sent a report to Chang'an, requesting approval of their execution.

Then the king received news of Zhang Sheng's arrest at the northern border as he attempted to cross into Yan from Xiongnu. Trussed up, Zhang was transported to the Yan capital Ji.

"Traitor!" shouted Lu Wan to his emissary as he was dragged in front of him in the Yan Palace.

"Great King, it is not what you think," said Zhang Sheng.

"As soon as I receive approval from Chang'an, I'll have you executed together with your entire family."

"Great King!" Zhang Sheng shouted at the top of his lungs. "Please allow me to brief you on my mission before you decide what you are going to do with me."

His anger cooling somewhat, Lu Wan instructed the guards to unbind Zhang and leave the room. Behind closed doors, Zhang Sheng informed him of Zang Yan's advice and his deal with the Xiongnu.

"It is treason against the Emperor!" fumed the king.

"Yes, it is. But it is the only way to save Yan and Your Highness."

"How so?" asked Lu Wan with suspicion.

"Your Highness, do you remember what happened to the other nonroyal kings like you?"

"Yes? What about them?"

"Your predecessor, Zang Yan's father, Zang Tu: beheaded...."

"Wait a minute! He rebelled against the throne."

"This is what the Han court wants you to believe. But Zang Yan told me that the Emperor provoked his father to rebel so that he could have an excuse to eliminate him."

"You don't say!"

"You don't have to believe it, but how about the others? For example, Hann Xin, Peng Yue, and Ying Bu—the three geniuses. All were eliminated on one excuse or another. Hannwang Xin was forced to defect to the Xiongnu, then perished. Zhang Er, king of Zhao, died early. His son was allowed to succeed, but was later thrown into jail. Then there is Wu Rui's son in Changsha. He seems to be doing fine. But Changsha is an unimportant kingdom with a small population. Yan is different. Not only is it much more populous, it also borders on Xiongnu territory. It is too important to be ruled by a nonroyal. Sooner or later, the Emperor has to replace you with a royal prince."

"The Emperor trusts me more than anyone else. We were born on the same day and grew up in the same neighborhood. We were the best of friends, and still are. Don't you know that I was the only one allowed to enter his campaign tent without an appointment when the Emperor was on campaign against Xiang Yu? Xiao He, Cao Shen, and Zhang Liang, none of them had that privilege."

"Yes, he did trust you. But no matter how hard you try, you cannot explain your recent defeat at the hands of the Xiongnu. Nor can you change the Emperor's mind about his plan to eliminate the kings whose surname is not Liu."

Lu Wan stared at the floor for a while. Then he looked up with a serious expression on his face. "But your family members are already in custody, waiting for an order from the court for their execution."

"Can you find some substitutes?"

"Substitutes?" The king fell silent for a while, then said, "All right, I'll see what I can do. But what am I supposed to do next?"

"Let me go north again to reconfirm the alliance I concluded with the Xiongnu so that you can have their backing in times of need."

After the meeting, the king ordered Zhang Sheng's "arrest." A few days later, Zhang and his family members were fetched from their prison cells for "interrogation" and, after changing into civilian clothes, were put into a sealed carriage and transported to a northern border town. From there, they were smuggled into Xiongnu territory.

After the "interrogation" was over, half a dozen prisoners on death row were sent into the prison cells previously occupied by the Zhangs.

***

LU WAN KING OF YAN continued to play the role of a loyal vassal. But, secretly, he sent an envoy to Chen Xi to negotiate a ceasefire. When the court order arrived approving his report, Lu Wan carried out the "execution" of Zhang Sheng and his family members in public.

Meanwhile, the tide began to turn against Chen Xi. General Zhou Bo won a crucial victory, capturing almost all of Chen's generals. General Fan Kuai fought a heated battle against the remnants of Chen's rebel army. In the process, Chen Xi himself got killed.

From the captured generals Zhou Bo learned that Lu Wan had concluded peace deals with the Xiongnu and Chen Xi.

***

THE EMPEROR WAS LYING in his sickbed in the residential basilica when he read Zhou Bo's report marked "urgent." It filled him with sorrow and anger. He summoned Shen Yiji marquis of Biyang, now a close courtier, for advice.

Shen said, "Since Your Majesty and Lu are good friends..."

"Good friends my ass!" the Emperor cut him off impatiently. "Just tell me what I ought to do."

"Yes, Your Majesty. How about sending a close adviser to summon him? This will test his loyalty and give him a face-saving opportunity to explain himself in person."

"Who will go on this mission?"

"If Your Majesty does not mind, I will."

"All right. Pay him a visit."

Shen Yiji's Visit to Yan (195 BCE)

MARQUIS SHEN YIJI was annoyed. When he arrived in the Yan capital Ji (in the southwest of Beijing), after a two-week journey, as imperial envoy, he expected to be greeted in the western suburb by the king himself, as was required by ritual, but was received by one of King Lu Wan's advisers instead (see Map 4).

Shen asked, "Where is the king?"

"The king has asked me to apologize on his behalf," answered the adviser. "He has been bedridden because of an illness."

The next morning, Shen Yiji went to the Yan Palace for a scheduled meeting with the king. To his chagrin, he only saw the king's deputy, and was told that the king was too sick to attend the meeting. Shen then asked to see the king at home, but was turned down. He delivered the imperial summons to the deputy and retired into the government guesthouse.

The following day, King Lu Wan held a secret meeting with his trusted officials in his residence.

"I can't see Shen Yiji now," the king said.

"How about later?" asked an adviser.

"Absolutely not. Let me try to explain. Now there are only two nonroyal kings left: Wu Chen king of Changsha and myself. Changsha is firmly under the court's control through Chancellor Li Cang, and Wu Chen is an inexperienced young man who can be removed anytime. Thus I remain the only thorn in the Emperor's side. Furthermore, because of Empress Lü's schemes, the two most powerful kings were executed: Hann Xin in spring, and Peng Yue in summer. That prompted the third great king, Ying Bu, to rebel, who was subsequently murdered. Now the Emperor is sick and has already entrusted much of his decision-making power to her. I am afraid that the Empress will go out of her way to kill off the nonroyal kings and meritorious senior officials. Shen Yiji's visit has only one purpose: to get me to go to Chang'an. But if I go, that will be the end of me."

"Couldn't Your Highness see Shen Yiji at least once?" asked another adviser.

"Shen Yiji is not only the Empress's man, but also an old fox. A meeting with him will probably arouse more suspicion. So we'll just wait until he leaves."

After staying in Ji for about a week, during which he made repeated requests to see the king but in vain, Shen Yiji departed, but not before being tipped off about Lu Wan's secret meeting. As soon as he arrived in Chang'an, Shen filed a scathing report on Lu Wan's suspicious behavior.

But the Emperor still could not make up his mind. Lu Wan was his only comrade-in-arms who was born on the same day and in the same year as the Emperor.

Then a top-ranking Xiongnu defector was brought in for interrogation. He revealed another startling fact: he had spotted a Yan envoy called Zhang Sheng at the Xiongnu court!

"Are you sure about that: Zhang Sheng was at the Xiongnu court?" the Emperor asked the Xiongnu general.

"Yes, Your Majesty. Let the Sky God be my witness: I am telling the truth."

"It can't be. I personally ordered the execution of Zhang together with his family."

"Your Majesty. I am aware of those orders. However, those who were executed were not the Zhangs, but other prisoners on death row."

The Emperor was stunned. He remained speechless for a while, his face white as silk, before he dismissed the defector.

It was early afternoon, and the Emperor decided to quit his work early. He stepped outside and mounted his palanquin, which took him to his residential basilica. He motioned away the eunuchs on duty, flung himself into bed, and started sobbing. *Why Lu Wan of all people? My best friend, my childhood buddy, whom I treated like my twin brother? How could he do this to me? Working hand in gloves with my enemies Chen Xi and the Xiongnu?*

He felt deeply hurt and betrayed, yet he could not bear to take action against him. In the end, he decided to call in his wife, Empress Lü, who had known Lu Wan very well, for consultation.

"What should I do with Lu Wan?" asked he as the Empress sat down.

"Your Majesty has no choice but to act firmly against him."

"What do you mean by 'firmly?'"

"Launching a military campaign to capture or destroy him."

"But he is my buddy! We have celebrated our birthdays together every year."

"His conduct—communication with the enemy—is an unpardonable crime. If it goes unpunished, it will have serious consequences for the empire and the dynasty. The court will lose its authority, and the imperial edicts will lose their credibility."

"But the chest wound I got from the last campaign is still unhealed."

"Your Majesty does not have to go personally. Someone else can lead the campaign."

The Emperor fell silent.

After the Empress' departure, he spent a long time pacing up and down in his sanctum and mulling over her suggestion. When he realized he could no longer put off the inevitable, he sat down and started dictating an edict to an attendant gentleman on the next military operation.

***

ABOUT TWO WEEKS LATER, a massive Han army marched into Yan. It consisted of troops from the Eastern Capital Luoyang and neighboring Zhao and Dai. Upon entering the flatlands south and east of Ji, they pitched camp. Commanding Officer Fan Kuai, under heavy escort, galloped to the front to assess the situation. His on-site reconnaissance and reports from army scouts confirmed early intelligence that the city was not heavily fortified nor was it garrisoned by a large army. Thereupon, he decided to start an onslaught on the city walls and gates as early as the following morning.

This hot-blooded butcher-turned-general had not changed that much since the days when he was a Mangdang outlaw under Liu Bang. Apparently, he wanted to accomplish the task at hand as soon as possible. However, this was not due to his impetuous temper, but the reality on the ground. When the infamous Yan winter arrived in a matter of weeks, the Han troops would not be able to survive the elements, let alone besiege and sack the city.

Furthermore, he had one more reason to be in a hurry. Before he set off on the campaign he was given a secret audience by his sister-in-law, Empress Lü. He recalled with perfect clarity the way a teary-eyed Empress fell on her knees and beseeched him.

Horrified, Fan Kuai rushed to help her to her feet, saying, "Just tell me what Your Majesty wants me to do."

"I want you to help Yingying. The Emperor could replace him as crown prince anytime, so long as Ruyi is alive. Should Ruyi become Emperor, that would be the end for all of us, because his mother, that slut, will grab power for herself. And her hatred for me knows no bounds."

"Your Majesty wants to make Ruyi disappear?"

"Can you do that?"

"Yes, I think so. On my way back, I can take Handan easily and find a way to get rid of him and his mentor Zhou Chang."

"Yes, that trouble-maker has to go too. But once you accomplish your Yan mission, stay there and wait until the Emperor goes to Heaven."

Fan Kuai nodded his head in agreement....

***

AFTER FAN KUAI ARRIVED in Yan, his secret mission had kept him constantly on edge. It was far more important than the defeat and capture of Lu Wan, because so much was at stake. If he pulled it off he would be the hero who saved the Lü clan from ruin. But a single false move could send him and his family to the gallows.

For his part, King Lu Wan was surprised by the sudden arrival of such a numerous army. Although he had been in liaison with the Xiongnu, he had not had time to conclude a military pact with them. Now it was too late to request military assistance. In a panic, the king took to his heels with an entourage of several thousands, mostly his dependents, attendants, palace ladies, and other servants.

Eventually Lu Wan and his people stopped at a place just south of the Great Wall. The king climbed onto the top of a hillock, stood there, and looked at the barren landscape of the far north. Buffeted by the howling wind of early spring, suddenly he felt a pang of compunction.

"Your Highness, are we going to cross over the Great Wall?" asked an attendant gentleman accompanying him.

"And join the Xiongnu?"

"Yes?"

"No. The Han forces have not come after us. I am certain that the Emperor has no desire to destroy us. Let's stay south of the Great Wall and wait."

"For what, Your Highness?"

"For the Emperor to get better and call the shots again."

"Then what?"

"I will make a trip to Chang'an to apologize in person."

"Are you sure you want to do that, Your Highness?"

"Yes, I am absolutely sure."

"What about your followers?"

"There are villages along the Great Wall. They can be quartered there for the time being."

The gentleman took leave of the king to issue the order.

The Exalted Progenitor (195 BCE)

THE CAMPAIGN OF YAN was remarkably successful. In less than two weeks, Fan Kuai had sacked the capital Ji and captured most of the Yan territory. Then on orders from the Emperor, Fan set up Liu Jian, one of the imperial princes, as the new king of the kingdom.

With the decisive victory over Yan, the Emperor finally could enjoy some peace and quiet in Chang'an. The only trouble was the old chest wound, which caused him much pain. Then he came down with a high fever, and had to be confined to bed in the Changle Palace. His women, Empress Lü, Lady Qi, and others, took turns to attend on him.

One morning, Empress Lü came, bringing with her an elderly man. They found the Emperor asleep.

The elderly man bent over and examined the patient for a while, and said to the Empress, "His Majesty is curable."

Suddenly, the Emperor woke up and asked the stranger, "Who the fuck are you?"

"This is Doctor Wei, a famed physician," the Empress said.

"I don't need another freaking physician! Get him out of here!" the Emperor roared hoarsely.

"Your Majesty...."

"Get the fuck out!" The Emperor then fell back to sleep.

The elderly man was led out of the room.

About half an hour later, the Emperor awoke again.

The Empress asked, "Could I bring Doctor Wei back?"

"What doctor?" the Emperor asked in perplexity.

"He was here a few moments ago. You drove him out."

"Did I? Well, I am sorry. Give him 50 catties of gold, and ask him not to come back."

"Why, Your Majesty?"

"I started out as a commoner with a three-foot sword in hand, and ended up conquering the world. I haven't done too badly, have I?" he asked rhetorically, with a light smile. "Isn't that the will of Heaven? Clearly, right now my life is in the hands of Heaven. No doctors, no matter how good, can change it. It is destiny."

Empress Lü said nothing.

"There are a few lingering regrets though," the Emperor continued. "I won't live to see Ruyi grow up. You must treat him *and* his mother well. Can you promise?" The Emperor paused to look intensely into her eyes.

"Yes, I promise. Your Majesty can rest assured that they will be given the most decent treatment they deserve," said the Empress.

"All right, I will take your word for it. Then there is our son Yingying. He is still weak and indecisive."

"He has made much progress under the tutelage of the Four White-hair Recluses. He will do better over time."

"I certainly hope so. Lastly, the Xiongnu. They continue to pose a threat."

"What can be done to keep them at bay?"

"The permanent removal of the Xiongnu threat should be a long-term goal. But we are not yet in a position to do so. We still have to build a strong cavalry. For now, in dealing with them, you must avoid confrontation, and must not give them an excuse to invade. 'Lack of forbearance in small matters will upset great plans,' as Confucius says."

The Empress nodded her head. The Emperor continued, "I feel that my life's journey is coming to an end very soon. It's time to look to the future."

"Your Majesty," the Empress said, with tears brimming her eyes, "I am very worried. Chancellor Xiao He is dying. After Your Majesty's passing, who is going to take his place?"

"This is what I like about you, Wife. You take a keen interest in government. But you are unlike the other women of power who only dabble in court affairs, you possess a sharp eye for politics. As for who is going to take Xiao He's place, undoubtedly, Cao Shen."

"After Cao Shen?"

"Wang Ling, perhaps. But he is a bit dull-witted. Chen Ping can help him. By the way, Chen Ping is highly intelligent, but is a bit unprincipled, hardly the material for the top leader. Zhou Bo, on the other hand, is honest and reliable, although he lacks literary talent. Still, only he can pacify the world for the Liu house. He can serve as defender-in-chief (*taiwei*)."

"Thereafter?"

"I don't know. That's too far into the future."

The Emperor fell asleep.

***

WHEN HE WOKE UP later that night, the Emperor saw Lady Qi in a gray garment, sitting on the edge of his bed, with tears on her face.

"Treasure," the Emperor greeted her, "I haven't seen you since yesterday. How have you been?"

"Fourth Brother, help Ruyi! He is in trouble."

"He is now in Handan and should be all right. Zhou Chang will do everything he can to protect him."

"But, as soon as you pass away, General Fan Kuai will attack Handan with an army from Yan and kill Ruyi."

"What?" asked the Emperor as he struggled to raise his body. Lady Qi bent over to help him. "You heard it from our informants in the Empress' household?"

"Yes, Fourth Brother."

"Butcher Fan! You fucking bastard!" the Emperor howled in a fit of anger.

Shortly after Lady Qi left, Chen Ping and Zhou Bo were summoned to the Emperor's sickroom. With a macabre look on his face, the Emperor said, "It has come to my attention that Fan Kuai has evil intentions toward Ruyi. My source has just confirmed it. Zhou Bo, I want you to take over command of Fan's army."

"Yes, Your Majesty!" said Zhou Bo.

"Chen Ping, I want you to go there and execute Fan Kuai on the spot!" the Emperor continued.

"Yes, Your Majesty. But Fan Kuai is the brother-in-law of the Empress."

"All the more reason to kill him!" the Emperor asserted. "Can you do it?"

"Yes, of course, Your Majesty," answered Chen Ping resignedly.

Once Fan Kuai's fate was settled, Chen Ping and Zhou Bo started a discussion with the Emperor about how best to accomplish their tasks. But shortly thereafter the Emperor fell asleep. Obviously, the conversation had fatigued him. The two top officials departed, each with a previously prepared edict on silk.

***

EARLY THE NEXT MORNING on June 1st, a court lady on duty went into the Emperor's sickroom and was terrified to find him lifeless. A palace physician was summoned. After a brief examination, he concluded that His Majesty had passed away in his sleep before dawn.

Upon his burial in the Changling Tomb Park on June 23rd, in the suburb of Chang'an, the deceased Emperor was given the temple name of "Exalted Progenitor" (Gaozu).

Epilogue

WHEN THE EXALTED PROGENITOR set out to conquer all under Heaven, he was already 47 years old. A medium-built, foul-mouthed peasant with a reputation as a ne'er-do-well, a womanizer, and a drunkard, who, though literate, never cared much about literature, he seemed to have a slim chance at success at a time when all the heroes in the realm contended for power and dominance. Against all odds, he defeated his rivals to found the Han dynasty, and quelled the numerous rebellions that challenged his rule.

He assumed the reins at time when the whole realm had been ravaged by incessant warfare. Initially, it was even impossible to assemble four horses of identical color for the imperial carriage. Chancellor Xiao He, as the leader of the bureaucracy, had to ride in an ox-drawn cart to work every day.

Inspired by the teachings of Laozi, the Exalted Progenitor implemented a "hands-off" policy, with minimal taxes and government interference. Consequently, the Han, several generations later, flourished into a great empire that encompassed the entire realm and extended deep into neighboring regions with a registered population that almost topped 60 million (in 2 CE).

What sets him apart from his rivals is a rare combination of several traits. First of all, he was second to none when it came to spotting talented men. He would appoint them to high office regardless of whether they were lowly peasants or members of the old aristocracy.

Second, he was exceptionally magnanimous and open-minded. He was never stingy in giving out rewards and was always ready to adopt new changes.

Third, he was an astute strategist. For instance, he had a profound understanding of the primacy of Guanzhong, which served as his base whence to conquer the realm.

Fourth, even though never a believer in Confucianism, essentially he practiced benevolence and righteousness, which stood in sharp contrast to the wanton brutality and blatant cronyism of Xiang Yu.

Fifth, he was an unusually good listener. Whether you were a common soldier or a top adviser, he would listen to your advice carefully, and act on it if he found that it made sense.

Sixth, he was possessed of a prodigious memory. He could remember the name of anyone he had met years before, whether he be a lowly peasant, a gatekeeper or a garrison soldier, a feat that made him immensely popular.

Of course, the Exalted Progenitor was also very lucky—having been helped along the way to power by a small group of highly talented individuals—Xiao He, Cao Shen, Zhang Liang, Hann Xin, Chen Ping, Liu Jing, Li Yiji, Shusun Tong, and Lu Jia, among others.

***

THE IMMEDIATE IMPACT OF the Exalted Progenitor's passing was felt on the northern frontier, where Lu Wan and his entourage were stranded. Lu had been hoping that, as soon as the Emperor had recovered, he would make a trip to Chang'an in repentance. But that was not to be. When the news of the Emperor's death arrived, Lu Wan lost all hope of returning. So he led his entourage of several thousands in crossing over the Great Wall and joining the Xiongnu.

In Chang'an, Crown Prince Liu Ying (posthumously known as Emperor Hui) ascended the throne. He had neither time nor energy to pursue Lu Wan. Thus the former king of Yan was allowed to spend the rest of his life among the barbarians free of harassment from the Han. But the fact of the matter was that, although the new Emperor, under the tutelage of the Four Recluses, had made much progress academically, he possessed neither the will nor the force of character to stand up to his challenger—his mother, now the Empress Dowager, who was in ascendancy and seemed to enjoy much support at court.

When Chen Ping returned from his mission to Yan, at the Empress Dowager's request, he went directly to her palace. As soon as Chen Ping was brought before the Empress Dowager, he threw himself on his knees, kowtowed three times, and said beseechingly, "Your guilty subject Chen Ping is asking for punishment."

"What are you guilty of?" asked a startled Empress Dowager.

"Failure to execute Fan Kuai in situ."

"What did you do with him?"

"I brought him back to Chang'an."

"Stand up, Chancellor Chen Ping," said the Empress Dowager. "You did the right thing. In fact, I would like to thank you personally and on behalf of the court."

Addressing her attendant gentlemen, she continued, "Here is my decree: set Fan Kuai free and restore his titles and rank forthwith."

Turning to Chen Ping, who was now on his feet, she said, "We need military talents like him, don't we?"

"Absolutely," echoed Chen Ping.

***

IGNORING THE YOUNG EMPEROR'S opposition and using her power as leader of the harem, Empress Dowager Lü imprisoned Lady Qi in the Eternal Alley, the area of the harem where court ladies who had committed crimes were incarcerated. On the Empress Dowager's orders, Lady Qi was constantly wearing a prisoner's drab uniform with a cangue on her neck. Every day from dawn till dusk, she was forced to pound rice, using a mortar and a pestle.

However, the Empress Dowager's greatest concern was not Lady Qi herself, but her son Prince Ruyi. Her previous plan to assassinate him by the hands of Fan Kuai had failed because of the intervention of the Exalted Progenitor. Now that the

Exalted Progenitor was dead, nobody could prevent her from trying to do it again. She issued a summons to Ruyi, now residing in Handan in Zhao. To her surprise, the fearless Chancellor Zhou Chang defied her order, and refused to send the young prince to the capital. The Empress Dowager then issued two more summonses; both were rejected by the chancellor. In a fit of anger, she summoned Zhou Chang himself. Zhou therewith left for Chang'an—he had no choice. She then sent the fourth summons to the ten-year-old Ruyi. And the young prince went on his way.

The young Emperor, though dominated by his mother, was determined to shield Ruyi from harm. He went as far as Bashang in the eastern suburb to welcome his little half-brother and settled him in his own palace. They dined together and played together, making it impossible for the Empress Dowager to get her way.

Early one morning, the Emperor went hunting while his little brother was fast asleep. He returned about three hours later and found Ruyi lying lifeless in bed with blood oozing from his orifices. Half a dozen palace maids kneeling in front of the bed were sobbing. The young prince had just been killed by poisoned wine.

The Emperor Liu Ying was overcome with sorrow and could not hold court for days following his half-brother's death. Eventually, when he made his appearance at court again, he was asked by his mother to see a "human pig." Before he knew it, he was led to a pigsty where he was horrified to see a human body without sight and hearing wallowing in mud. The Empress Dowager then said coldly, "This is Lady Qi, Ruyi's mother." At that, the Emperor broke down and sobbed violently.

While the Empress Dowager's inveterate hatred for the "slut" could explain her heinous act against her, it is anybody's guess why she wanted to traumatize her son with the horrific image of the mutilated body. Whatever the reason, because of this experience, for more than a year, the Emperor Liu Ying was unable to hold court once. He then submitted a request to abdicate, which was rejected by the Empress Dowager. Eventually, however, mother and son worked out a compromise. The Emperor would hold on to his imperial title while the Empress Dowager would take over the reins as regent.

The young Emperor continued to live in the palace, spending much of his time drinking until he passed away at age 22.

The Empress Dowager then placed a toddler on the throne. He was allegedly the son of the deceased Emperor Liu Ying (Emperor Hui). But, as rumor had it, the toddler was the descendant of an unrelated woman, who had been killed by the Empress Dowager's hatchet men. However, that was hardly the issue. The boy, who was still in his swaddling clothes, was too young to rule. In fact, the Empress reigned in her own right, and the reign period was named after her not the toddler.

The biggest challenge for the Empress Dowager came from the outside. The Xiongnu *chanyu* Modu, who had come close to capturing the Exalted Progenitor, had little respect for his wife, the new ruler. In a letter, delivered by a Xiongnu emissary, the *chanyu* requested the hand of another Han princess, and hinted in unembellished terms at the possibility of having some fun with the Empress Dowager for the sake of Xiongnu-Han friendship.

An incensed Empress Dowager summoned a special meeting of her top military officers. The issues under discussion included whether the court should execute the *chanyu*'s emissary and invade Xiongnu. General Fan Kuai was the first to speak, offering to lead an army of 100,000 to attack the Xiongnu in their lair. That triggered a raucous debate among the officers. At length, the Empress Dowager did not follow her brother-in-law's proposal, and instead sent her own emissary to Xiongnu to conclude one more marriage alliance. In spite of her anger, she realized that the Han military was still no match for the Xiongnu cavalry. The *chanyu* Modu jumped at the chance. It was hoped that henceforth the northern frontier would be free from Xiongnu raids for a long time.

This allowed the Empress Dowager to focus attention on the domestic front. When the toddler Emperor was about four years old, someone told him about the death of his birthmother. The little boy was brought to tears. He pounded the table with his tiny fist, vowing to revenge her death when he grew up. Soon the Empress Dowager got wind of it, and had him removed from the throne and later killed. Another toddler was then placed on the throne. And the Empress Dowager continued to rule unchallenged.

For the remainder of her rule, the Empress Dowager was obsessed with a desire to bolster the power of her own Lü clan. A separate Ancestral Temple was set up to honor her own ancestors, and three male members of the Lü clan were made kings, which was clearly a violation of the rule that "no one of nonroyal descent should be allowed to be king" laid down by the Exalted Progenitor himself. But that was precisely her point. She wanted to make her own clan so powerful that she would be able to pass the reins on to a *Lü*, putting an end to the dominance of the *Lius* for good. The timing was propitious as well, because hardly any senior officials were likely to stand in her way. In fact, although many were disillusioned, hardly anyone had the guts to voice their dissent.

Lu Jia, for instance, was so discouraged by what he saw that gave up his work on philosophy, resigned his official posts, and moved out of the capital. He divided up much of the wealth he had received after his Nanyue mission among his five sons, all of whom were married and had their own households. He then took turns to live with them, promising that whoever housed him at the time of his death would inherit the rest of his riches, which were still substantial. But of course, being filial, the sons and daughter-in-laws would have welcomed him even without the promise.

It is important to note that by then Xiao He, Cao Shen, and Zhang Liang had all passed on. Concerning Zhang Liang, I must add that, for a long time, he had lived in reclusive retirement. As a pious practitioner of the Huangdi-Laozi cult, he led a content, low-profiled life. Before he died he managed to make a trip to the Gucheng Mountain (southwest of Jinan and Pingyin, Shandong). At the foot of the mountain, he found a smooth-faced yellow stone. As he stood in front of it, he could feel the presence of the grotesque-looking old man he had met on the Xiapi Bridge, who had given him the *Taigong's Art of War*. Zhang Liang then had the stone moved to his home and passed away shortly thereafter. Following the instructions of his will, the yellow stone was buried with him.

In the end, only one person, Wang Ling, openly objected to the Empress Dowager's scheme. But the Empress Dowager was undaunted and soon found an excuse to strip Wang of his substantive powers. Chen Ping and Zhou Bo, it would seem, had finally gone over to the Empress' camp, much to the chagrin of Wang Ling.

Unbeknownst to the Empress dowager and other Lüs, however, Lu Jia, although officially in retirement, still maintained active contact with his former colleagues. On a secret visit to Chen Ping, he revealed his plan for the revival of the Liu house and persuaded Chen Ping to join him. Acting on this plan, Chen Ping, the top leader of the bureaucracy, formed a secret alliance with Zhou Bo, the top leader of the military.

Before long, the Empress dowager fell ill and, after a terrifying encounter with a monster, later identified as the ghost of Prince Ruyi, expired.

*　*　*

IN THE HAIR-RAISING showdown between the Lü camp and the anti-Lü camp that followed, the latter gained the upper hand, after Zhou Bo had seized control of the military. Chen Ping's support as head of officialdom guaranteed a relatively smooth transfer of power.

Prince Liu Heng was then chosen as the Emperor (posthumously known as Emperor Wen). Emperor Wen was the Exalted Progenitor's son by Consort Bo, who had been Wei Bao's wife before being accepted as the Exalted Progenitor's consort. So by now, the physiognomist Xu Fu's prophecy was finally fulfilled, and Bo's son became a man of great nobility.

Emperor Wen turned out to be a great ruler. In his reign the Han was more peaceful and prosperous than ever. Under his son, Liu Qi (Emperor Jing), peace and prosperity continued.

But Emperor Jing's rule was soon challenged by Liu Pi, the prince with that "rebel look," whose kingdom of Wu, like several other kingdoms ruled by the imperial princes, had slipped out of the court's control over time. When Emperor Jing confronted them, they started a civil war known in history as the Rebellion of the Seven Kingdoms (in 154 BCE). In the end, the generals (especially Luan Bu who had been serving as chancellor and leading military officer in the kingdom of Yan) sided with the Emperor. This enabled him to crush the rebellion, reassert central authority, and ensure that the transfer of power to his son Liu Che, Emperor Wu, was peaceful (see Map 5).

In spite of his cruel streak, Emperor Wu was the one who broke the dominance of the Xiongnu on the northern frontier, and embraced Confucianism as the only state-sanctioned philosophy.

However, it was the Exalted Progenitor Liu Bang who laid the groundwork for Han ascendancy that has persisted to this day, 289 years since the founding of the dynasty!

Bibliography

Bielenstein, Hans. *The Bureaucracy of Han Times*. Cambridge: Cambridge UP, 1980.

Dubs, Homer H., trans. *The History of the Former Han Dynasty*, vol. 1. Baltimore: Waverly, 1938.

Lewis, Mark Edward. *The Early Chinese Empires: Qin and Han*. Cambridge, MA: Belknap, 2007.

Nienhauser, William H. Jr., ed. *The Grand Scribe's Records*. Weiguo Cao et al., trans., vol. 2: *The Basic Annals of Han China*. Bloomington: Indiana UP, 2002.

Sima, Qian / Watson, Burton, trans. *Records of the Grand Historian: Han Dynasty I*. New York: Columbia UP, 1993.

Twitchett, Denis, and Michael Loewe, eds. *The Cambridge History of China*. Vol. 1: The Ch'in and Han Empires, 221 BC–AD 220. Cambridge: Cambridge UP, 1986.

Chronology

770–476 BCE Spring and Autumn (SA) Period

475–221 Warring States (WS) Period

221–207 Qin Dynasty

221 The First Emperor founds the Qin dynasty.

218 Zhang Liang 張良 makes a failed attempt on the life of the First Emperor.

214 Qin dislodges the Xiongnu from Henandi 河南地 and builds the Great Wall.

213 The First Emperor orders the burning of books.

212 The First Emperor orders a large labor force to build palaces in Guanzhong 關中 and elsewhere, including the Epang 阿房 Palace in Xi'an; executes 460-plus scholars.

210 The First Emperor dies. His son Huhai 胡亥 is placed on the throne by Li Si 李斯 and Zhao Gao 趙高.
Fusu 扶蘇 is ordered to commit suicide.

209 Chen Sheng 陳勝 and Wu Guang 吳廣 rebel; Chen declares himself king.
Liu Bang 劉邦 rebels in north Jiangsu.
Xiang Liang 項梁 and Xiang Yu 項羽 (Xiang Ji) rebel in south Jiangsu.

207 Huhai is killed in a palace coup, succeeded by Ziying 子嬰.
Liu Bang conquers Guanzhong and enters Xianyang 咸陽; Qin falls.

206 Liu Bang survives the Hongmen banquet and flees to Hanzhong 漢中.
Xiang Yu enfeoffs various warlords as kings, including Liu Bang as king of Han.

206–202	Chu-Han War.
205	Han general Hann Xin 韓信 defeats the Wei army under King Wei Bao 魏豹 and annexes Wei.
	Liu Bang sacks Pengcheng 彭城 before being routed by Xiang Yu.
	Hann Xin defeats the Zhao army under Chen Yu 陳餘 at the battle of the Jingxing Pass 井陘關 .
204	Liu Bang leaves Xingyang 滎陽 , his de facto capital in the Central Plain; Xingyang falls to Xiang Yu.
	Liu Bang's adviser Li Yiji 酈食其 persuades Tian Guang 田廣 king of Qi to submit.
	Han general Hann Xin, advised by Kuai Che 蒯徹 , attacks and conquers much of Qi territory, causing Li Yiji's death.
	Liu Bang and his rival Xiang Yu meet in Guangwu and exchange accusations.
203	Han general Hann Xin defeats Qi and Chu forces at the battle of Gaomi 高密 and conquers Qi. Liu Bang launches the final campaign against Xiang Yu; Peng Yue and Hann Xin join the campaign after being granted enfeoffments.
202	Defeated by Liu Bang, Xiang Yu takes his own life at Wujiang 烏江 .
	Liu Bang founds the [Western] Han and reigns as its first emperor (r. 202–195 BCE).
	Zang Tu 臧荼 king of Yan declares independence before he is captured and killed.

202 BCE–8 CE Western Han Dynasty

201 BCE	Hann Xin is humiliated and demoted.
	Hannwang Xin 韓王信 king of Hann joins Xiongnu against Han. Siege of Baideng 白登 .
199	First marriage alliance (proposed by Liu Jing 劉敬) with the Xiongnu *chanyu* Modu 冒頓 .

197–196	Chen Xi 陳豨 War
196	Hann Xin is executed.
	Hannwang Xin is killed in battle.
	Peng Yue is executed.
	Lu Jia 陸賈 visits Zhao Tuo 趙佗 and confers on Zhao on behalf of Han the title of king of Nanyue 南越.
	Ying Bu 英布 War.
195	Lu Wan 盧綰 king of Yan plans to defect to Xiongnu.
	Liu Bang dies.
	Liu Ying 劉盈 (Emperor Hui 惠帝; r. 195–188 BCE) succeeds, but Empress Dowager Lü 呂太后 holds power.
187–180	Empress Dowager Lü rules in her own right.
180	Empress Dowager Lü dies; power returns to the Lius after the Lüs have been purged.
	Liu Heng 劉恆 (Emperor Wen 文帝; r. 180–157 BCE) succeeds.
157	Liu Qi 劉啟 (Emperor Jing 景帝; r. 157–141 BCE) succeeds.
141	Liu Che 劉徹 (Emperor Wu 武帝; r. 141–87 BCE) succeeds.

8–23 CE   Wang Mang's 王莽 Xin Dynasty

25–220   Eastern Han Dynasty

Glossary

___ (underline): present-day place name

bold: key term

cap.: capital (*du* 都)

co.: county (*xian* 縣)

com.: commandery (*jun* 郡)

mts.: mountains

pal.: palace (*gong* 宮)

plc.: place; settlement

SA: Spring and Autumn (the period before the Warring States)

WS: Warring States (the period before the Qin dynasty)

Pronunciation

a = a as in f**a**thers

c = zz as in pi**zz**a

ch = ch as in **ch**ina

e or ê = olo as in c**olo**nel without the *r* sound (except after i, u or ü, y)

e (after i, u or ü, y) = e as in r**e**d

er = er as in dinn**er** (Am.)

i = ee as in d**ee**d (except after sibilants: c, ch, s, shi, z, zh)

i (after sibilants: c, ch, s, shi, z, zh) = the vowelized sound of the consonant

j = g as in **g**ee

o = o as in f**o**reign

q = ch as in **ch**eese (approx.)

u = oo as in f**oo**d (except after j, q, x)

u (after j, q, x) = ü (Ger. umlaut)

ü = ü (Ger. umlaut)

x = ch as in i**ch** (Ger.), or *sh* as in **sh**eep (approx.)

z = ds as in wor**ds**

zh = j, as in **J**oe (approx.)

- Anyang 安陽 : co. Seat: in north <u>Henan</u>.
- Anyi /än-yē/ 安邑 : capital of Wei (northwest of <u>Xiaxian</u>, southwest <u>Shanxi</u>).
- Ao Granary (Aocang /ao-tsäng/ 敖倉): northeast of <u>Xingyang</u>, <u>Henan</u>.
- Bai Qi /bai chē/ 白起 : Qin top general.
- **Baideng** 白登 Hill: northeast of Pingcheng.
- Baili Xi /bai-lē shē/ 百里奚 : Qin chancellor in Spring and Autumn times.
- Baoye Vale 褒斜谷 : in Hanzhong.
- **Bashang** /bä-shäng/ 霸上 : plc. southeast of Xianyang.
- Ben He /ben hê/ 賁赫 : counselor under Ying Bu.
- Bi 畢 (Net): stellar lodge.
- Boji 薄姬 . *See* Madam Bo.
- Canhe /tsan-hê/ 參合 : town in the northernmost part of <u>Shanxi</u>.
- Cao Jiu 曹咎 : Xiang Yu's general.
- **Cao Shen** /tsao shen/ 曹參 (–190 BCE): Liu Bang's top official.
- Chai Wu 柴武 : top general under Liu Bang.
- **Chang'an** 長安 : Han capital in <u>Xi'an</u>, <u>Shaanxi</u>.
- Changle 長樂 (Long-lasting Joy) Palace: in Chang'an. *See also* Xingle 興樂 .
- Changshan /chäng-shän/ 常山 : commandery; known as Hengshan 恆山 until 179 BCE.
- Changyi /chäng-yē/ 昌邑 : co. Seat: south of <u>Juye</u>, <u>Shandong</u>.
- *chanyu* /chän-yü/ 單于 : king of the Xiongnu tribal confederation.
- **Chen Ping** 陳平 (–178 BCE): Liu Bang's top adviser; Marquis of Quni 曲逆 (<u>Shunping</u>, <u>Hebei</u>).
- **Chen Sheng** /chen shêng/ 陳勝 (–208 BCE): late Qin rebel leader.
- **Chen Xi** /chen shē/ 陳豨 (–196 BCE): superior chancellor (*xiangguo* / shēängguoh/ 相國) of Zhao.
- Chen Yu /chen yü/ 陳餘 : late Qin rebel leader; friend of Zhang Er.
- Chen Ze /chen dzeh/ 陳澤 : Zhang Er's general.
- Chen 陳 : com. Seat: <u>Huaiyang</u>, <u>Henan</u>.

- Chen 郴 : co. Seat: <u>Chenzhou</u>, south <u>Hunan</u>.
- Chencang /chen-tsäng/ 陳倉 : co. Seat: east of <u>Baoji</u>, <u>Shaanxi</u>.
- **Chenggao** 成皋 : town west of <u>Xingyang</u>, <u>Henan</u>.
- Chengwu 成武 : co. Seat: southeast of Dingtao (in southwest <u>Shandong</u>).
- Chenliu 陳留 : co. Seat: southeast of <u>Kaifeng</u>, <u>Henan</u>
- Chiyou /chih-you/ 蚩尤 : militant sovereign of far antiquity.
- Chu Huaiwang 楚懷王 . *See* King Huai of Chu.
- **Chu** 楚 : state in the central and lower valleys of the Yangzi vanquished by Qin (223 BCE) and revived by Xiang Liang and Xiang Yu.
- *Classic of Documents* (Shujing 書經): Confucian classic.
- *Classic of Songs* (Shijing 詩經): Confucian classic.
- commandery (*jun* 郡): one of the dozens of local administrative divisions.
- community head (*tingzhang* /ting-jang/ 亭長): WS–Qin-Han unranked grass-roots leader.
- Concubine Yú (Yuji /yü-jē/ 虞姬): Xian Yu's lover.
- Cong 樅 . *See* General Cong.
- Consort Li (Liji /lē-jē/ 驪姬): Duke Xian of Jin's 晉獻公 consort; femme fatale.
- Dai Vale 代谷 : in <u>Fanshi, Shanxi</u>.
- Daliang /dä-lēäng/ 大梁 : cap. of WS Wei to 225 BCE; NW of <u>Kaifeng</u>, <u>Henan</u>. *See* Xunyi.
- Dang /däng/ 碭 : com. Seat: south of <u>Shangqiu</u>, <u>Henan</u>.
- Dapple (Zhui /jui/ 騅): Xiang Yu's warhorse.
- Daze /dä-dzeh/ 大澤 Township (*xiang* 鄉): in <u>Suzhou</u>, <u>Anhui</u>; southwest of <u>Xuzhou</u>, <u>Jiangsu</u>.
- *ding* 鼎 : bronze ritual vessel with three (tripod) or four legs (quadripod).
- Dingtao 定陶 : co. Seat: northwest of <u>Dingtao</u>, <u>Shandong</u>.
- Dong Yi 董翳 (King of Di 翟): Qin general; enfeoffed by Xiang Yu.
- Dong 東 : com. in west <u>Shandong</u> and north <u>Henan</u>.
- Dong'e /dong-ê/ 東阿 : co. Seat: south of <u>Liaocheng</u>, <u>Shandong</u>.

- Dongcheng 東城 : co. Seat: northwest of <u>Chuzhou</u>, <u>Anhui</u>.

- Donghu 東胡 : nomadic people in <u>Manchuria</u>.

- Dongyuan 東垣 : co. Seat: northeast of <u>Shijiazhuang</u>, <u>Hebei</u>.

- Duke Xian of Jin (Jin Xiangong /jin shian-gong/ 晉獻公) (–651 BCE): SA sovereign of Jin.

- Emperor Jing. *See* Liu Che 劉啟 .

- Emperor Wen. *See* Liu Heng 劉恆 .

- Emperor Wu. *See* Liu Qi 劉徹 .

- **Empress Lü** (Lühou 呂后) (241–180 BCE; r. 187–180 BCE) [Ms. Lü; Empress Dowager Lü]: wife of Liu Bang; mother of Liu Ying 劉盈 .

- Epang /ê-päng/ 阿房 : pal. built by the First Emperor in Xianyang.

- Exalted Progenitor. *See* Liu Bang 劉邦 .

- **Fan Kuai** 樊噲 (242–189 BCE): Liu Bang's general; brother-in-law of Empress Lü.

- Fan Li 范蠡 : Yue top official.

- **Fan Zeng** /fän dzêng/ 范增 (278–204 BCE) [Second Father]: chief counselor of Xiang Liang and Xiang Yu.

- **Feng** 豐 : co. Seat: west of <u>Peixian</u>, <u>Jiangsu</u>; Liu Bang's hometown.

- **First Emperor** (259–210 BCE) [Ying Zheng 嬴政 ; Qin Shihuang 秦始皇]: founding emperor of the Qin dynasty.

- Four White-hair Recluses of Mount Shang (Shangshan sihao 商山四皓): four famous Qin scholars who served as Crown Prince Liu Ying's mentors.

- Fuchai 夫差 : King of Wu in SA times.

- Fusu 扶蘇 : the First Emperor's eldest son.

- Gaixia /gai-shёä/ 垓下 : plc. SE of <u>Lingbi</u>, <u>Anhui</u>; location of the last battle between Chu and Han that ended Xiang Yu's life (202 BCE).

- Gaomi 高密 : co. Seat: NW of <u>Gaomi</u>, <u>Shandong</u>.

- Gaoyang 高陽 : township SW of <u>Qixian</u>, <u>Henan</u>.

- Gaozu 高祖 . *See* Liu Bang.

- General Cong /tsong/ 樅 : Liu Bang's general.

- Goujian 勾踐 : King of Yue in SA times.

- Gouzhu /gou-ju/ 勾住 Mountains: north and west of <u>Daixian</u>, <u>Shanxi</u>.

- Gu River 谷水 : it flowed from the west of Pengcheng, and joined the Si River 泗水 at Pengcheng.

- Guan Gao 貫高 : chancellor of the Han kingdom of Zhao.

- Guan Ying 灌嬰 : Liu Bang's top general.

- Guangwu 廣武 : plc. NE of <u>Xingyang</u>, <u>Henan</u>.

- **Guanzhong** /guän-jong/ 關中 : Wei River valley in south <u>Shaanxi</u>.

- Guling 固陵 : co. Seat: south of <u>Taikang</u>, in central <u>Henan</u>.

- *hai* 醢 : paste made from human flesh.

- Han Wudi 漢武帝 . *See* Liu Che 劉徹 .

- **Han** 漢 : dynasty founded by Liu Bang in 202 BCE.

- **Handan** 邯鄲 : Zhao cap. (in south <u>Hebei</u>).

- Hangu 函谷 Pass: east of <u>Lingbao</u>, <u>Henan</u>.

- Hann 韓 [Han]: WS state in south <u>Henan</u>.

- Hann Cheng 韓成 (–206 BCE): King of Hann, killed by Xiang Yu.

- Hann Fei /hän fei/ 韓非 : 1. Qin Legalist. 2. *Hann Fei*: collection of writings by Hann Fei.

- Hann Guang /hän guäng/ 韓廣 : King of Yan; King of Liaodong 遼東 .

- **Hann Xin** /hän shēn/ 韓信 (231–196 BCE): Liu Bang's general-in-chief; King of Qi; King of Chu; Marquis of Huaiyin. *See also*: Hannwang Xin.

- **Hannwang Xin** /hän-wäng shēn/ 韓王信 (–196 BCE) [King of Hann; Hann Xin]: Hann royal; Liu Bang's general.

- **Hanzhong** 漢中 : southernmost part of <u>Shaanxi</u> (south of Guanzhong).

- Henandi 河南地 : area south of the Heshui in the northern part of the <u>Ordos</u> <u>Loop</u>.

- Hong Conduit (Honggou 鴻溝): canal from <u>Kaifeng</u> to <u>Huaiyang</u>, <u>Henan</u>.

- **Hongmen** 鴻門 : plc. east of Xianyang; venue of the Hongmen banquet (206 BCE).

- Hu Zhe /hu jê/ 扈輒 : general under Peng Yue.

- Huainan 淮南 : kingdom renamed from Jiujiang 九江 in 203 BCE.

- Huaiyin 淮陰 : co. Seat: east of <u>Qingjiang</u>, <u>Jiangsu</u>.

- Huangdi 黃帝 . *See* Yellow Emperor.

- **Huhai** /hu-hai/ 胡亥 (230–207 BCE): second emperor of the Qin.

- Ji Xin /jē shēn/ 紀信 : Liu Bang's general.

- Jiang Taigong /jiäng taigong/ 姜太公 [Taigong]: late Shang and early Zhou strategist.

- Jianglü 將閭 . *See* Prince Jianglü.

- Jin Xiangong 晉獻公 . *See* Duke Xian of Jin.

- Jing 荊 : kingdom south of the Huai, headed by Liu Jia 劉賈 .

- Jingju 景駒 . *See* King Jingju.

- Jingxing /jēng-shēng/ 井陘 Pass: west of <u>Shijiazhuang</u>, <u>Hebei</u>.

- Jinyang /jēn-yäng/ 晉陽 : seat of Taiyuan com., SW of <u>Taiyuan</u>, <u>Shanxi</u>.

- Jiujiang 九江 : kingdom in north Anhui, headed by Ying Bu 英布 ; capital: Lù 六 .

- Jiuyuan 九原 : com. in the <u>Ordos</u> <u>Loop</u>.

- Julu 巨鹿 : com. Seat: east of <u>Xingtai</u>, south <u>Hebei</u>.

- Juye /jü-yeh/ 鉅野 Moors: north of <u>Juye</u>, <u>Shandong</u>.

- King Huai of Chu (Chu Huaiwang 楚懷王): 1. (–296 BCE): kidnapped by Qin in 299 BCE. 2. (–206 BCE) [Xiong Xin 熊心]: descendant of 1, set up by Xiang Liang 項梁 as Chu king; later named Yidi /yi-di/ 義帝 (Righteous Emperor).

- King Jingju (Jingju Wang /jing-jü wang/ 景駒王): Chu king set up by a former general of Chen Sheng.

- **Kuai Che** 蒯徹 (fl. 203–196 BCE) [Kuai Tong 蒯通]: Hann Xin's close adviser.

- **Kuaiji** (Guiji) 會稽 : com. Seat: <u>Suzhou</u>, <u>Jiangsu</u>.

- **Lady Qi** (Qi Furen /chē fu-ren/ 戚夫人) (–194 BCE): Liu Bang's concubine; Liu Ruyi's mother.

- *li* 里 [measure of distance]: 1 *li* was slightly shorter than half a kilometer (or 0.31 mile) in Qin and Han times.

- Li Bing /lē ~/ 李冰 : Qin governor of Shu Commandery.

- Li Cang /lē tsäng/ 利蒼 : chancellor of Changsha under Wu Chen.

- Li Shang /lē shäng/ 酈商 : Li Yiji's brother; Liu Bang's general.

- **Li Si** /lē sih/ 李斯 (284–208 BCE): Qin chancellor.
- **Li Yiji** /lē yē-jē/ 酈食其 (–204 BCE) [Lord of Guangye /guäng-yeh/ 廣野]: chief adviser of Liu Bang.
- Li You 李由 : Li Si's son; governor of Sanchuan Commandery.
- Li Zuoche /dzuo-chê/ 李左車 [Lord of Guangwu 廣武]: Zhao strategist.
- Licheng 歷城 : town in Jinan, Shandong.
- Liji 驪姬 . *See* Consort Li.
- Linxiang /lēn-shēäng/ 臨湘 : co. Seat: Changsha, Hunan; cap. of the kingdom of Changsha.
- Linzi /lēn-dzih/ 臨淄 : Qi cap. in east Shandong.
- Liu 留 : co. Seat: southeast of Peixian, Jiangsu.
- **Liu Bang** /lēu-bäng/ 劉邦 (256–195 BCE; r. 202–195 BCE) [Lord of Pei; King of Han; Gaozu 高祖 (Exalted Progenitor)]: founder of the Han dynasty.
- Liu Che 劉徹 (157–87 BCE; r.141–87 BCE): son of Liu Qi 劉啟 ; Emperor Wu of Han (Han Wudi 漢武帝).
- Liu Fei 劉肥 : Liu Bang's non-heir son by Ms. Cao /tsao/ 曹 ; King of Qi.
- Liu Heng 劉恆 (203–157 BCE; r. 180–157 BCE): Liu Bang's son by Madam Bo 薄 ; Emperor Wen of Han (Han Wendi 漢文帝).
- Liu Jia 劉賈 : Liu Bang's cousin; King of Jing 荊 .
- Liu Jian 劉建 : Liu Bang's non-heir son; King of Yan 燕 .
- Liu Jiao 劉交 : Liu Bang's brother; King of Chu 楚 .
- **Liu Jing** 劉敬 (fl. 202–199 BCE) [Lou Jing 婁敬]: Liu Bang's top adviser; Marquis of Jianxin /jian-shin/ 建信 .
- **Liu Luyuan** /lēu lu-yüan/ 劉魯元 (*ca.* 218 BCE–) [Yuanyuan]: daughter of Liu Bang and Empress Lü.
- Liu Pi 劉濞 : Liu Bang's nephew; King of Wu 吳 .
- Liu Qi /chē/ 劉啟 (r. 157–141 BCE): son of Liu Heng 劉恆 ; Emperor Jing of Han (Han Jingdi 漢景帝).
- Liu Ruyi 劉如意 (-194 BCE): son of Liu Bang by Lady Qi.

- Liu Xi /lēu shē/ 劉喜 (Liu Bang's elder brother); King of Dai 代 .
- **Liu Ying** 劉盈 (*ca.* 211–188 BCE) [Emperor Hui of Han (Han Huidi 漢惠帝); Yingying]: son of Liu Bang and Empress Lü.
- Long Ju /~ jü/ 龍且 : Xiang Yu's top general.
- Lord of Xinling /shin-ling/ 信陵 : famous nobleman in the WS state of Wei.
- Lou Jing 婁敬 . *See* Liu Jing 劉敬 .
- Lu Jia 陸賈 (ca. 240–170 BCE): Liu Bang's emissary to Nayue; thinker.
- Lü Matong 呂馬童 : Xiang Yu's officer who joins Liu Bang.
- **Lu Wan** /lu wan/ 盧綰 (–194 BCE): Liu Bang's close friend and follower; King of Yan 燕 .
- Lü Ze /lü dzê/ 呂則 : Liu Bang's general; Empress Lü's elder brother.
- Lù 六 [Lu]: co. Seat: north of <u>Lu'anshi</u>, <u>Anhui</u>.
- Luan Bu 欒布 : friend of Peng Yue; Han general.
- Lühou 呂后 . *See* Empress Lü.
- **Luoyang** 洛陽 : city east of <u>Luoyang</u>, <u>Henan</u>.
- Madam Bo (Boji 薄姬): concubine of Wei Bao 魏豹 ; consort of Liu Bang.
- Mangdang /mäng-däng/ 芒碭 : mts. that lie in four modern provinces: <u>Henan</u>, <u>Anhui</u>, <u>Shandong</u>, and <u>Jiangsu</u>.
- Manqiu Chen /män-chēu chen/ 曼丘臣 : general under Hannwang Xin and Chen Xi.
- Mao 昴 (Mane): stellar lodge.
- Mayi /mä-yē/ 馬邑 : co. Seat: <u>Shuozhoushi</u>, north <u>Shanxi</u>.
- Meng Tian /mêng tēän/ 蒙恬 : Qin general.
- Meng Yi /mêng yē/ 蒙毅 : Qin senior official; Meng Tian's brother.
- **Modu** /moh du/ 冒頓 (–174 BCE): Xiongnu *chanyu* after Touman.
- Mr. Xue /shüeh/ 薛 : former chancellor of the kingdom of Chu.
- Ms. Lü. *See* Empress Lü.
- Ms. Qi. *See* Lady Qi.
- Nanshan 南山 . *See* South Mountains.

- Nanyang 南陽 : com. in <u>Nanyang</u> (in <u>Henan</u>), <u>Suizhou</u> (in <u>Hubei</u>) et al.
- Nanyue /nän-yüeh/ 南越 : state founded by Zhao Tuo. It lay in <u>Guangdong</u>, <u>Guangxi</u>, and north <u>Vietnam</u>.
- Nanzheng /nän-jêng/ 南鄭 : co. Seat: in south <u>Shaanxi</u>.
- *New Discourses* (Xinyu /shin-yü/ 新語): book by Lu Jia 陸賈 .
- Panyu /pän-yü/ 番禺 : co.; town (co. seat; com. seat) in <u>Guangzhou</u>, <u>Guangdong</u>.
- **Pei** 沛 : co. Seat: in <u>Peixian</u>, <u>Jiangsu</u>; north of Pengcheng; Liu Bang's adopted hometown.
- **Peng Yue** 彭越 (–196 BCE): chancellor of Wei; King of Liang 梁 .
- **Pengcheng** 彭城 : cap. of Xiang Yu in <u>Xuzhou</u>, <u>Jiangsu</u>.
- Pingcheng 平城 : town northeast of <u>Datong</u>, <u>Shanxi</u>.
- Pingyuan 平原 : co. Seat: south of <u>Pingyuan</u>, <u>Shandong</u>.
- Poyang /po-yäng/ 番陽 : co. Seat: northeast of Poyang, north Jiangxi.
- Prince Jianglü /jēäng-lü/ 將閭 : Qin prince.
- Puban 蒲坂 : plc. in <u>Yongji</u>, <u>Shanxi</u>.
- Qi Furen 戚夫人 . *See* Lady Qi.
- Qin /chēn/ 秦 : 1. Zhou state based in <u>Shaanxi</u>. 2. first imperial dynasty based on the state of Qin.
- Qin Shihuang 秦始皇 . *See* First Emperor.
- Qing Bu /chēng bu/ 黥布 . *See* Ying Bu.
- Qingyi /chēng-yē/ 青衣 : co. Seat: <u>Leshan</u>, <u>Sichuan</u>.
- Ren Xiao /ren shēao/ 任囂 : Qin general.
- Righteous Emperor. *See* King Huai of Chu 2.
- Robber Zhi [dao Zhi /dao jih/ 盜蹠]: most notorious robber of the SA period.
- Sanchuan 三川 : com. in north and NW <u>Henan</u>. Seat: Luoyang.
- Second Father. *See* Fan Zeng 范增 .
- Shangshan sihao 商山四皓 . *See* Four White-hair Recluses of Mount Shang.
- Shang 上 : com. in east Shaanxi.

- Shaqiu /shä-chēu/ 沙丘 Palace: south of <u>Julu</u>, <u>Hebei</u>.

- Shen Buhai 申不害 : Hann Legalist philosopher of the WS period.

- **Shen Yiji** 審食其 (–177 BCE) [Marquis of Biyang 辟陽]: favorite courtier of Empress Lü.

- Shen 參 (Triaster): stellar lodge.

- *Shijing* 詩經 . See *Classic of Songs.*

- *Shujing* 書經 . See *Classic of Documents.*

- **Shusun Tong** 叔孫通 (fl. 202–196 BCE) [Lord of Jisi 稷嗣]: ritual scholar and official.

- Si River 汜水 : it ran past Chenggao (in east <u>Henan</u>).

- Si River 泗水 : it ran by Pengcheng, Xiapi, etc. (in <u>Jiangsu</u>).

- Sima Ang /sih-mä äng/ 司馬卬 : enfeoffed by Xiang Yu as king of Yin 殷 .

- Sima Xin /sih-mä shēn/ 司馬欣 [Saiwang 塞王 (King of Sai)]: Qi general; enfeoffed by Xiang Yu.

- Sishui /sih-shui/: 1. 泗水 : plc. east of <u>Peixian</u>, <u>Jiangsu</u>. *Cf.* Si River. 2. *See* Si River 汜水 ; Si River 泗水 .

- Song Yi 宋義 (–207 BCE): Chu top general.

- South Mountains [Nanshan 南山 ; Zhongnanshan 終南山]: the Qinling Mountains in south <u>Shanxi</u>.

- Sui He /sui hê/ 隨何 (fl. 205 BCE): Liu Bang's envoy to Ying Bu 英布 .

- Suiyang /sui-yäng/ 睢陽 : co. Seat: south of <u>Shangqiu</u>, <u>Henan</u>.

- Sun Bin 孫臏 : Sun Wu's descendant; Qi strategist in WS times.

- Taiyuan 太原 : com. in <u>Shanxi</u>.

- Three Article Code (*yuefa sanzhang* 約法三章): laws Liu Bang first issued in Xianyang in 207 BCE.

- Tian Guang /tēän guäng/ 田廣 (–204 BCE): King of Qi.

- Tian Heng /tēän hêng/ 田橫 (–202 BCE): younger brother of Tian Rong; King of Qi.

- Tian Ken 田肯 : Liu Bang's counselor.

- Tian Rong 田榮 : Qi general; father of Tian Guang.

- *tingzhang* /tēng-jäng/ 亭長 . *See*: community head

- Tongdi 銅鞮 : plc. south of <u>Qinxian</u>, <u>Shanxi</u>.

- Touman 頭曼 (−209 BCE): Xiongnu *chanyu*; father of Modu 冒頓 .

- Tu Sui 屠睢 : Qin general.

- Waihuang /wai-huäng/ 外黃 : co. Seat: northwest of <u>Minquan</u>, <u>Henan</u>.

- Wang Chong 王充 : leading philosopher of the Eastern Han.

- Wang Huang 王黃 : general under Hannwang Xin and Chen Xi.

- Wang Jian 王翦 : Qin general.

- Wang Ling 王陵 : Han senior official.

- Wang Yi 王翳 : Han officer.

- Wei Bao 魏豹 (−204 BCE): King of [West] Wei.

- Wei Jiu 魏咎 : King of Wei under Chen Sheng.

- Wéi River 濰水 : it ran past <u>Gaomi</u>, <u>Shandong</u>.

- Wei Wuzhi /wei wu-jih/ 魏無知 : Liu Bang's adviser.

- Wen Zhong /wen jong/ 文種 : SA Yue top official; forced to commit suicide.

- Wu Chen 吳臣 : son of Wu Rui 吳芮 ; King of Changsha.

- Wu Chen 武臣 : Chen Sheng's friend.

- Wu Guang /wu guäng/ 吳廣 (−208 BCE): co-leader of the first Qin rebellion.

- Wu Qi 吳起 : Lu, Wei, Chu strategist in WS times.

- **Wu Rui** 吳芮 (−202 BCE): King of Hengshan 衡山 under Xiang Yu; King of Changsha 長沙 under Liu Bang.

- Wu She 武涉 : Xiang Yu's envoy to Hann Xin.

- Wu Zixu /~ dzih-shü/ 伍子胥 : SA Chu official who fled to Wu; suicide by order.

- Wujiang /wu-jēäng/ 烏江 : plc. NE of <u>Hexian</u> and SW of <u>Nanjing</u>.

- **Xiahou Ying** /shēä-hou yēng/ 夏侯嬰 (−172 BCE) [Lord of Teng 滕公]: close friend and follower of Liu Bang.

- **Xiang Bo** /shēäng ~/ 項伯 (−192 BCE): younger brother of Xiang Liang; uncle of Xiang Yu.

- **Xiang Liang** /shēäng lēäng/ 項梁 (−208 BCE) [Lord of Wuxin /wu-shin/ 武信]: son of Xiang Yan; uncle of Xiang Yu.

- Xiang Yan /shēäng yän/ 項燕 : WS Chu general.

- **Xiang Yu /shēäng** yü/ 項羽 (232–202 BCE) [Xiang Ji 項籍 ; Lord of Lu 魯公 ; Hegemonic King of West Chu (Xichu bawang 西楚霸王)]: nephew of Xiang Liang; grandson of Xiang Yan; archrival of Liu Bang.

- Xiang Zhuang /shēäng juäng/ 項莊 : cousin of Xiang Yu; nephew of Xiang Liang.

- Xiangcheng /shēäng-chêng/ 襄城 : co. Seat: in Henan.

- **Xianyang** /shēän-yäng/ 咸陽 : Qin cap. north of Xi'an, Shaanxi.

- Xiao /shēao/ 蕭 : co. Seat: in north Anhui and near Xuzhou, Jiangsu.

- **Xiao He** /shēao hê/ 蕭何 (257–193 BCE): top Han official under Liu Bang.

- **Xiapi** /shēä-pē/ 下邳 : co. Seat: SE of Xuzhou, Jiangsu.

- Xiayang /shēa-yäng/ 夏陽 : co. Seat: SW of Hancheng, Shaanxi.

- Xiayi /shēa-yē/ 下邑 : co. Seat: Dangshan, Anhui.

- Xingle /shēng-lê/ 興樂 (Rising Joy): Qin pal.; converted to Changle under Han.

- **Xingyang** /shēng-yäng/ 滎陽 : city in Henan.

- Xinling /shēn lēng/ 信陵 . *See* Lord of Xinling.

- *Xinyu* /shēn-yü/ 新語 . *See New Discourses*.

- **Xiongnu** /shēong-nu/ 匈奴 : northern nomadic people.

- Xiuwu /shēu-wu/ 修武 : plc. west of Xinxiang, north Henan.

- Xu Fu /shü ~/ 許負 : Qin physiognomist.

- Xue /shüeh/ 薛 : co. Seat: south of Tengzhoushi, Shandong.

- Xunyi /shün-yē/ 浚儀 : co. Seat: Kaifeng, Henan. *See* Daliang.

- Yan Le /yän lê/ 閻樂 : Qin magistrate of Xianyang County.

- Yangdi 陽翟 : seat of Yingchuan 潁川 com. in Yuzhou, Henan.

- Yangzhou /yäng-joe/ 陽周 : co. Seat: north of Zichang, Shaanxi.

- Yanmen 雁門 : com. It lay in north Shanxi and part of Inner Mongolia.

- *yanzhi* /yän-jih/ 閼氏 : consort of a Xiongnu *chanyu* (king).

- Yao 堯 : legendary sage king.

- Yellow Emperor [Huangdi /huäng-di/ 黃帝]: legendary king.

- **Ying Bu** /yēng bu/ 英布 (–196 BCE): King of Jiujiang 九江 ; King of Huainan 淮南 .

- Yingchuan 潁川 : com. in Xuchang, Yuzhou et al., central Henan. Seat: Yangdi 陽翟 (Yuzhou).

- Yingying: *see* Liu Ying 劉盈 .

- Yinling 陰陵 : co. Seat: south of Bengbu, Anhui.

- Yong Chi /yong chih/ 雍齒 : late Qin rebel; enfeoffed by Liu Bang.

- Yongcheng 庸城 : town south of Suzhou, in north Anhui.

- Yongqiu /yong-chēu/ 雍丘 : co. Seat: in east Henan.

- Yuan 宛 : seat of Nanyang com., in Nanyang, Henan.

- Yuanyuan. *See* Liu Luyuan 劉魯元 .

- Yue Yue 樂說 : Hann Xin's retainer.

- *yuefa sanzhang* 約法三章 . *See* Three Article Code.

- **Yueyang** 櫟陽 (NE of Lintong, Shaanxi): early cap. of Liu Bang.

- Yuezhi /yüeh-jih/ 月氏 : nomadic people in Gansu.

- Yúji 虞姬 [Yuji]. *See* Concubine Yú.

- Yunmeng /yün-mêng/ 雲夢 : plc. near Jingzhoushi, south Hubei.

- Yuyang /yü-yäng/ 漁陽 : plc. north of Beijing.

- Zang Tu /dzäng ~/ 臧荼 : King of Yan.

- Zang Yan /dzäng ~/ 臧衍 : Zang Tu's son.

- **Zhang Ao** /jäng ~/ 張敖 (–182 BCE): son of Zhang Er; King of Zhao; Marquis of Xuanping /shüan-ping/ 宣平 .

- **Zhang Er** /jäng ~/ 張耳 (–202 BCE): King of Zhao; Chen Yu's 陳餘 good friend.

- **Zhang Han** /jäng ~/ 章邯 (–205 BCE): top Qin general under Huhai; King of Yong 雍 under Xiang Yu.

- **Zhang Liang** /jäng lēäng/ 張良 (–186 BCE): top adviser of Liu Bang.

- Zhang Sheng /jäng shêng/ 張勝 : Lu Wan's 盧綰 emissary.

- Zhang Yan /jäng yän/ 張黶 : Zhang Er's 張耳 general.

- **Zhao Gao** /jao ~/ 趙高 (–207 BCE): Qin eunuch, chancellor.

- **Zhao Tuo** /jao ~/ 趙佗 (–137 BCE): Qin general; founder of the State of Nanyue.

- Zhao Xie /jao shēeh/ 趙歇 : Zhao king.

- Zhending /jen-/ 真定 : Han co. Seat: <u>Zhengding</u>, <u>Hebei</u>.

- Zheng /jêng/ 鄭 : co. Seat: <u>Huaxian</u>, <u>Shaanxi</u>.

- Zheng Chang /jêng chäng/ 鄭昌 : King of Hann under Xiang Yu.

- **Zhongli Mo** /jong-lē moh/ 鍾離昧 (–201 BCE): Xiang Yu's top general.

- **Zhou Bo** /joe boh/ 周勃 (–169 BCE): Liu Bang's top general.

- **Zhou Chang** /joe chäng/ 周昌 (–192 BCE): Zhou Ke's cousin; official under Liu Bang.

- Zhou Ke /joe kê/ 周苛 : Liu Bang's censor-in-chief.

- Zhou Wen /joe wen/ 周文 : general under Chen Sheng.

- Zhou Yin /joe ~/ 周殷 : commander-in-chief of Xiang Yu's army.

- *zhu* /ju/ 筑 : a musical instrument similar to a zither.

- Zhui 騅 . *See* Dapple.

- Zixiang /dzih-shēang/ 茲鄉 : village.

- **Ziying** /zih-yēng/ 子嬰 (–206 BCE): Qin sovereign after Huhai 胡亥 .

From Peasant to Emperor: The Life of Liu Bang

ISBN: 978-986-6286-71-1

DOI: 10.978.9866286/711

Publishing Date: August, 2018

Price: US$ 24.00 / NT$ 500

Author: Victor Cunrui Xiong

Chief Editor: Huei-Chu Chang

Executive Editor: Yi-Chun Liao

Cover Designer: Alan Chang

Typesetting: Yu-Chen Liu

General Manager: Chris Cheng

Publishing Specialist: John Zhang

Publisher: Airiti Press

18F, No. 80, Sec. 1, Chenggong Rd., Yonghe Dist., New Taipei City 234, Taiwan

Tel: +886-2-2926-6006

Fax: +886-2-2923-5151

E-mail: press@airiti.com